2021-22

Planning to Change the World

A PLAN BOOK FOR SOCIAL JUSTICE TEACHERS

Editors
Thomas Nikundiwe, Education for Liberation Network
Carla Shalaby, University of Michigan
Margaret Kavanagh, Education for Liberation Network
Gretchen Brion-Meisels, Harvard Graduate School of Education

Designer
Shira Evergreen, www.shirari.com

Researchers and Writers
Damaris Altomerianos
Amber Bennett
Hayley Breden
Teresa Bunner
Nicole Cirino
Lizzie Fortin
Rita Hathaway
Mel Katz
Esther Kim
Kara Lawson
Ai Miller
Erika Mittag
Julie Sizer
Ann Van Etten-Janey
Kaya Waltzer
Ursula Wolfe-Rocca

This book belongs to:
School:
Grade:

"I am convinced that the world I envision and want to inhabit is possible. I believe that it exists already in fragments. This is a core belief and perhaps this is why I don't despair."

- Mariame Kaba, abolitionist, organizer, and educator

Portrait to the left by Laura Baran

This year's cover illustration is inspired by photos of Berkeley Forest School, which aims to "instigate a culture of active citizens to live in relationship with the land, and with awareness of our global community." **BerkeleyForestSchool.org**

DEDICATED TO

This year's book is dedicated to John Lewis, one of the Founding Fathers of the American Civil Rights Movement. He joined the struggle at a very young age and quickly rose in the ranks of the movement's icons to become a fearless warrior and trusted leader. Lewis was one of the original Freedom Riders – young people who risked their lives to end segregation in public transportation in the South. Dedicated to the notion of nonviolent protest, Lewis and the other Freedom Riders were assaulted and arrested countless times. He was elected Chairman of the Student Nonviolent Coordinating Committee (SNCC) and was one of the principal organizers of the historic March on Washington for Jobs and Freedom in 1963. At 23 years old, Lewis was the youngest speaker to address the gathered throng, giving a fiery speech that ruffled feathers, but established his legitimacy on the national stage. He later led the Selma to Montgomery March for Voting Rights, where he was severely beaten by police in an event that would go down in history as Bloody Sunday, a turning point in the struggle for civil rights for Black Americans. John Lewis often used the term "good trouble," calling on young people to, "Get in good trouble, necessary trouble, and redeem the soul of America." He believed that America would one day live up to its promise of "liberty and justice for all." But he knew it wouldn't happen without a fight – a battle he waged his entire adult life, first as an organizer and protester, and later as a congressman for 33 years. He fought for his "beloved community," never giving up or giving in. We owe a debt of gratitude to John Lewis for his dedication to the cause, and so while we dedicate this edition of *Planning to Change the World* to him, we simultaneously lift and recognize the many overlooked women in the American Civil Rights Movement, several of whom are named and celebrated in this year's edition, along with exceptional new teaching resources shining a light on their contributions.

Finally, we also dedicate this year's edition to the countless lesser-known freedom fighters lost to COVID and killed by our systems of policing and prison, who struggled humbly and mightily in their everyday work and actions across the globe, and who are dearly missed by their immediate and extended families and their own beloved communities.

Facebook @justiceplanbook

Twitter @EdLibPlanBook

Introduction

Planning to Change the World is a plan book for educators who believe that young people can and already do create meaningful social change. It is produced by the Education for Liberation Network and is published in partnership with Rethinking Schools. All proceeds from sales of the book support these two organizations.

The information and ideas featured on these pages come from teachers, parents, young people, organizers, and activists who, like you, struggle daily to put their values into practice but recognize the urgency of doing so. Our hope is to support school-based, home-based, and community-based educators to translate their visions of a just education into concrete activities for and with young people. *Planning to Change the World* is packed with important social justice birthdays and historical events—especially those that often get left out of mainstream textbooks—as well as lesson plans and teaching resources, words of wisdom from visionary leaders, and more. This book also connects you to a national community of educators who are committed to teaching freedom, so you might feel less isolated in the work you do.

In this edition, as always, we include a special feature highlighting the work practicing teachers. This year's feature—which would not have been possible without our incredible guest editor, Sarah Garton—describes an innovative new Ethnic Studies BIPOC Mentorship Network launched by our first-ever local chapter of the Education for Liberation Network (EdLib Minnesota). Our hope is that this feature supports readers to envision and imagine mentorship as multidirectional rather than two-way and top-down, and that you might use the feature to consider your own community-based mentorship program to counter the feelings of isolation associated with doing critical and radical work all alone in your school building.

We hope, as we do each year, that this edition of the plan book provides a small bit of support and inspiration for every day of your year, and that you can feel the love and energy we send through its pages. We recognize that while the work of teaching was deemed essential this past year, teachers were treated as essential workers but not as essential human beings who deserve the care, protection, gratitude, and compensation commensurate with their essential daily work. We see you, and we stand alongside you through the pages of this book. Please take good care of yourselves and each other, now and always.

In Love, Struggle, and Solidarity,
Thomas, Carla, Margaret and Gretchen

About our organization

education
for liberation
network

The Education for Liberation Network (www.edliberation.org) is a national coalition of teachers, community activists, researchers, youth and parents who believe a good education should teach people—particularly low-income youth and youth of color—to understand and challenge the injustices their communities face. The network provides a space for members to share knowledge and work together to create tools for liberatory education. By building alliances that cross the boundaries of geography, occupation, and age, we hope to nurture communities of thoughtful, socially-engaged people and to maximize the impact of their work

Education for Liberation Network would like to thank the following people for their vital assistance in creating this edition: Tracy Buenavista, Cati de los Rios, Ron Espiritu, Brian Lozenski, Natalia Ortiz, and Bree Picower.

School year at a glance

AUGUST **2021**

S	M	T	W	T	F	S
1	2	3	4	5	6	7
8	9	10	11	12	13	14
15	16	17	18	19	20	21
22	23	24	25	26	27	28
29	30	31				

SEPTEMBER **2021**

S	M	T	W	T	F	S
			1	2	3	4
5	6	7	8	9	10	11
12	13	14	15	16	17	18
19	20	21	22	23	24	25
26	27	28	29	30		

OCTOBER **2021**

S	M	T	W	T	F	S
					1	2
3	4	5	6	7	8	9
10	11	12	13	14	15	16
17	18	19	20	21	22	23
24	25	26	27	28	29	30
31						

NOVEMBER **2021**

S	M	T	W	T	F	S
	1	2	3	4	5	6
7	8	9	10	11	12	13
14	15	16	17	18	19	20
21	22	23	24	25	26	27
28	29	30				

DECEMBER **2021**

S	M	T	W	T	F	S
			1	2	3	4
5	6	7	8	9	10	11
12	13	14	15	16	17	18
19	20	21	22	23	24	25
26	27	28	29	30	31	

JANUARY **2022**

S	M	T	W	T	F	S
						1
2	3	4	5	6	7	8
9	10	11	12	13	14	15
16	17	18	19	20	21	22
23	24	25	26	27	28	29
30	31					

FEBRUARY **2022**

S	M	T	W	T	F	S
		1	2	3	4	5
6	7	8	9	10	11	12
13	14	15	16	17	18	19
20	21	22	23	24	25	26
27	28					

MARCH **2022**

S	M	T	W	T	F	S
		1	2	3	4	5
6	7	8	9	10	11	12
13	14	15	16	17	18	19
20	21	22	23	24	25	26
27	28	29	30	31		

APRIL **2022**

S	M	T	W	T	F	S
					1	2
3	4	5	6	7	8	9
10	11	12	13	14	15	16
17	18	19	20	21	22	23
24	25	26	27	28	29	30

MAY **2022**

S	M	T	W	T	F	S
1	2	3	4	5	6	7
8	9	10	11	12	13	14
15	16	17	18	19	20	21
22	23	24	25	26	27	28
29	30	31				

JUNE **2022**

S	M	T	W	T	F	S
			1	2	3	4
5	6	7	8	9	10	11
12	13	14	15	16	17	18
19	20	21	22	23	24	25
26	27	28	29	30		

JULY **2022**

S	M	T	W	T	F	S
					1	2
3	4	5	6	7	8	9
10	11	12	13	14	15	16
17	18	19	20	21	22	23
24	25	26	27	28	29	30
31						

How to use this book

First, a note about the dates featured in this book. There are so many events and people that could be included in a planner like this, we had to find a way to narrow the possibilities. So for this calendar, we chose significant anniversaries and birthdays, which generally means (with a few exceptions) anniversaries/birthdays that fall on the 10-year mark (e.g. 10th anniversary of Hurricane Katrina and the 120th anniversary of the *Plessy v. Ferguson* decision).

The weekly planning pages include several special features:

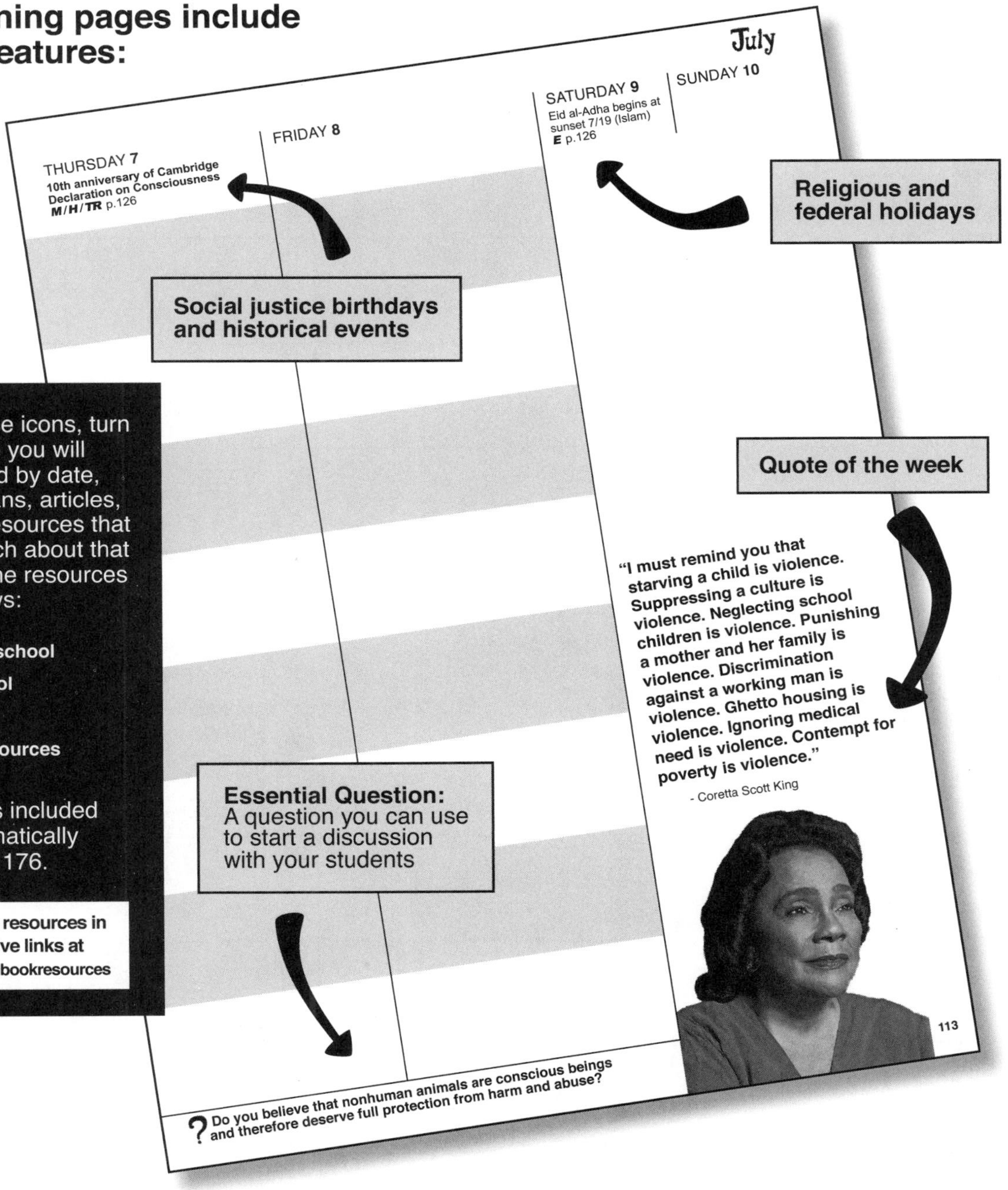

When you see these icons, turn to page 120, where you will find a list, organized by date, of online lesson plans, articles, videos and other resources that you can use to teach about that event or person. The resources are coded as follows:

E	**Elementary school**
M	**Middle school**
H	**High school**
TR	**Teacher Resources**

All of the resources included are also listed thematically beginning on page 176.

You can view all of the resources in this book online with live links at www.ediberation.org/planbookresources

This book has other important features:

- Reproducible social justice awards for students (pages 214-215)
- A list of organizations through which you can meet teachers who share your concerns and access additional resources (page 216)
- "Teacher 2 Teacher" special features: *An Introduction to the Education for Liberation Minnesota's Ethnic Studies BIPOC Mentorship Network* (pages 56-59) and, reprinted from our 2018-19 edition, *15 Everyday Ways to Affirm TGNC (Trans and Gender Nonconforming) Students* (pages 210-213)

Long-term planning

2021

August

8/21 190th anniversary of Nat Turner's rebellion

SUNDAY	MONDAY	TUESDAY	WEDNESDAY	THURSDAY	FRIDAY	SATURDAY
1	2	3	4	5	6	7
8	9	10	11	12	13	14
15	16	17	18	19	20	21
22	23	24	25	26	27	28
29	30	31	1	2	3	4

September

9/11 20th anniversary of the 9/11 terrorist attacks

SUNDAY	MONDAY	TUESDAY	WEDNESDAY	THURSDAY	FRIDAY	SATURDAY
29	30	31	1	2	3	4
5	6	7	8	9	10	11
12	13	14	15	16	17	18
19	20	21	22	23	24	25
26	27	28	29	30	1	2

Long-term planning

2021

October

10/24 30th anniversary of the First National People of Color Environmental Leadership Conference

SUNDAY	MONDAY	TUESDAY	WEDNESDAY	THURSDAY	FRIDAY	SATURDAY
26	27	28	29	30	1	2
3	4	5	6	7	8	9
10	11	12	13	14	15	16
17	18	19	20	21	22	23
24	25	26	27	28	29	30
31	1	2	3	4	5	6

November

11/7 60th anniversary of the first openly gay person to run for public office

SUNDAY	MONDAY	TUESDAY	WEDNESDAY	THURSDAY	FRIDAY	SATURDAY
31	1	2	3	4	5	6
7	8	9	10	11	12	13
14	15	16	17	18	19	20
21	22	23	23	25	26	27
28	29	30	1	2	3	4

Long-term planning 2021-22

December

12/10 Grace Thorpe, Native American and environmental activist, born (1921-2008)

SUNDAY	MONDAY	TUESDAY	WEDNESDAY	THURSDAY	FRIDAY	SATURDAY
28	29	30	1	2	3	4
5	6	7	8	9	10	11
12	13	14	15	16	17	18
19	20	21	22	23	24	25
26	27	28	29	30	31	1

January

1/11 110th anniversary of the Bread and Roses Strike

SUNDAY	MONDAY	TUESDAY	WEDNESDAY	THURSDAY	FRIDAY	SATURDAY
26	27	28	29	30	31	1
2	3	4	5	6	7	8
9	10	11	12	13	14	15
16	17	18	19	20	21	22
23	24	25	26	27	28	29
30	31	1	2	3	4	5

Long-term planning 2022

February

2/26 10th anniversary of Trayvon Martin's murder

SUNDAY	MONDAY	TUESDAY	WEDNESDAY	THURSDAY	FRIDAY	SATURDAY
30	31	1	2	3	4	5
6	7	8	9	10	11	12
13	14	15	16	17	18	19
20	21	22	23	24	25	26
27	28	1	2	3	4	5

March

3/28 80th anniversary of the arrest of Minoru Yasui for breaking Japanese American curfew

SUNDAY	MONDAY	TUESDAY	WEDNESDAY	THURSDAY	FRIDAY	SATURDAY
27	28	1	2	3	4	5
6	7	8	9	10	11	12
13	14	15	16	17	18	19
20	21	22	23	24	25	26
27	28	29	30	31	1	2

Long-term planning

April

4/1 90th anniversary of the Chicago School Children's Strike

SUNDAY	MONDAY	TUESDAY	WEDNESDAY	THURSDAY	FRIDAY	SATURDAY
27	28	29	30	31	1	2
3	4	5	6	7	8	9
10	11	12	13	14	15	16
17	18	19	20	21	22	23
24	25	26	27	28	29	30

May

5/6 140th anniversary of the Chinese Exclusion Act

SUNDAY	MONDAY	TUESDAY	WEDNESDAY	THURSDAY	FRIDAY	SATURDAY
1	2	3	4	5	6	7
8	9	10	11	12	13	14
15	16	17	18	19	20	21
22	23	24	25	26	27	28
29	30	31	1	2	3	4

Long-term planning 2022

June

6/23 50th anniversary of Title IX

SUNDAY	MONDAY	TUESDAY	WEDNESDAY	THURSDAY	FRIDAY	SATURDAY
29	30	31	1	2	3	4
5	6	7	8	9	10	11
12	13	14	15	16	17	18
19	20	21	22	23	24	25
26	27	28	29	30	1	2

July

7/16 Ida B. Wells, educator, journalist, and activist, born (1862-1931)

SUNDAY	MONDAY	TUESDAY	WEDNESDAY	THURSDAY	FRIDAY	SATURDAY
26	27	28	29	30	1	2
3	4	5	6	7	8	9
10	11	12	13	14	15	16
17	18	19	20	21	22	23
24	25	26	27	28	29	30
31	1	2	3	4	5	6

August

MONDAY **2**	TUESDAY **3**	WEDNESDAY **4**
		Barack Obama, 44th US President, born (1961) ***E/M*** p.120 **10th anniversary of the Environmental Justice Interagency Memorandum of Understanding (EJ MOU)** ***M/H*** p.120

? Where do you see examples of environmental racism in your community or communities around you?

THURSDAY **5**
40th anniversary of Air Traffic Controllers' strike *H/TR* p.120

FRIDAY **6**
Hiroshima Day *E/M/H* p.120

SATURDAY **7**

SUNDAY **8**

"We, the People, recognize that we have responsibilities as well as rights; that our destinies are bound together; that a freedom that only asks what's in it for me, a freedom without a commitment to others, a freedom without love or charity or duty or patriotism, is unworthy of our founding ideals and those who died in their defense."

- Barack Obama

August

MONDAY **9**	TUESDAY **10**	WEDNESDAY **11**
International Day of the World's Indigenous Peoples *E/M/H* p.120	Muharram begins at sunset 8/10 (Islam) ***E*** p.120	

? ***Why are Tribal Nations considered sovereign governments, and why does it matter?***

THURSDAY **12**

International Youth Day
E/M/H p.120

140th anniversary of the founding of the United Brotherhood of Carpenters and Joiners of America ***H*** p.121

FRIDAY **13**

60th anniversary of the border closure between East and West Berlin ***H*** p.121

SATURDAY **14**

SUNDAY **15**

"This is really why I made my daughters learn to garden – they would always have a mother to love them, long after I am gone."

- Robin Wall Kimmerer, member of the Citizen Potawatomi Nation, professor, and author of *Braiding Sweetgrass*

August

MONDAY **16**	TUESDAY **17**	WEDNESDAY **18**
		Amelia Boynton, civil rights activist, born (1911-2015) *E/M/H* p.121 **Carter Camp, Indigenous rights activist and AIM leader, born (1941-2013) *M/H/TR*** p.121

***?* What are some possible explanations for the fact that the role of women leaders during the Civil Rights movement has so often been minimized or overshadowed?**

THURSDAY **19**

230th anniversary of Benjamin Banneker's challenging Thomas Jefferson's support for slavery *E/H* p.121

FRIDAY **20**

SATURDAY **21**

190th anniversary of Nat Turner's rebellion *M/H* p.121

SUNDAY **22**

10th anniversary of Martin Luther King, Jr. Memorial opening to the public *H/TR* p.121

"I think that we need to recognize that there are as many genders as there are people in the world. And that even the word 'man' and the word 'woman' conceal more than they elucidate."

- Alok Vaid-Menon, gender non-conforming writer and performance artist

August

MONDAY **23**	TUESDAY **24**	WEDNESDAY **25**
International Day for the Remembrance of the Slave Trade and Its Abolition ***E/M/H*** p.121	**10th anniversary of exposé of NYPD Islamophobic policing** ***E/H/TR*** p.122	

THURSDAY **26**

Women's Equality Day *M/H* p.122

50th anniversary of the First Women's Equality Day *M/H* p.122

FRIDAY **27**

SATURDAY **28**

SUNDAY **29**

Krishna Janmashtami (Hinduism) ***E*** p.122

"People ask me sometimes: When do you think it will be enough? When will there be enough women on the Court? And my answer is: When there are nine."

- Ruth Bader Ginsburg

In which areas do you believe there is still the most work to do in achieving full equality for women in the US? What about globally?

August

MONDAY **30**

TUESDAY **31**

100th anniversary of the Battle of Blair Mountain ***E/M/H*** p.122

September

WEDNESDAY **1**

80th anniversary of Nazi decree requiring Jews to wear yellow stars ***E/M/H/TR*** p.123

10th anniversary of Plan EJ 2014 ***M/H*** p.123

THURSDAY **2**

FRIDAY **3**

120th anniversary of Alabama's constitution mandating segregation *M/H* p.123

SATURDAY **4**

SUNDAY **5**

"We're nothing without the Earth."

- Joelle Zgheib, Lebanese youth climate activist

? What are some of the strategies used to disenfranchise Black voters today?

September

MONDAY **6**	TUESDAY **7**	WEDNESDAY **8**
Labor Day ***M/H/TR*** p.126 Rosh Hashanah begins the evening of 9/6/2021, ends 9/8/2021 (Judaism) ***E*** p.123		**International Literacy Day *E/M/H*** p.123

THURSDAY **9**

50th anniversary of the Attica Prison uprising *H/TR* p.123

FRIDAY **10**

SATURDAY **11**

40th anniversary of Silver Spring monkey lab raid *E/M/H* p.124

20th anniversary of the 9/11 terrorist attacks *E/M/H/TR* p.124

SUNDAY **12**

Pedro Albizu Campos, Puerto Rican independence activist, born (1891-1965) *H/TR* p.124

? How and why is the label "terrorist" unevenly applied?

"Los jóvenes tienen el deber de defender su patria con las armas del conocimiento."

- Pedro Albizu Campos, Puerto Rican Independence activist

September

MONDAY **13**	TUESDAY **14**	WEDNESDAY **15**
140th anniversary of Lewis Latimer's first patent *E/M* p.124	**110th anniversary of the *Congreso Mexicanista H*** p.124	**First day of Hispanic Heritage Month *E/M/H*** p.124 Yom Kippur begins at sunset on 9/15/2021 and ends at sunset on 9/16/2021 (Judaism) ***TR*** p.125

September

THURSDAY **16**

Mexican Independence Day
TR p.125

FRIDAY **17**

SATURDAY **18**

170th anniversary of Fort Defiance (AZ) *M/H* p.125

SUNDAY **19**

First Day of Banned Books Week *E/M/H/ TR* p.125

140th anniversary of Tuskegee Institute p.125

? In your opinion, is there ever an acceptable reason to ban a book?

"A dangerous book will always be in danger from those it threatens with the demand that they question their assumptions. They'd rather hang on to the assumptions and ban the book."

- Ursula K. Le Guin, writer

September

MONDAY **20**	TUESDAY **21**	WEDNESDAY **22**
130th anniversary of the Cotton Pickers' strike p.125 **Henry Stephens Salt, animal rights and social reform activist, born (1851-1939)** ***E*** p.125 **40th anniversary of Solidarity Day** ***TR*** p.125 **10th anniversary of repeal of "Don't Ask, Don't Tell"** ***H*** p.125 **Arsham Parsi, LGBTQI+ activist, born (1981)** ***M/H*** p.126	**International Day of Peace** ***E/M/H/TR*** p.126 First day of Sukkot begins at sunset 9/21/2021, ends at sunset 9/27 (Judaism) ***E*** p.126 **40th anniversary of Belize's independence from Britain** ***E*** p.126 **10th anniversary of the execution of Troy Davis** ***H/TR*** p.126	**World Car-Free Day** ***E/M/H*** p.126

? In the places around the world where being queer is still considered a crime, what strategies do activists and organizers use in their struggle for LGBTQ+ liberation?

THURSDAY **23**

George Jackson, Black Panther Party member, born (1941-1971) ***H/TR*** p.126

Amzie Moore, civil rights activist, born (1911-1982) ***M/H/TR*** p.127

FRIDAY **24**

SATURDAY **25**

50th anniversary of the repeal of the Emergency Detention Act of 1950 ***E/M*** p.127

40th anniversary of swearing-in of Sandra Day O'Connor to Supreme Court ***H*** p.127

SUNDAY **26**

"I don't want to die and leave a few sad songs and a hump in the ground as my only moment. I want to leave a world that is liberated from trash, pollution, racism, nation states, nation state wars and armies, from pomp, bigotry, parochialism, a thousand different brands of untruth, and licentious, usurious economics."

- George Jackson, Black Panther Party member, author, and activist

September

MONDAY **27**	TUESDAY **28**	WEDNESDAY **29**
200th anniversary of Mexico's independence from Spain *E* p.127	**130th anniversary of Black longshoreman's strike *H*/*TR*** p.127	

October

THURSDAY **30**

30th anniversary of the military coup in Haiti ***M/H*** p.127

FRIDAY **1**

First day of Disability Employment Awareness Month ***E/M/H/TR*** p.128

World Vegetarian Day/First Day of Vegetarian Awareness Month ***M/H/TR*** p.128

First day of LGBT History Month ***E/M/H/TR*** p.128

170th anniversary of the Jerry Rescue ***E/M*** p.128

Anfesia Shapsnikoff, Aleut leader and educator, born (1901-1973 ***E*** p.128

October

SATURDAY **2**

SUNDAY **3**

"If collective access is revolutionary love without charity, how do we learn to love each other? How do we learn to do this love work of collective care that lifts us instead of abandons us, that grapples with all the deep ways in which care is complicated?"

- Leah Lakshmi Piepzna-Samarasinha, queer disabled femme writer, organizer, performance artist, and educator

? ***What are the environmental benefits of vegetarianism?***

October

MONDAY **4**	TUESDAY **5**	WEDNESDAY **6**
70th anniversary of Burglund HS walkout *H* p.128	**World Teachers' Day *TR*** p.128 **40th anniversary of *Seminole Tribe v. Butterworth* *E/M*** p.128	First day of Navaratri (Hinduism) ***E*** p.129

***?* How have school walkouts been used historically as a powerful form of youth protest and activism, and how and where do you see them used today?**

THURSDAY **7**

20th anniversary of the War in Afghanistan *M/H* p.129

FRIDAY **8**

Jesse Jackson, civil rights leader, Baptist minister, and politician, born (1941) *E/M/H* p.129

SATURDAY **9**

SUNDAY **10**

"It's time for America to get right."

- Fannie Lou Hamer

October

MONDAY **11**	TUESDAY **12**	WEDNESDAY **13**
National Coming Out Day ***M/H/TR*** p.129 **Indigenous Peoples Day (US)** ***E/M/H*** p.129 **20th anniversary of California Senate Bill 828** ***H*** p.129	**110th anniversary of Society of American Indians** ***E/M*** p.129	**100th anniversary of the founding of the Order of the Sons of America** ***E / M*** p.130

? How can organizing strengthen a group's ability to demand and advance their rights?

THURSDAY **14**

40th anniversary of the Democratic Dussehra (Hinduism) ***E*** p.130

FRIDAY **15**

White Cane Safety Day ***E*** p.130

170th anniversary of The Second National Woman's Rights Convention ***M/H*** p.130

SATURDAY **16**

World Food Day ***E/M/H/TR*** p.130

130th anniversary of the death of Sarah Winnemucca, Paiute writer and activist (1844-1891) ***H*** p.130

SUNDAY **17**

International Day for the Eradication of Poverty ***M/H*** p.130

Vernon Bellecourt, American Indian Movement activist, born (1931-2007) ***H/TR*** p.130

150th anniversary of President Grant's declaring martial law over KKK violence in SC ***M/H*** p.130

***?** In what ways do modern forms of White supremacist terrorism look similar to or different from the KKK?*

"We are a living people with a vibrant culture, and we refuse to have our identity trivialized and degraded. Indians are people, not mascots for America's fun and games."

- Vernon Bellecourt, founding member of the American Indian Movement (AIM)

October

MONDAY **18**	TUESDAY **19**	WEDNESDAY **20**

THURSDAY **21**

FRIDAY **22**

National Day of Protest to Stop Police Brutality *E/M/H* p.131

SATURDAY **23**

SUNDAY **24**

150th anniversary of the Chinese Massacre of 1871 *TR* p.131

30th anniversary of the First National People of Color Environmental Leadership Conference *E/M* p.131

? How might learning the long history of racism, violence, and discrimination against Asian Americans strengthen our ability to analyze, name, and fight against it today?

"I think all of us are waking up to the fact that we are interdependent and that we have to start to make some pretty significant changes in the way that we value our relationships, especially our caregiving relationships, if we're to make it through."

- Ai-Jen Poo, labor organizer, Director of the National Domestic Workers Alliance

October

MONDAY 25

40th anniversary of swearing-in of Sandra Day O'Connor to Supreme Court *H* p.131

TUESDAY 26

Intersex Awareness Day *M/H/TR* p.131

20th anniversary of the Patriot Act *H* p.131

WEDNESDAY 27

Nawal El Saadawi (Arabic: نوال السعداوي) Egyptian feminist writer, activist, physician, and psychiatrist, born (1931-2021) *H* p.132

? How are claims of "patriotism" sometimes used to justify White supremacy, wars, and the stripping of basic human rights?

THURSDAY **28**

FRIDAY **29**

SATURDAY **30**

SUNDAY **31**

130th anniversary of the Coal Creek War
M/H/TR p.132

120th anniversary of Silas Esters' lynching
H/TR p.132

El Día de los Muertos **(Day of the Dead), begins on 10/31 and ends on 11/2** ***E*** p.132

Halloween
E/M/H p.132

"They said, 'You are a savage and dangerous woman.' I am speaking the truth. And the truth is savage and dangerous."

- Nawal El Saadawi, Egyptian feminist writer and activist

November

MONDAY **1**	TUESDAY **2**	WEDNESDAY **3**
First day of National American Indian Heritage Month *E/M/H* p.133 **World Vegan Day *E/M/H*** p.133 **190th anniversary of the beginning of the Choctaw removal *E/M*** p.133 **40th anniversary of Antigua's and Barbuda's independence from Britain** p.133	**Election Day *M/H*** p.133  	

November

THURSDAY 4

Diwali (Deepavali), Indian Festival of Lights (Hinduism, Sikhism, Jainism, and Buddhism) ***E*** p.123

FRIDAY 5

SATURDAY 6

SUNDAY 7

90th anniversary of the deaths of Black women after Georgia hospital refused care ***H/TR*** p.133

180th anniversary of *The Creole* Revolt ***TR*** p.133

60th anniversary of the first openly gay person to run for public office ***M/H*** p.134

210th anniversary of the Battle of Tippecanoe ***E/M/H/TR*** p.134

Daylight Saving Time Ends

? *Why are the rebellions and revolts of enslaved people so often omitted from textbooks?*

"We know we cannot be kind to animals until we stop exploiting them – exploiting animals in the name of science, exploiting animals in the name of sport, exploiting animals in the name of fashion, and yes, exploiting animals in the name of food."

- César Chávez

November

MONDAY **8**	TUESDAY **9**	WEDNESDAY **10**
		Samuel Gridley Howe, abolitionist, and educator of blind people, born (1801-1876) ***H/TR*** p.134

? When and how does a physical or mental variation become a "disability"?

THURSDAY **11**

Veterans Day *H/TR* p.134

190th anniversary of Nat Turner's execution *H* p.134

140th anniversary of George Frederick Keller's "A Statue for Our Harbor" *E/M/TR* p.134

FRIDAY **12**

Sor Juana Ines de la Cruz, writer and advocate for women's rights, born (1651-1695) *M/H* p.134

SATURDAY **13**

30th anniversary of Audre Lorde's being named Poet Laureate of New York *H/TR* p.135

SUNDAY **14**

"I want to live the rest of my life, however long or short, with as much sweetness as I can decently manage, loving all the people I love, and doing as much as I can of the work I still have to do."

- Audre Lorde

November

MONDAY **15**	TUESDAY **16**	WEDNESDAY **17**
140th anniversary of the Federation of Organized Trades and Labor Unions *E/M/H* p.135		**International Students' Day *E*** p.135 **60th anniversary of the Albany Movement *H/TR*** p.135

THURSDAY **18**

FRIDAY **19**

SATURDAY **20**

Transgender Day of Remembrance

E/M/H/TR p.135

? What is required from each of us to protect the lives of transgender people?

SUNDAY **21**

"Just because so many things are in conflict does not mean that we ourselves should be divided."

- Sophie Scholl, German student and anti-Nazi activist

November

MONDAY **22**	TUESDAY **23**	WEDNESDAY **24**
	Mamie Till Mobley, educator, activist, and mother of Emmett Till, born (1921-2003) ***H*** p.135	**Arundhati Roy, Indian author and activist, born (1961)** ***H*** p.135

***?** Can you think of examples of women who became activists because of their identities and experiences as mothers?*

THURSDAY **25**

Thanksgiving/Day of Mourning *E/M/H/TR* p.136

110th anniversary of the *Plan de Ayala* *M/H* p.136

FRIDAY **26**

Buy Nothing Day *E/M/H* p.136

Fur-Free Friday *E* p.136

160th anniversary of the state of West Virginia *H* p.136

Mahalia Jackson, gospel singer and civil rights activist, born (1911-1972) *E/M/H* p.136

SATURDAY **27**

SUNDAY **28**

First day of Hanukkah begins at sunset on 11/28/2021 (Judaism) ***E*** p.136

"It is not that I dwell on the past. But the past shapes the way we are in the present and the way we will become what we are destined to become. It is only because I have finally understood the past, accepted it, embraced it, that I can fully live in the moment. And hardly a moment goes by when I don't think about Emmett, and the lessons a son can teach a mother."

- Mamie Till-Mobley, educator, activist, and mother of Emmett Till

November

MONDAY **29**

Wendell Phillips, abolitionist and activist, born (1811-1884) ***E*** p.136

TUESDAY **30**

December

WEDNESDAY **1**

World AIDS Day ***M/H*** p.137

THURSDAY **2**

FRIDAY **3**

International Day of Persons with Disabilities *H*/*TR* p.137

SATURDAY **4**

SUNDAY **5**

"We are now struggling for a new world which is based on peace, which is based on love, which is based on justice, which is based on accountability, based on human rights."

- Tawakkol Karman, Yemeni activist and Nobel Peace Prize laureate

***?** How is the fight for disability rights different from the struggle for disability justice?*

December

MONDAY **6**	TUESDAY **7**	WEDNESDAY **8**
	80th anniversary of the attack on Pearl Harbor *E/M/H* p.137	

THURSDAY **9**

60th anniversary of Tanganyika's (now Tanzania) independence from Britain p.137

FRIDAY **10**

International Human Rights Day ***E/M/H/TR*** p.137

International Animal Rights Day ***E/M/H*** p.137

Grace Thorpe, Native American and environmental activist, born (1921-2008) ***M/H*** p.137

10th anniversary of Tawakkol Karman's Nobel Peace Prize ***H/TR*** p.138

SATURDAY **11**

SUNDAY **12**

"Migration is an expression of the human aspiration for dignity, safety, and a better future. It is part of the social fabric, part of our very makeup as a human family."

- Ban Ki-moon, South Korean politician and former Secretary-General of the United Nations

? What rights should all animals have?

MONDAY **13**	TUESDAY **14**	WEDNESDAY **15**
		230th anniversary of the adoption of the Bill of Rights *E/M/TR* p.138 **10th anniversary of National Institutes of Health's (NIH) ending funding for new experiments on chimps *M/H*** p.138

THURSDAY **16**

FRIDAY **17**

SATURDAY **18**

International Migrants Day *H* p.138

50th anniversary of Alaska Native Claims Settlement Act *H* p.138

? How did the exploitation of natural resources adversely affect Native American communities? How does it affect these communities today?

SUNDAY **19**

"There is so much that able-bodied people could learn from the wisdom that often comes with disability. But space needs to be made. Hands need to be reached out. People need to be lifted up."

- Alice Wong, author, research consultant, and disability rights activist

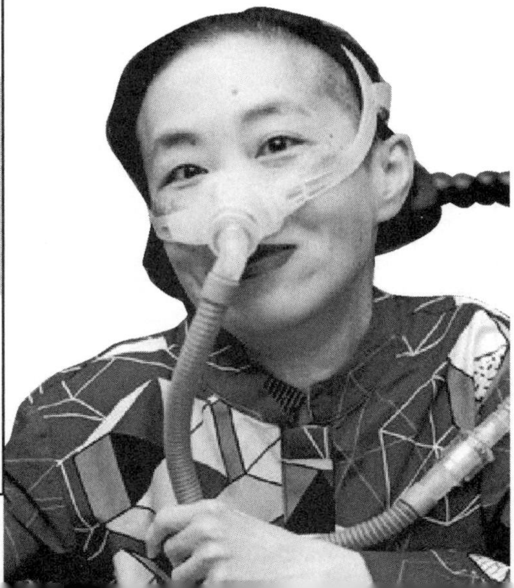

December

MONDAY **20**	TUESDAY **21**	WEDNESDAY **22**
50th anniversary of UN Declaration on the Rights of "Mentally Retarded" People *E*/*H*/*TR* p.138 **10th anniversary of largest women's demonstration in modern Egyptian history *H*** p.139	**Winter Solstice (Northern Hemisphere) *E*** p.139	**Soyal, the New Year's celebration of the Hopi and Zuni *E*** p.139

? ***What unique role do activist women play in justice movements in the Middle East?***

THURSDAY **23**

FRIDAY **24**

70th anniversary of Libya's independence p.139

SATURDAY **25**

Christmas
E/M/H/TR p.139

70th anniversary of Harry T. Moore's murder *H/TR* p.139

Clara Barton, nurse and humanitarian, born (1821-1912) *M/H/TR* p.139

SUNDAY **26**

First day of Kwanzaa (Umoja = Unity) p.139

"I try to be as honest about what I see and to speak rather than be silent, especially if it means I can save lives or serve humanity."

- Sandra Cisneros,
Mexican American author

December

MONDAY **27**	TUESDAY **28**	WEDNESDAY **29**
Second day of Kwanzaa (Kujichagulia = Self-determination) ***E*** p.139 **190th anniversary of the Baptist War (aka Christmas Rebellion)** ***M/H*** p.140 **30th anniversary of Minnesota's ruling for same-sex guardianship** ***E*** p.140	**Third day of Kwanzaa (Ujima = Collective Work and Responsibility)** ***M/H/TR*** p.140	**Fourth day of Kwanzaa (Ujamaa = Cooperative Economics)** ***H/TR*** p.140

? What is the relationship between freedom and self-determination?

THURSDAY **30**

Fifth day of Kwanzaa (Nia = Purpose) ***E/M/H*** p.140

30th anniversary of ***El Pueblo para el Aire y Agua Limpio v. Kings County Board of Supervisors*** ***E/M/H/TR*** p.140

FRIDAY **31**

New Year's Eve ***E*** p.140

Sixth day of Kwanzaa (Kuumba = Creativity) p.140

SATURDAY **1**

Seventh day of Kwanzaa (Imani = Faith) ***E/M*** p.141

130th anniversary of Ellis Island Immigration Center ***E/M*** p.141

60th anniversary of Illinois becoming the first state to repeal anti-sodomy laws ***TR*** p.141

40th anniversary of the publication of Lois Marie Gibbs' ***Love Canal: My Story*** ***H*** p.141

SUNDAY **2**

"Though we tremble before uncertain futures / may we meet illness, death, and adversity with strength / may we dance in the face of our fears."

- Gloria Anzaldúa, Chicana writer, poet, scholar, and activist

Teacher 2 Teacher

An Introduction to the Education for Liberation Minnesota's Ethnic Studies BIPOC Mentorship Network

THE INAUGURAL COHORT OF THE ETHNIC STUDIES BIPOC MENTORSHIP NETWORK, INCLUDING MENTORS, MENTEES, AND EDLIB MN ORGANIZING COMMITTEE MEMBERS INCLUDE:

Janaan Ahmed, Natalia Benjamin, Cristeta Boarini, Rose Brewer, Anita Chikkatur, cory cochrane, Sylvia Fred, Sarah Garton, Maria-Renee Grigsby, Sophia Grigsby, Lowana Greensky, Jonathan Hamilton, Carmen Higueros, Maria Higueros-Canny, Emmanuel Ifonlaja, Katie Johnston-Goodstar, Jenny Kordosky, Khadijah Lamah, Naomi Ono LeBeau, Robert Lin, Brian Lozenski, Meredith McCoy, Anthony Minus Angelina Momanyi, mk nguyen, Kleber Ortiz, Corina Pastrana, Jimmy Patino, Nathan Perez, Tracy Pham, Iana Phillips, Madeleine Pinkerton, A'nia-Nicole Rae, Malachi Raymond, Adam Savariego, Terrance Shambley, Cassandra Sheppard, Nate Taylor, Daniel Teshome (Sahille), Diamond Thlang, Shakita Thomas, Angelica Torralba-Olague, Lauretta Towns, David Traslavina, Pang Yang, Maheen Zaman

Background

In July 2019, the Twin Cities (Minneapolis and St. Paul, MN) hosted our biennial Free Minds, Free People Conference. Though a national conference, the volunteer-led, year-long planning process leans heavily on the local delegation to make the gathering a reality. During the intensive planning process in 2019, the conference organizers in the Twin Cities formed an identity and a community that, following the conference, became the Education for Liberation Network's first local chapter: EdLib Minnesota.

One of the first projects Ed Lib MN created was the *Ed Lib Minnesota BIPOC Ethnic Studies Learning Community* – a unique and powerful mentorship model designed to advance ethnic studies teaching, learning, and advocacy in and beyond Minnesota classrooms. We feature their *Learning Community* in this year's Teacher 2 Teacher because there is so much to learn from how they approach their work, the role of relationships in what they do, and their important conception of who can and should be a mentor. Following an introduction to the nuts and bolts of the *Learning Community*, Sarah Garton – a high school social studies teacher and one of the coordinators of the network – offers a glimpse into the work they embarked on during the 2020-2021 school year. Following that are testimonials from Sarah's fellow cohort members.

Overview

The Ed Lib Minnesota BIPOC Ethnic Studies Learning Community uses a collaborative group mentoring model that builds relationships among K-12 educators (mentees) and the following mentors: higher ed Ethnic Studies faculty, youth, veteran K-12 teachers, youthworkers, and artists. Representatives from each of these groups come together in a small collaborative cohort with the goal of supporting one another and, along with the larger group of members in the Learning Community, working to strengthen the development of Ethnic Studies content knowledge and pedagogy in Minnesota.

In the inaugural year of the Learning Community, there were 50 members including 20 mentee educators, 20 mentors (five youth, five youthworkers, five faculty, and five artists), and 10 members of EdLib MN who coordinate the network. The hope is to recruit a new group of mentors and mentees each year. Most of the members are in the Twin Cities Metro area, but there are three Indigenous members who live on reservations, and one member from Rochester, MN. The large group of 50 meets every other month on Saturday mornings. In the months between, the network breaks into five cohorts of nine people (four mentee educators, four mentors – youth, youthworker, faculty, and artist – and one liaison from EdLib MN). One of the key innovations EdLib MN uses is the idea of horizontal rather than hierarchical mentorship, in which everyone has expertise and everyone has something to learn.

A Glimpse into the Learning Community

by Sarah Garton

The 2019 Free Minds, Free People Conference brought us all together. After months of planning and then hosting that inspirational space, we met again and asked ourselves: How do we move now toward liberatory education in Mni Sota Makoce? Ms Norma, the educational leader from El Colegio, a liberation-based high school in Minneapolis, said, "We need spaces for teachers to be together." As a new teacher, I'd been wondering: where are all the ethnic studies teachers?

We are so abundant in our TC education community: radical professors, Wobblies, mural artists, poets, policy heads, youth workers, paras holding it down, student activist coalitions, and YPAR crews, but the cities can be really siloed. There was a state grant available for teacher mentorship. We weren't really sure what we were creating as we applied; we just knew we hadn't really felt it yet, but knew how much we needed it. We got the grant and then the pandemic hit. George Floyd was murdered. Our cities were filled with rage and hope for abolitionist futures. In the wake of it all, our network applications went out asking: do you care about ethnic studies in the classroom? Bring your knowledge! So much of the outreach in the first few months was shedding a feeling of scarcity of knowledge and experience, instead offering a multidirectional flow of mentoring. Let's all come to the table. We value you and everything you are. You belong.

As with ethnic studies curricula, you first need to look to your own community ecosystem. Who's in the room? What do they need and want? There's not a real play-by-play for how to do this in your community; instead, we hope to inspire you for what's possible if you get together and ask: what do we see and what do we want to do together? And just as with the work of abolition, this work is a horizon and a constant struggle. Breaking down hierarchies of knowledge is long work, and still needs logistics and organization even if you want to embrace your messiness. Our organizing committee meets at least twice a month to plan our network gatherings of more than 50 teachers where we have community members and artists featured, talk about what's new with policy and social studies standards, and really hash out the theory and lessons. We also use these occasions to get to know each other. Especially during the pandemic, just seeing the network on a Saturday morning has been nourishing – Black, Brown, Indigenous teachers, youth, and academics not only from the Twin Cities, but from all the way up north Red Lake down to Rochester. Our relationships are what make us stronger, and we hope to build on them for years to come.

TIPS FOR STARTING YOUR OWN LEARNING COMMUNITY!

1. Allow ample time for connection and community.
2. Doing this work requires trust.
3. We were able to build relationships organizing for FMFP, and that translated to this: Ongoing relationships!
4. Find a common time to meet that is recurring and takes into account shifting schedules.
5. Look for small grant opportunities that don't require hours of writing.
6. Keep the work manageable and break it into small tasks.
7. Arts integration is key!
8. Roll deep – you need time and space for organizers to be able to step up and to step away to take care of life responsibilities. Planning, getting interpreters, and finding speakers all takes time and different perspectives.

Malachi (Youth Member)

More times than not, this work isn't a straight line; it's messy, confusing, and complex. Challenge previously learned information and be willing to learn from those you surround yourself with as they have a plethora of amazing knowledge.

I see everyone in the cohort as a "teacher" or rather an educator. We all have areas of expertise and areas where we want to grow. We identified these areas in the first few meetings so we know how we can help each other continue to grow and learn when we're in this cohort.

Angelina (Classroom Teacher)
This experience pushed me to write an elementary Black studies curriculum with another teacher at my school. We shared it with our building community, and it is currently being taught. This cohort, the organizing work of the Education for Liberation and the Youth 4 Ethnic Studies group, emboldened me. It was easy to push past resistance from my administration because I felt the support of my cohort and the ongoing organizing in support of ethnic studies in Minnesota and across the country.

Something to keep in mind as you create this kind of community is that relationships need time, effort, and intention to grow.

Maheen (Professor)
Prior to my engagement with Ed Lib, I have engaged ethnic studies and critical race theory from the intersection of Asian American and American Muslim Studies perspectives. Working with my cohort has pushed me to be even more interdisciplinary and to fully commit to education as a public good beyond academia… [T]he fellowship in Ed Lib's Mentoring Network has been a critical catalyst in my transformation.

If there is one suggestion I have to offer to future participants, it would be to come to this work as an intentional interpreter rather than a passive consumer of discourse and to have that direct sense of engagement shaped by the empathy of a good listener.

Anthony (Classroom Teacher)
Just accept the invite. It sounds very simple, but I overlooked my invite multiple times before I clicked "Yes." The time to speak is now!

The space allows me to free myself from thoughts of having to stay quiet. Questions that I have asked myself, students, and colleagues from the Ed Lib space are: How do we embrace challenges? How do we attack hurdles? How do we unite as a community of learners and leaders? Why am I, or are we, afraid? What are we afraid of? What do I aspire to be?

Adam (Professor)
Try to be wary of not entering what I call the "Oppression Olympics." One's own individual experience should not dismiss others, but rather find commonalities between the experiences and ask what we can do together.

January

MONDAY **3**	TUESDAY **4**	WEDNESDAY **5**
230th anniversary of Mary Wollstonecraft's *A Vindication of the Rights of Women* *E/M* p.141 **170th anniversary of the arrival of the first Chinese laborers in Hawaii *H*** p.141		

What examples do you know of in which workers were (and are) explicitly incited to turn against each other on the basis of race and/or country of origin?

THURSDAY **6**

190th anniversary of the founding of New England Anti-Slavery Society ***M/H*** p.141

110th anniversary of New Mexico's becoming 47th state p.141

FRIDAY **7**

SATURDAY **8**

110th anniversary of the founding of the African National Congress (ANC) ***M/H*** p.141

20th anniversary of "No Child Left Behind." ***TR*** p.142

SUNDAY **9**

"Enslave the liberty of but one human being and the liberties of the world are put in peril."

- William Lloyd Garrison, American abolitionist, suffragist, and social reformer

January

MONDAY **10**	TUESDAY **11**	WEDNESDAY **12**
Bodhi Day (Buddhism) ***E/M*** p.142	**National Human Trafficking Awareness Day *M/H*** p.142 **110th anniversary of the Bread and Roses Strike *E/M/H/TR*** p.142	

? ***What is the power of unionized labor? Who benefits when unions are dissolved or workers are prevented from organizing?***

THURSDAY **13**

FRIDAY **14**

SATURDAY **15**

SUNDAY **16**

190th anniversary of Alabama's declaring sovereignty over Creek and Cherokee peoples *E/TR* p.142

Religious Freedom Day *E/M/H* p.142

"Until we get equality in education, we won't have an equal society."

- Sonia Maria Sotomayor, Supreme Court Justice

January

MONDAY **17**	TUESDAY **18**	WEDNESDAY **19**
Martin Luther King, Jr. Day (Observed) ***E/M/H*** p.143  **Muhammad Ali, champion boxer and human rights activist, born (1942-2016)** ***M/H/TR*** p.143 **60th anniversary of Executive Order 10988** ***M/H*** p.143	**60th anniversary of the temporary closing of Southern University** ***M/H*** p.143	**10th anniversary of Ava DuVernay's Sundance Film Festival Best Director Award** ***M/H/TR*** p.143

? ***What specific role do athletes play in the struggle for civil and human rights, both historically and today?***

THURSDAY **20**

FRIDAY **21**

SATURDAY **22**

90th anniversary of the peasant uprising in El Salvador *E* p.143

110th anniversary of lynching in Hamilton, GA *M/H* p.143

SUNDAY **23**

"My job is to restore dignity. Society told them that they were not beautiful, they were not amazing, that they will never make it. A big part of my job is to reassure them that they were lied to. And once I'm able to do that, I want them to dream."

- Ruby Corado, LGBTQ activist and founder of Casa Ruby

January

MONDAY **24**	TUESDAY **25**	WEDNESDAY **26**
	50th anniversary of Shirley Chisholm's announcing her candidacy for President *E/M/H/TR* p.144 **80th anniversary of the lynching of Cleo Wright in Sikeston, MO *M/H*** p.144 **40th anniversary of *Merrion v. Jicarilla Apache Tribe* *H*** p.144	**Bessie Coleman, first Black and first Native American woman pilot, born (1892-1926) *E*** p.144

? Besides running for office, what key roles do Indigenous, Black, and other Women of Color play in political life?

THURSDAY **27**

FRIDAY **28**
Margo Tamez, scholar, poet, and Indigenous rights advocate, born (1962) *M/H* p.144

SATURDAY **29**
20th anniversary of Mee Moua's election to the Minnesota State Senate *E/M*/p.144

SUNDAY **30**
50th anniversary of Northern Ireland's Bloody Sunday p.144

"If trauma be inherited, so be resilience."

- Elizabeth Acevedo, Dominican poet

January

MONDAY **31**

February

TUESDAY **1**

First day of African American History Month *E/M/H/TR* p.146

First day of the annual Black Lives Matter at School Week of Action *E/TR* p.146

Lunar New Year *E* p.126

Tet (Vietnamese New Year) ***E/M/H*** p.146

Langston Hughes, poet, author, playwright, born (1902-1967) *E/M* p.146

WEDNESDAY **2**

510th anniversary of Taíno leader Hatuey's execution in Cuba *M/H* p.146

? ***When people say, "All Lives Matter," how are they undermining the significance and validity of the demand that we acknowledge that "Black Lives Matter"?***

February

THURSDAY **3**

FRIDAY **4**

SATURDAY **5**

SUNDAY **6**

120th anniversary of Thomas Brown's lynching
H/TR p.147

? ***In what ways does structural racism contribute to the disproportionate number of African Americans with HIV diagnoses?***

"1. End 'zero tolerance' discipline and implement restorative justice
2. Hire more Black teachers
3. Mandate Black history and ethnic studies in K-12 curriculum
4. Fund counselors, not cops."

- BLM at School Demands

February

MONDAY **7**	TUESDAY **8**	WEDNESDAY **9**
National Black HIV/AIDS Awareness Day ***H*** p.147	**110th anniversary of the San Diego Free Speech Fight** ***H*** p.147	

? ***Which limits on free speech, if any, do you believe are appropriate or necessary?***

THURSDAY **10**

FRIDAY **11**

Lydia Maria Child, abolitionist and author, born (1802-1880) ***E*** p.147

SATURDAY **12**

SUNDAY **13**

"We must break down arbitrary borders around the world not only for immigration but also the borders and labels we put on people, the assumptions we make about other humans, how they live and what they believe."

- Cecilia Chung, civil rights and LGBTQ activist, HIV/AIDS awareness advocate

February

MONDAY **14**	TUESDAY **15**	WEDNESDAY **16**
Valentine's Day *E/M* p.147	Parinirvana (Nirvana) Day (Buddhism) ***E*** p.147	Ash Wednesday/first day of Lent (Christianity) ***M/H/TR*** p.147

THURSDAY **17**

Huey Newton, civil rights activist and Black Panther Party co-founder, born (1942-1989) ***H*** p.147

FRIDAY **18**

SATURDAY **19**

80th anniversary of President Franklin D. Roosevelt's order to intern Japanese Americans p.147

160th anniversary of the Anti-Coolie Act ***E*** p.148

SUNDAY **20**

? How did the US government justify the internment of Japanese people during World War II, and where do you hear echoes of these kinds of arguments today?

"The movement is contagious, and the people in it are the ones who pass on the spirit."

- Yuri Kochiyama, Japanese American civil rights activist

February

MONDAY **21**

Presidents Day *E/M* p.148

International Mother Language Day *TR* p.148

TUESDAY **22**

190th anniversary of the Female Anti-Slavery Society *E/M/H/TR* p.148

20th anniversary of Monsanto PCB verdict *H/TR* p.148

WEDNESDAY **23**

THURSDAY **24**

FRIDAY **25**

40th anniversary of Wisconsin's civil rights protections for LGBT people *E* p.148

SATURDAY **26**

60th anniversary of *Bailey v. Patterson* *E/M* p.148

50th anniversary of the Buffalo Creek Disaster *H/TR* p.148

10th anniversary of Trayvon Martin's murder *E/M/H* p.149

SUNDAY **27**

"If you talk to a man in a language he understands, that goes to his head. If you talk to him in his language, that goes to his heart."

- Nelson Mandela

? What motivates governments to create laws against certain marriages?

February

MONDAY **28**

Mahashivaratri (Hinduism) ***H/TR*** p.149

80th anniversary of White mobs rioting against racial integration in Detroit *H* p.149

March

TUESDAY **1**

First day of Women's History Month *E/M/TR* p.150

180th anniversary of *Commonwealth v. Hunt* *E/M* p.150

150th anniversary of Yellowstone National Park *E* p.150

80th anniversary of the Japanese internment proclamation *M/H* p.150

WEDNESDAY **2**

Ash Wednesday/first day of Lent (Christianity) ***M/H/TR*** p.150

10th anniversary of Iowa's "Ag-Gag" law *E/M/H* p.150

130th anniversary of People's Grocery lynching *M/H* p.150

110th anniversary of HR 409 hearings on Lawrence Strike *H* p.151

THURSDAY **3**

180th anniversary of first US child labor law regulating working hours *E/M* p.151

50th anniversary of the Center for Independent Living *M/H* p.151

FRIDAY **4**

140th anniversary of Anti-Chinese Demonstration Day *M/H* p.151

Miriam Makeba, South African singer and activist, born (1932-2008) *E/M/H* p.151

SATURDAY **5**

SUNDAY **6**

"Age is wisdom if one has lived one's life properly."

- Miriam Makeba, South African musician and activist

***?* Who profits and benefits from child labor globally? Do you?**

March

MONDAY **7**	TUESDAY **8**	WEDNESDAY **9**
80th anniversary of the death of Lucy Parsons *H* p.151	**240th anniversary of the Gnadenhutten Massacre of Lenape (Ohio) *E/M*** p.151	**Walter Mercado, television personality, born (1932-2019) *H*** p.152

THURSDAY **10**

100th anniversary of the arrest of Mahatma Gandhi for sedition
M/H p.152

50th anniversary of the first National Black Political Convention *H* p.152

FRIDAY **11**

SATURDAY **12**

SUNDAY **13**

Daylight Saving Time begins

First Day of Deaf History Month
E/M/H p.152

"Where there is love there is life."

- Mahatma Gandhi

What reasons could there be for the government and law enforcement to target and arrest so many of the most notable and celebrated activists, both historically and today?

MONDAY **14**	TUESDAY **15**	WEDNESDAY **16**
	International Day Against Police Brutality *H* p.152 **80th anniversary of Norwegian teachers resisting Nazi curriculum *H*** p.152	Purim begins at sunset on 3/16 (Judaism) ***E*** p.152 **230th anniversary of Denmark's abolition of the slave trade *H*** p.152

***?* Who and what do the police successfully serve and protect?**

THURSDAY **17**

Bayard Rustin, civil rights and LGBTQ+ rights activist, born (1912-1987) *E/M* p.153

FRIDAY **18**

First Day of Holi (Hinduism) ***E*** p.153

Fred Shuttlesworth, civil rights activist, born (1922-2011) *M/H/TR* p.153

30th anniversary of White South Africans voting to negotiate an end to Apartheid *M/H/TR* p.153

SATURDAY **19**

60th anniversary of Algerian independence
H p.153

SUNDAY **20**

170th anniversary of the publication of *Uncle Tom's Cabin*
E/M/H/TR p.153

"When an individual is protesting society's refusal to acknowledge his dignity as a human being, his very act of protest confers dignity on him."

- Bayard Rustin

March

MONDAY **21**	TUESDAY **22**	WEDNESDAY **23**
World Down Syndrome Day *E* p.153 **International Day for the Elimination of Racial Discrimination *TR*** p.153 **Zackie Achmat, South African LGBTQ and AIDS activist, born (1962) *H*** p.153 **10th anniversary of Juan Felipe Herrera's being named California Poet Laureate *H*** p.154	**World Water Day *E/M/H*** p.154 **50th anniversary of *Eisenstadt v. Baird* *H*** p.154	**90th anniversary of the Norris-LaGuardia Act *E*** p.154

? ***Should anyone have to pay for access to clean water?***

THURSDAY **24**

190th anniversary of the Treaty of Cusseta *E/M/H* p.154

Dorothy Height, educator and civil rights activist, born (1912-2010) *H* p.154

40th anniversary of the Sanctuary Movement (also called the Overground Railroad) *M/H* p.154

FRIDAY **25**

SATURDAY **26**

SUNDAY **27**

"Let's detox our cluttered academic brain. That's what the poet does. People call it daydreaming, detoxing our minds and taking care of that clutter. It's being able to let in call letters from the poetry universe."

- Juan Felipe Herrera, poet, teacher, and activist

March

MONDAY **28**

50th anniversary of Barbara Jordan's election as President of the Texas Senate *E/M* p.155

80th anniversary of the arrest of Minoru Yasui for breaking Japanese American curfew *M/H* p.155

TUESDAY **29**

WEDNESDAY **30**

220th anniversary of Indian Intercourse Act of 1802 *M/H* p.155

? How are curfews used as a tool to thwart protest? What recent examples of this can you think of?

THURSDAY **31**

César Chávez Day *E/M/H* p.126

60th anniversary of the National Farmworkers of America (NFWA) *E* p.155

FRIDAY **1**

First day of Arab American Heritage Month *TR* p.156

First day of Sexual Assault Awareness Month *E/H/TR* p.156

First day of National Poetry Month *E/M/H* p.156

90th anniversary of the Chicago School Children's Strike *E/M* p.156

April

SATURDAY **2**

First Day of the month of Ramadan (Islam) ***E/H/TR*** p.156

SUNDAY **3**

"I have rested in the shade of trees that others planted before me, so it behooves me to plant trees for those who come after me, that they may rest in their shade."

- Minoru Yasui,
Japanese American activist

April

MONDAY **4**	TUESDAY **5**	WEDNESDAY **6**
Dorothea Dix, social reformer, mental health activist, and advocate for women nurses, born (1802-1877) ***H/TR*** p.157	**190th anniversary of the Black Hawk War** ***TR*** p.157	**310th anniversary of slave revolt in New York** ***E/M/H*** p.157 **Rose Schneiderman, union organizer and women's rights activist, born (1882-1972).** ***E/M/H*** p.157

? ***How are nurses and physicians uniquely and powerfully positioned to exercise activism in certain areas of political struggle?***

THURSDAY **7**

World Health Day *H* p.157

Harry Hay, LGBTQ activist and labor organizer, born (1912-2002) *H* p.157

FRIDAY **8**

National Day of Silence *M/H* p.126

Vesak (Buddhism) ***E*** p.157

SATURDAY **9**

70th anniversary of the Bolivian National Revolution *H/TR* p.157

SUNDAY **10**

50th anniversary of the United Nations Biological Weapons Convention *H* p.158

130th anniversary of the Cuban Revolutionary Party (PRC) *E/M* p.158

"This is not the first time girls have been burned alive in the city. Every week I must learn of the untimely death of one of my sister workers. Every year thousands of us are maimed. The lives of men and women are so cheap, and property is so sacred. There are so many of us for one job it matters little if 146 of us are burned to death."

- Rose Schneiderman, feminist and union organizer

April

MONDAY **11**	TUESDAY **12**	WEDNESDAY **13**

THURSDAY **14**

70th anniversary of Ralph Ellison's *Invisible Man* H p.158

Vaisakhi (Sikhism) ***E/M/TR*** p.158

FRIDAY **15**

First day of Passover begins at sunset on 4/15 (Judaism) ***E/M*** p.158

Good Friday (Christianity) p.158

130th anniversary of the founding of *Kawkab America* H p.158

Cornelia (Corrie) ten Boom, Holocaust resister, born (1892-1983) *H* p.158

SATURDAY **16**

Hanuman Jayanti (Hinduism) ***M/H*** p.159

110th anniversary of Harriet Quimby's flight over the English Channel *E/M* p.159

160th anniversary of the Compensated Emancipation Act *H/TR* p.159

SUNDAY **17**

Easter (Christianity) ***E*** p.159

"Like bones to the human body, the axle to the wheel, the wing to the bird, and the air to the wing, so is liberty the essence of life."

- José Martí, Cuban revolutionary

? ***What do you know about Sikhism? How could you learn more?***

April

MONDAY **18**	TUESDAY **19**	WEDNESDAY **20**
		10th anniversary of the Racial Justice Act *H* p.159

THURSDAY **21**

FRIDAY **22**
Earth Day *H/TR* p.159

SATURDAY **23**

SUNDAY **24**
Armenian Genocide Remembrance Day
M/H p.159

"There's never been as much hope as there is today. As a kid on the front lines of probably one of the most depressing issues that our world has ever faced, I can tell you that there is more hope than there is apathy in the world. And there's so much left to fight for."

- Xiuhtezcatl Roske-Martinez, climate activist and hip-hop artist

? How can caring for the environment lead to a more just society?

April

MONDAY **25**	TUESDAY **26**	WEDNESDAY **27**
	160th anniversary of the Chinese Police Tax law *H* p.159	Yom HaShoa – Holocaust Remembrance Day – begins at sundown on 4/27 (Judaism) ***M/H*** p.159

THURSDAY **28**

FRIDAY **29**

30th anniversary of the Los Angeles uprising *M/H* p.159

60th anniversary of Linus Pauling's protest of nuclear testing *H* p.160

SATURDAY **30**

International Jazz Day *E* p.160

70th anniversary of the English translation of *The Diary of Anne Frank E/M/H/TR* p.160

130th anniversary of the lynching of Ephraim Grizzard *H* p.160

SUNDAY **1**

First day of Asian Pacific American Heritage Month *E/M/H/TR* p.161

First Day of Mental Health Awareness Month *TR* p.161

International Workers' Day/ May Day *H/TR* p.161

First Day of National Bike Month *H* p.161

30th anniversary of the Asian Pacific American Labor Alliance *E* p.161

? What is the role of music in social movements?

"Honor the hands that harvest your crops."

- Dolores Huerta

May

MONDAY **2**	TUESDAY **3**	WEDNESDAY **4**
First day of National Children's Book Week *E/M* p.161 Eid al-Fitr begins at sunset on 5/2 (Islam) ***E/M/H*** p.161 **Mabel Hampton, dancer, domestic worker, and lesbian activist, born (1902-1989) *H*** p.161	**World Press Freedom Day *H*** p.161 **National Teachers' Day *H/TR*** p.162	

***?** If teachers are considered to be essential workers, are they compensated and respected accordingly?*

THURSDAY **5**

Cinco de Mayo *E/M/H/TR* p.162

FRIDAY **6**

International No Diet Day *M/H* p.162

140th anniversary of the Chinese Exclusion Act *E/M/H* p.162

SATURDAY **7**

National Barrier Awareness Day *E/M/H/TR* p.162

SUNDAY **8**

Mother's Day *E/M/H/TR* p.162

"I have been a lesbian all my life, for 82 years, and I am proud of myself and my people. I would like all my people to be free in this world, my gay people and my Black people."

- Mabel Hampton, dancer, domestic worker, and LGBTQ activist

May

MONDAY **9**	TUESDAY **10**	WEDNESDAY **11**
10th anniversary of Manal al-Sharif's Václav Havel Prize for Creative Dissent ***M/H*** p.163 **190th anniversary of the Treaty of Payne's Landing** ***H*** p.163	**150th anniversary of Victoria Woodhull's becoming the first woman nominated for president** ***E/M*** p.163	**50th anniversary of César Chávez's hunger strike** ***E/M*** p.163

THURSDAY **12**

120th anniversary of the Anthracite Coal Strike *E/M* p.163

FRIDAY **13**

20th anniversary of amendment to Animal Welfare Act limiting the definition of "animal" *M/H* p.163

SATURDAY **14**

World Fair Trade Day *E/M/TR* p.163

SUNDAY **15**

International Conscientious Objectors Day *M/H* p.164

80th anniversary of the Women's Army Auxiliary Corp (WAC) *M/H* p.164

? Do women who serve in the Army today enjoy all the rights and benefits afforded to male soldiers?

"This history is not your fault, but it is absolutely your responsibility. "

- Nikki Sanchez, Indigenous media maker and environmental educator

May

MONDAY **16**	TUESDAY **17**	WEDNESDAY **18**
	International Day Against Homophobia, Biphobia and Transphobia (IDAHOBIT) ***E/M/H/TR*** p.164	**170th anniversary of the first state compulsory education law** ***H*** p.164

? Should schooling be compulsory?

THURSDAY **19**

FRIDAY **20**

160th anniversary of the Homestead Act *H* p.164

180th anniversary of the Seneca Treaty of Buffalo Creek *H* p.164

120th anniversary of end of US occupation of Cuba *H* p.164

20th anniversary of East Timor's independence from Indonesia p.164

SATURDAY **21**

90th anniversary of Amelia Earhart's transatlantic solo flight. *E/M* p.164

SUNDAY **22**

150th anniversary of the Amnesty Act of 1872 *H* p.165

20th anniversary of the conviction of Bobby Cherry *E/M/H* p.165

"Performance is a form of advocacy [and] a form of catharsis."

- Samar A., queer Jordanian activist

May

MONDAY **23**	TUESDAY **24**	WEDNESDAY **25**
William Ellsworth ("Dummy") Hoy, deaf major league baseball player, born (1862-1961) ***E/M*** p.165		**African Liberation Day** ***E/M/H/TR*** p.165

THURSDAY **26**

National Sorry Day (Australia)
E/M p.165

FRIDAY **27**

130th anniversary of White mob destroying Memphis office of Ida B. Wells' newspaper
M/H p.165

SATURDAY **28**

130th anniversary of the founding of the Sierra Club
M/H p.165

SUNDAY **29**

80th anniversary of the National Japanese American Student Relocation Council
E/M/H p.165

30th anniversary of the EPA report "Reducing Risk for All Communities"
E/M/H p.166

Laverne Cox, transgender actor, born (1972) ***TR*** p.166

10th anniversary of Dolores Huerta's Presidential Medal of Freedom ***M/H*** p.166

"No pride for some of us without liberation for all of us."

- Marsha P. Johnson, queer liberation activist

? ***Why is it a problem to have White people so overrepresented in the field of journalism?***

May

MONDAY 30

Memorial Day *E/H/TR* p.166

80th anniversary of the arrest of Fred Korematsu *E/M* p.166

TUESDAY 31

June

WEDNESDAY 1

First day of Caribbean American Heritage Month *E/M/H* p.167

First day of Lesbian, Gay, Bisexual and Transgender Pride Month *E/M/H/TR* p.167

THURSDAY **2**

FRIDAY **3**

30th anniversary of the Earth Summit
E/M/H p.167

SATURDAY **4**

Shavuot begins at sunset on 6/4 (Judaism) ***E*** p.167

UN Day of Innocent Children Victims of Aggression *E* p.167

110th anniversary of first Minimum Wage law in the US
M/H p.167

50th anniversary of Angela Davis's acquittal in Jonathan Jackson case *TR* p.167

SUNDAY **5**

Christy Brown, painter and poet, born (1932-1981)
M/H p.168

? How is the struggle to raise the minimum wage to $15/hour part of the movement for racial justice?

"I came to you tardy and late, as I usually do to the better things in my life."

- Christy Brown, Irish painter, poet, and artist

June

MONDAY **6**	TUESDAY **7**	WEDNESDAY **8**
	130th anniversary of the arrest of Homer Plessy *H* p.168	**10th anniversary of Razan Ghazzawi's Human Rights Defenders at Risk award *H*/*TR*** p.168

THURSDAY **9**

FRIDAY **10**

200th anniversary of Martin's Act ***E/M/H/TR*** p.168

150th anniversary of the 8-hour workday victory celebration ***H/TR*** p.168

SATURDAY **11**

20th anniversary of the Bari and Cherney decision ***H*** p.168

20th anniversary of CCN's victory over Shell Oil Corp ***M/H*** p.168

SUNDAY **12**

World Day Against Child Labor ***E/M/H*** p.169

40th anniversary of the Anti-Nuclear Proliferation Demonstration in Central Park ***H*** p.169

? What is an ecofeminist, and what does environmental justice have to do with feminism?

"Democracy only works when we work for it. When we fight for it, when we demand it."

- Stacey Abrams, American politician, lawyer, voting rights activist, and author

MONDAY **13**	TUESDAY **14**	WEDNESDAY **15**
		60th anniversary of SDS Port Huron Statement ***H*** p.169 **40th anniversary of** ***Plyler v. Doe*** ***E/M/H*** p.169 **Anthony Coelho, Congressman and disability rights advocate, born (1942)** ***M/H*** p.169

THURSDAY **16**

International Day of the African Child *H* p.169

100th anniversary of the Cable Act *H* p.169

FRIDAY **17**

70th anniversary of the signing of Decree 900 in Guatemala *E/M/H/TR* p.169

50th anniversary of the Watergate burglary *M/H* p.170

SATURDAY **18**

Autistic Pride Day *E/M/H* p.170

210th anniversary of the start of War of 1812 *M/H* p.170

200th anniversary of the arrest of Denmark Vesey *H* p.170

SUNDAY **19**

Juneteenth *E/H* p.170

Father's Day *E/M* p.170

40th anniversary of the murder of Vincent Chin *E/H* p.171

? What is neurodiversity, and why is it important for young people to learn about it?

"When it comes to human rights, you shouldn't wait to be asked."

- Arsham Parsi, exiled Iranian LGBTQ rights activist

June

MONDAY **20**	TUESDAY **21**	WEDNESDAY **22**
World Refugee Day *E/M/H* p.171	**Summer Solstice (Northern Hemisphere) *E*** p.171	**250th anniversary of the Somerset ruling *H*** p.171

THURSDAY 23

50th anniversary of Title IX *E/M/H* p.171

FRIDAY 24

40th anniversary of ILGWU strike in New York's Chinatown *H* p.171

SATURDAY 25

60th anniversary of *Engel v. Vitale* *H* p.171

50th anniversary of openly gay William Johnson's ordination as a Christian minister *H* p.172

40th anniversary of *Island Trees Board of Education v. Pico* *TR* p.172

190th anniversary of the Battle of Velasco *H* p.172

SUNDAY 26

International Day in Support of Victims of Torture *H* p.172

National HIV Testing Day *TR* p.172

? Is there any text you believe is appropriate for all students to be required to recite in a public school?

"We are born with the breath of survival. It is our birthright to learn the breath of thriving."

- Aimee Inglis, queer, femme, Osage/Wazhazhe organizer

MONDAY **27**	TUESDAY **28**	WEDNESDAY **29**
70th anniversary of the McCarran-Walter Act *M/H* p.172 **Paul Laurence Dunbar, poet and author, born (1872-1906) *E/M*** p.172		**Henry Gerber, gay rights activist, born (1892-1972) *H*** p.172

? How is poetry used as a tool for social change?

THURSDAY **30**

FRIDAY **1**

David Ross Brower, environmentalist, born (1912-2000) *H* p.173

60th anniversary of Rwanda's and Burundi's independence from Belgium *H* p.173

10th anniversary of the publication of *The Wrong Complexion for Protection* *H* p.173

120th anniversary of the Land Allotment Acts *E/M* p.173

SATURDAY **2**

SUNDAY **3**

"We don't inherit the earth from our ancestors; we borrow it from our children."

- Author unknown

July

MONDAY **4**	TUESDAY **5**	WEDNESDAY **6**
US Independence Day ***M/H/TR*** p.173 **60th anniversary of Algerian independence, granting women's right to vote and stand for election** ***H*** p.173		**130th anniversary of the Homestead Strike** ***H*** p.173

THURSDAY **7**

10th anniversary of Cambridge Declaration on Consciousness

M/H/TR p.173

FRIDAY **8**

SATURDAY **9**

Eid al-Adha begins at sunset 7/19 (Islam)

E p.174

SUNDAY **10**

"I must remind you that starving a child is violence. Suppressing a culture is violence. Neglecting school children is violence. Punishing a mother and her family is violence. Discrimination against a working man is violence. Ghetto housing is violence. Ignoring medical need is violence. Contempt for poverty is violence."

- Coretta Scott King

? Do you believe that nonhuman animals are conscious beings and therefore deserve full protection from harm and abuse?

MONDAY **11**

130th anniversary of Coeur d'Alene miners' strike *H* p.174

TUESDAY **12**

WEDNESDAY **13**

? ***What makes a strike "successful" in your opinion?***

THURSDAY **14**

FRIDAY **15**

160th anniversary of the Battle of Apache Pass *E/M* p.174

SATURDAY **16**

Ida B. Wells, educator, journalist, and activist, born (1862-1931) *E/M* p.174

SUNDAY **17**

"Justice is not a flexible tool. Unless we all do our part to ensure that justice is applied equally to all human beings, we are a party to its abuse. We must stand together to protect the rights of others."

- Leonard Peltier, Native American civil rights activist

July

MONDAY **18**	TUESDAY **19**	WEDNESDAY **20**

THURSDAY **21**

FRIDAY **22**

SATURDAY **23**

70th anniversary of the Egyptian Revolution *M/H* p.174

SUNDAY **24**

50th anniversary of Tuskegee syphilis experiment exposé *H/TR* p.174

? Today, how are the poor disproportionately mistreated in medical and other scientific studies?

"Youth are finally letting their voices be heard and letting others know it is our time to make decisions."

- Anthony Tamez-Pochel, founding member of the Chi-Nations Youth Council

July

MONDAY **25**	TUESDAY **26**	WEDNESDAY **27**

THURSDAY **28**

90th anniversary of attack on Bonus Army *H/TR* p.174

FRIDAY **29**

SATURDAY **30** SUNDAY **31**

"These days I've learned to write my past from right to left, and my present from left to right."

- Ahmed Badr, Iraqi American artist and activist

***?* What examples do you know of protests organized by current or retired soldiers?**

List of resources by month

To see an online version of this list with live links, visit: www.edliberation.org/planbookresources

Key E = Elementary School M = Middle School H = High School TR = Teacher Resources

August Resources

4 Barack Obama, 44th US President, born (1961). Obama was born in Hawaii to a White mother from Kansas and a Black father from Kenya. In law school, Obama became the first Black president of the *Harvard Law Review*. He later taught constitutional law at the University of Chicago. He went on to work as a community organizer, then won election to the Illinois State Senate and the US Senate. On November 4, 2008, Obama made history by becoming the first Black President of the United States.

Barack Obama: Son of Promise, Child of Hope, by Nikki Grimes. Even as a boy, Barack knew he wasn't quite like anybody else, but through his journeys he found the ability to listen to Hope and become what he was meant to be: a bridge to bring people together. This is the moving story of our 44th President, told by Nikki Grimes and illustrated by Bryan Collier, both winners of the Coretta Scott King Award. (**E**) bit.ly/3laT3LD; printable educator's guide: bit.ly/2ufyRkV

Of Thee I Sing: A Letter to My Daughters, by Barack Obama. In this tender, beautiful letter to his daughters, President Obama writes a moving tribute to 13 groundbreaking Americans and the ideals that have shaped our nation. (**E, M**) bit.ly/2EqAcq0

10th anniversary of the Environmental Justice Interagency Memorandum of Understanding (EJ MOU). The EJ MOU encapsulated agency responsibilities outlined in the 1994 Executive Order 12898, "Federal Actions to Address Environmental Justice in Minority Populations and Low-Income Populations." The EO directed Federal agencies to make environmental justice part of its mission and to work with other agencies on environmental justice issues as members of the EJ Interagency Working Group (IWG). The EJ MOU broadened the reach of the EJ IWG and formalized agency commitments to environmental justice.

Analyzing Environmental Justice, by Learning for Justice. This lesson helps students understand how pollution disproportionately affects people who are poor and members of racial and ethnic minorities. It also teaches them how to use a map to locate environmental injustice. (**M, H**) bit.ly/39AiJN6

---

5 40th anniversary of Air Traffic Controllers' strike. On August 3, almost 13,000 air traffic controllers went on strike in response to stalled negotiations with the federal government over demands for increased pay and shortened workweeks. On August 5th, President Ronald Reagan fired 11,359 striking air-traffic controllers, arguing they violated his return-to-work order. This resulted in federal decertification of PATCO and barred striking employees from federal service for life.

1981 Strike Leaves Legacy for American Workers, by Kathleen Schalch for NPR. An informational article about the effects of the 1981 Air Traffic Controllers strike. Also includes a timeline of events related to the strike and "Voices from 1981," a small collection of firsthand audio recordings. (**H, TR**) n.pr/3wn6Kwf

---

6 Hiroshima Day. This annual observance is held to remember the dropping of the first atomic bomb on the Japanese city of Hiroshima on August 6, 1945.

Haiku and Hiroshima: Teaching About the Atomic Bomb, by Wayne Au. Lesson for high school students on the bombing of Hiroshima, using haiku and the film *Barefoot Gen*. (**H**) bit.ly/2SdYmL4

A Bowl Full of Peace: A True Story, by Caren Stelson. In this moving nonfiction picture book, award-winning author Caren Stelson tells the story of Sachiko Yasui's experiences during and survival of the atomic bombing of Nagasaki, and brings her message of peace to a young audience. (**E, M**) carenstelson.com/books/

---

9 International Day of the World's Indigenous Peoples. In 2010, the United Nations declared August 9 as the day in which Indigenous Peoples would be honored. The annual commemoration is intended to raise awareness of the 370 million people worldwide whose traditions, cultures, and identities have been exploited and violated for centuries.

Standing with Standing Rock: A Role Play on the Dakota Access Pipeline, by Ursula Wolfe-Rocca, Bill Bigelow, and Andrew Duden. This role play helps students recognize the issues at stake in the historic struggle of the Standing Rock Sioux to block construction of the Dakota Access Pipeline. (**E, M, H**) bit.ly/2j9JkW3

---

10 Muharram begins at sunset 8/10 (Islam). Muharram is the beginning of the first lunar month of the Islamic calendar. It is often considered the second holiest month, after Ramadan.

My Name is Bilal, by Asma Mobin-Uddin. In this book, Bilal feels the need to hide his Muslim religion for fear he will be teased by other students. (**E**) bit.ly/2JvurtS

Salaam – A Muslim American Boy's Story, by Trish Brown. This is a biography about a Muslim American boy named Imran, who likes to do the same things that most children his age enjoy. Not everyone understands what it means to be Muslim, and through his story, Imran shows that Muslims strive to be good people, just as those of other faiths do. (**E**) bit.ly/2C8BsOk

---

12 International Youth Day. This UN holiday recognizes efforts of the world's youth to change global society for the better and promotes ways to encourage their active involvement in making positive contributions to their communities.

Kids on the March: 15 Stories of Speaking Out, Protesting, and Fighting for Justice, by Michael Long. Long before they could vote, kids have spoken up, walked out, gone on strike, and marched for racial justice, climate protection, gun control, world peace, and more. *Kids on the March* tells the stories of these protests, from the March of the Mill Children, who walked out of factories in 1903 for a shorter workweek, to 1951's Strike for a Better School, which helped build the case for *Brown v. Board of Education*, to the 21st century's most iconic movements, including March for Our Lives, the Climate Strike, and the Black Lives Matter protests reshaping our nation. (**E, M, H**) bit.ly/2RtCjVb

No Voice Too Small: Fourteen Young Americans Making History, edited by Lindsay Metcalf, Keila Dawson, and Jeanette Bradley. Mari Copeny demanded clean water in Flint. Jazz Jennings insisted, as a transgirl, on playing soccer with the girls' team. From Viridiana Sanchez Santos's quinceañera demonstration against anti-immigrant policy to Zach Wahls's moving declaration that his two moms and he were a family like any other, *No Voice Too Small* celebrates the young people who know how to be the change they seek. (**E, M**) bit.ly/3uM5TU9

140th anniversary of the founding of the United Brotherhood of Carpenters and Joiners of America. The United Brotherhood of Carpenters and Joiners of America is one of the largest trade unions in North America. Unlike most trade unions at the time, both Black and White workers were allowed to join from the beginning of the union.

Labor Unions and Working Conditions: United We Stand, a lesson plan by the Library of Congress. Students work with primary source documents from the Library of Congress online collections to study the working conditions of US laborers at the turn of the century and consider the question: "Was there a need for organized labor unions?" (**H**) bit.ly/3rISYRe

---

13

60th anniversary of the border closure between East and West Berlin. Following World War II, Germany was divided into four zones. Technically, the Soviets controlled Berlin, but it was split into two parts. Desperate to leave Soviet-controlled East Germany, millions of people escaped to the Western side. In August 1961, East German soldiers began laying down barbed wire and bricks as a barrier between East Berlin and the democratic Western section of the city. Two days later, construction began on the Berlin Wall, which remained in place until 1989.

The Berlin Wall and Beyond: An Online High School Curriculum, by Sarah Tellier. With six units of lesson plans, activities, discussion questions, primary source documents, and analysis worksheets, this website offers the tools that educators need to teach their students about the Berlin Wall, post-World War II Europe, and the Cold War through interactive activities, videos, photos, and other media. (**H**) bit.ly/3wpHBRx

---

18

Amelia Boynton, civil rights activist, born (1911-2015). Amelia Boynton was a civil rights pioneer from Alabama, who started her activism through voting rights campaigns and eventually became the first Black woman to run for Congress in Alabama. In 1965, Boynton helped organize and participated in the march from Selma to Montgomery, AL, which, because of the brutal attacks by police, came to be known as "Bloody Sunday." She was awarded the Martin Luther King, Jr. Medal of Freedom in 1990.

They Dared! by PBS. A collection of short videos (no more than 4 minutes) celebrating strong and determined Alabama women who dared to make a difference, including Amelia Boynton Robinson, Gwendolyn Patton, Hellen Keller, and more. (**E, M, H**) pbs.org/show/they-dared

---

Carter Camp, Indigenous rights activist and AIM leader, born (1941-2013). Camp was an American Indian Movement (AIM) activist, playing a leading role in the 1972 Trail of Broken Treaties and later in the AIM caravan to Washington, DC, where "Red Power" advocates occupied the Bureau of Indian Affairs offices. In 1973, he helped lead the Wounded Knee (SD) occupation, which lasted 73 days and resulted in the deaths of two protesters. He later focused on the Keystone Pipeline for its negative impact on tribal lands.

Alcatraz Is Not an Island, by PBS. This PBS website provides lesson plans and resources for teaching about the American Indian Movement. (**M, H**) bit.ly/2dZjx4I

19

230th anniversary of Benjamin Banneker's challenging Thomas Jefferson's support for slavery. Benjamin Banneker was a Black scientist, writer, and farmer who worked to invalidate the belief that White people were intellectually superior to Black people. In a public letter, he confronted Thomas Jefferson, Secretary of State at the time, about his pro-slavery stance and how it contradicted the principles of freedom and equality espoused by the Declaration of Independence, which Jefferson co-authored.

Created Equal: How Benjamin Banneker Challenged Jefferson on Race and Freedom, by Facing History and Ourselves. A reading on Banneker's challenge to Jefferson's pro-slavery stance, with selections from both Banneker's letter and Jefferson's response. (**H**) bit.ly/2PxSsbv

Dear Benjamin Banneker, by Andrea Davis Pinkney and Brian Pinkney. Benjamin Banneker was born free when most Black people in the United States were still enslaved. It troubled him that not all Black people were free. An accomplished astronomer and mathematician, he decided to take a stand against slavery by writing to then-Secretary of State Thomas Jefferson. This is the story of their extraordinary correspondence. (**E**) bit.ly/3sKExgQ

21

190th anniversary of Nat Turner's rebellion. Nat Turner, an enslaved preacher, led a slave rebellion in Southampton, VA that killed about 55 White slaveholders. Although fewer than 60 people took part in the uprising, White mobs tortured and murdered hundreds of Black people. Southern states passed laws designed to suppress Black rebellion and censor abolitionists, putting an end to the emancipation movement in that region. Turner was captured and executed along with 16 of his followers.

Nat Turner, by Kyle Baker. This graphic novel depicts the evils of slavery in this moving and historically accurate story of Nat Turner's slave rebellion. Told nearly wordlessly, every image resonates with the reader as the brutal story unfolds. (**M, H**) bit.ly/3vj6wpu; teaching guides at abramsbooks.com/resources

---

22

10th anniversary of Martin Luther King, Jr. Memorial opening to the public. Although open to the public on the 22nd, the memorial's official dedication was scheduled for August 28, 2011, to coincide with the 48th anniversary of the March on Washington for Jobs and Freedom. However, the ceremony was postponed until October because of Hurricane Irene. The memorial is located at 1964 Independence Avenue, S.W., a reference to the year the Civil Rights Act of 1964 became law.

The Speech: The Story Behind Dr. Martin Luther King Jr.'s Dream, by Gary Younge. Younge brings to life the fascinating chronicle of King's "I Have a Dream" speech and other events surrounding the March on Washington. The book is short, engaging, accessible and contains thoughtful analyses of race and racism in America in the 50 years since the march. (**H, TR**) bit.ly/19JfxW2

23

International Day for the Remembrance of the Slave Trade and Its Abolition. In 1791, enslaved African people staged a revolt in current-day Haiti, demanding freedom and independence. This uprising was a turning point in human history and is marked by UNESCO as an official day to pay tribute to those who fought for freedom, and to inspire all peoples of the world to fight against servitude, racism, prejudice, racial discrimination, and social injustice.

Teaching Hard History: A Framework for Teaching American Slavery, by Learning for Justice. Most students leave high school without an adequate understanding of the role slavery played in the development of the United States or how its legacies still influence us today. To try to remedy this, Teaching Tolerance developed a comprehensive guide for teaching and learning this critical topic at the middle and high school levels. Includes primary sources, podcasts, webinars, and more. (**M, H**) bit.ly/2FUocgs

Born on the Water, by Nikole Hannah-Jones and Renée Watson, the 1619 Project. The 1619 Project's lyrical picture book chronicles the consequences of slavery and the history of Black resistance in the United States. A young student receives a family tree assignment in school, but she can trace back only three generations. Grandma gathers the whole family, and the student learns that 400 years ago, in 1619, their ancestors were stolen and brought to America by White slave traders. But before that, they had a home, a land, and a language. She learns how the people said to be born on the water survived. (**E, M**) bit.ly/2RyPhRJ

---

24 10th anniversary of exposé of NYPD Islamophobic policing. The first in a series of damning exposés of the Islamophobic and illegal practices of the NYPD was published by the Associated Press. Among other outrageous acts, the AP found that hundreds of mosques and student groups were investigated and infiltrated with no evidence of wrongdoing. In addition, the CIA, which is prohibited from operating on US soil, helped set up many of these schemes. The series won a Pulitzer Prize and led to a congressional investigation.

Classroom Resources for Educating about Muslims, by teachingwhilemuslim.org. A compilation of resources, lesson plans, and curriculum guides to help fill the gap in educating about the experiences and history of Muslims all over the world, and to combat Islamophobia in our schools and communities. (**TR**) bit.ly/2JitGo4

American Islamophobia: Understanding the Roots and Rise of Fear, by Khaled Beydoun. Using his unique lens as a critical race theorist and law professor, Khaled A. Beydoun captures the many ways in which law, policy, and official state rhetoric have fueled the frightening resurgence of Islamophobia in the United States. (**H, TR**) bit.ly/3fRy3Jx

Under My Hijab, by Hena Khan. With cheerful rhyming text and charming illustrations, this picture book provides a friendly introduction to hijabs for all readers and celebrates the many Muslim women and girls who choose to wear them. Free teacher's guide at this site. (**E**) leeandlow.com/books/under-my-hijab

---

26 Women's Equality Day. Established in 1971, the date commemorates the day the 19th Amendment to the US Constitution went into effect in 1920, giving American women full voting rights.

Women and Social Movements in the United States, 1600 to 2000. This *Teacher's Corner* website offers more than 100 documents and lesson plans for teaching the role of women in American history. (**M, H**) bit.ly/bmuSYJ

50th anniversary of the First Women's Equality Day. Established in 1971, the date commemorates the day the 19th Amendment went into effect, giving American women full voting rights in 1920. On August 26, 1970, the National Organization for Women organized a Women's Strike for Equality. The strike drew national attention to the Women's movement. The following year, Bella Abzug introduced a bill designating August 26 as Women's Equality Day.

Women's Suffrage, by Justice for Education. Students will explore, using primary and secondary documents, how over a period of 75 years a movement of American women used nonviolent measures to persuade both federal and state governments to allow women to vote. In 1920, the 19th amendment to the Constitution was passed, securing women's right to vote. (**M, H**) bit.ly/2IOoO9c

Vanguard: How Black Women Broke Barriers, Won the Vote, and Insisted on Equality for All, by Martha Jones. In *Vanguard*, acclaimed historian Martha Jones offers a new history of African American women's political lives in America. She recounts how they defied both racism and sexism to fight for the ballot, and how they wielded political power to secure the equality and dignity of all persons. From the earliest days of the republic to the passage of the 1965 Voting Rights Act and beyond, Jones excavates the lives and work of Black women--Maria Stewart, Frances Ellen Watkins Harper, Fannie Lou Hamer, and more--who were the vanguard of women's rights, calling on America to realize its best ideals. (**H**) bit.ly/39JVwse

---

29 Krishna Janmashtami (Hinduism). Krishna is believed to be the eighth incarnation of Vishnu. This Hindu celebration of Krishna's birth is observed by fasting, praying and singing, dancing, and staying up until midnight to exchange gifts. In temples and homes, images of Krishna's infancy are placed in swings and cradles.

The Fantastic Adventures of Krishna, by Demi. *The Fantastic Adventures of Krishna* tells the enchanting tale of the child Krishna, who is sent by the God Vishnu to aid humanity. Hidden among the poor cowherds, Krishna uses his miraculous powers to fight an evil demon king who has overthrown the peaceful kingdom of Mathura. The story of Krishna, dating to the 8th century BCE, and forming an integral part of Hinduism, is beautifully brought to life by award-winning author and illustrator, Demi. (**E**) bit.ly/2VbP1ax

---

31 100th anniversary of the Battle of Blair Mountain. More than 10,000 coal miners in West Virginia rose up against mining company owners over low wages and poor working conditions. Armed warfare erupted between mine workers and a force of 3,000 police, deputies, and local militiamen brought in by the anti-union county sheriff, in addition to state police and coal company security. Eventually, federal troops were called in to end one of the largest labor uprisings in US history.

Battle of Blair Mountain, by David Rovics. This song is about the biggest battle in the West Virginia Coal Mine War of 1920-1921. The site includes the lyrics, link to the audio, and a link to the book on which the song is based. (**M, H**) bit.ly/3eynOJm

***Celebrate People's History: The Poster Book of Resistance and Revolution,* 2nd Edition**, edited by Josh MacPhee. These posters pay tribute to the longstanding human legacy of revolution, creative activism, and grassroots organizing. In this book, contemporary artists imagine and interpret often overlooked events and figures in movements for racial justice, women's rights, queer liberation, labor organizing, and environmental conservation. Includes a poster about the Battle of Blair Mountain. (**E, M, H**) bit.ly/3rXauSo

September Resources

1 **80th anniversary of Nazi decree requiring Jews to wear yellow stars**. Singling out Jewish people as "others" wasn't a new idea by the Nazis. It had been going on as far back as 807 CE. In the Nazi era, local jurisdictions began requiring Jews to wear emblems or badges to identify themselves. An official decree on September 1, 1941, required all Jews in Germany and occupied Poland to wear a yellow Star of David on their clothing. Failure to comply could result in beatings or death.

U.S. Holocaust Memorial Museum. USHMM provides resources for students and educators. It includes samples of primary documents and suggested lessons and activities for students and teachers. (**E, M, H, TR**) bit.ly/A0dotD

10th anniversary of Plan EJ 2014. Plan EJ 2014, named in recognition of the 20th anniversary of President Clinton's executive order 12898, was intended to integrate Environmental Justice into all EPA programs, policies, and activities. Clinton's order had called on every federal agency to identify and address the disproportionately high adverse effects their programs, policies, and activities had on minority and low-income populations. It seems strange that it took them 20 years to get around to it, but maybe better late than never.

Cast Away: Poems for Our Time, by Naomi Shihab Nye. With poems about food wrappers, lost mittens, plastic straws, refugee children, trashy talk, the environment, connection, community, responsibility to the planet, politics, immigration, time, junk mail, trash collectors, garbage trucks, all that we carry and all that we discard, this is a rich, engaging, moving, and sometimes humorous collection for readers ages 12 to adult. (**M, H**) bit.ly/2PwZGwz

---

3 **120th anniversary of Alabama's constitution mandating segregation**. Alabama adopted a state constitution that was designed to disenfranchise Black voters. It also prohibited interracial marriages and mandated segregated schools. Because of that pesky 14th Amendment, it had to appear race-neutral, but in reality, registrars were trained to decrease Black registration. Although it has been amended, the constitution and a few of its discriminatory provisions are still in place.

Amend: The Fight for America. In this student-friendly Netflix series, Will Smith hosts an examination of the evolving, often lethal, fight for equal rights in America through the lens of the US Constitution's 14th Amendment. (**M, H**) bit.ly/3qKZiHs

---

6 **Labor Day**. Labor Day honors the social and economic achievements of American workers and pays tribute to the contributions workers have made to the strength, prosperity, and wellbeing of the country.

What Rights Do We Have? by Bill Bigelow and Norm Diamond. A teaching activity that provides teachers with five units centered around labor movements, history, and rights. (**M, H, TR**) bit.ly/1kaTKy8

The Five Basic Steps to Organizing a Union. Student-friendly step-by-step guide to starting a union from the United Electrical, Radio and Machine Workers of America's website. (**M, H, TR**) bit.ly/VVGMxk

---

Rosh Hashanah begins the evening of 9/6/2021, ends 9/8/2021 (Judaism). Rosh Hashanah is the Jewish New Year.

Apples and Pomegranates: A Rosh Hashanah Seder, by Rahel Musleah. This children's book acts as a guideline for celebrating the Jewish New Year. Traditional foods and the sequence in which they are eaten are described. Each chapter includes the history of the food, an activity, recipes, and more. (**E**) bit.ly/2ShDgLT

---

8 **International Literacy Day**. International Literacy Day gives children and communities a chance to rediscover the joys of reading while raising awareness about those without access to formal education.

Freedom Libraries: The Untold Story of Libraries for African Americans in the South, by Mike Selby. Although illegal, racial segregation was strictly enforced in a number of American states, and public libraries were not immune. Numerous libraries were desegregated on paper only: there would be no cards given to African Americans, no books for them read, and no furniture for them to use. It was these exact conditions that helped create Freedom Libraries. More than 80 of these parallel libraries appeared in the Deep South, staffed by civil rights voter registration workers. (**H**) bit.ly/3se9QPV

Little Libraries, Big Heroes, by Miranda Paul. The inspiring story of how the Little Free Library organization brings communities together through books, from founder Todd Bol's first installation to the creation of more than 75,000 mini-libraries around the world. Includes an author's note and bibliography. (**E**) bit.ly/3wUFeGQ

Feed Your Mind: A Story of August Wilson, by Jen Bryant. As a child, August Wilson, the two-time Pulitzer Prize-winning playwright, read soup can labels and cereal boxes. When his mother took him to the library, his whole world opened up. After facing intense prejudice at school from both students and some teachers, August dropped out. However, he continued reading and educating himself independently. *Feed Your Mind* is told in two acts, revealing how Wilson grew up to be one of the most influential American playwrights. The book includes an author's note, a timeline of August Wilson's life, a list of Wilson's plays, and a bibliography. (**M, H**) bit.ly/3dWMlG8

---

9 **50th anniversary of the Attica Prison uprising**. Inmates at the state prison in Attica, NY were frustrated with chronic overcrowding, censorship of letters, and deplorable and dehumanizing living conditions. In a spontaneous uprising, the inmates went on a rampage and were met with lethal force. 43 people died, including 39 killed by the police and prison guards who fired indiscriminately into an area where hostages were being held. It was the deadliest prison uprising in US history.

We Do This 'til We Free Us: Abolitionist Organizing and Transforming Justice, by Mariame Kaba. In this collection of essays and interviews, Kaba reflects on the deep work of abolition and transformative political struggle. The book asks questions about justice beyond the punishment system, transforming how we deal with harm and accountability, and finding hope in collective struggle for abolition. (**H, TR**) bit.ly/3lfelaV; discussion guide at bit.ly/3fDoUUK

Steps to End Prisons and Policing: A Mixtape on Transformative Justice, by the Just Practice Collaborative. This mixtape is an offering of nourishment and care to the abolitionist community. Learn from some of the people who have been practicing and thinking about and creating organizations around Transformative Justice over the last two decades. (**H, TR**) bit.ly/3vsjVLb

Attica Prison Uprising 101 - A Short Primer, by Mariame Kaba. This publication about the Attica Prison uprising of 1971 is not intended to be a curriculum guide, but a brief primer for educators and organizers. It includes a timeline of events (with primary sources); testimonies from Attica prisoners; poetry by Attica prisoners; sample activities for youth; and other suggested resources. (**H, TR**) bit.ly/3sZrIOT

---

11 40th anniversary of Silver Spring monkey lab raid. An undercover worker from the animal-rights group People for the Ethical Treatment of Animals (PETA) alerted police to cruel treatment of monkeys at a research lab in Silver Spring, MD. The lab's raid led to a groundbreaking investigation resulting in important additions to the Animal Welfare Act and growing public scrutiny of the abuse that animals endure in experimentation.

TeachKind Materials, from PETA. PETA offers FREE classroom kits at both the primary and secondary levels that include comic books, informational leaflets and magazines on Humane Education topics, as well as sticker sheets and other materials. (**E, M, H**) bit.ly/2H49QM4

20th anniversary of the 9/11 terrorist attacks. Two hijacked planes crashed into the World Trade Center in NYC, one into the Pentagon, and one into a field in Pennsylvania, killing nearly 3,000 people, including more than 400 first responders. In response to the attacks, the US government started a war in Afghanistan that continues today, and enacted measures that infringe on civil liberties in the name of security. There has also been a dramatic increase in hate crimes toward Muslims and anyone appearing to be of Middle Eastern descent.

Teaching Elementary Students in Times of Crisis, by Marieke van Woerkom for Morningside Center for Social Responsibility. Written in 2021, this blog post provides some basic guidelines for opening up discussion on difficult issues with your elementary and middle school students. (**E, TR**) bit.ly/3cthnV7

Teaching on Days After: Dialogue & Resources for Educating Toward Justice, initiated by Alyssa Haley Dunn. This Facebook group is a space for progressive educators to share resources and support for teaching on "days after" major historical events. (**TR**) bit.ly/3cv9nTB

Countering Islamophobia, by Learning for Justice. This lesson helps students explore, confront, and deconstruct stereotypes targeted at Muslims. Students will learn about the impact of Islamophobia and create an anti-Islamophobia campaign to display in school. (**H**) bit.ly/2R8ggDc

Resources for Students and Teachers from the 9/11 Memorial & Museum. Links to virtual school programs and field trips, lesson plans, and other teaching materials about the events of 9/11 and how the attacks continue to impact our lives. (**E, M, H, TR**) 911memorial.org/learn/students-and-teachers

A Few Books about 9/11, a blog post by Pernille Ripp. From a practicing classroom teacher, a collection of recommended books for use with younger students about September 11, 2001. (**E, M**) bit.ly/3wng2bB

We Too Sing America: South Asian, Arab, Muslim, and Sikh Immigrants Shape Our Multiracial Future, by Deepa Iyer. Renowned activist Deepa Iyer asks whether hate crimes should be considered domestic terrorism and explores the role of the state in perpetuating racism through detentions, national registration programs, police profiling, and constant surveillance. Reframing the discussion of race in America, she addresses the complexity and diversity of the South Asian community and provides ideas from the front lines of post-9/11 America. (**H**) bit.ly/1KtM1pM

---

12 Pedro Albizu Campos, Puerto Rican independence activist, born (1891-1965). Campos was known as a powerful orator who condemned US imperialism and promoted Puerto Rican independence. He criticized the enslavement of Puerto Ricans to US economic and political interests, including tax breaks given to US corporations, compulsory military service for Puerto Ricans, and the despotism the US employed. He called for racial and national pride, emphasizing the importance of bravery and valor and the power of the human will over tyrannical military might.

War Against All Puerto Ricans: Revolution and Terror in America's Colony, by Nelson A. Denis. The website for this book includes a historical overview of Puerto Rico's struggle for independence, and a wealth of related resources, including video clips and other multimedia. Includes a section on Albizu Campos. (**H, TR**) bit.ly/2lOJDVL

---

13 140th anniversary of Lewis Latimer's first patent. Latimer, a self-taught Black inventor, worked with Hiram Maxim at U.S. Electric Lighting Company. While working there in 1881, Latimer patented a carbon filament for the incandescent lightbulb, which was safer and more durable than the paper filament invented by Thomas Edison. The invention helped make electric lighting practical and affordable for the average household. Latimer also worked with Alexander Graham Bell on the design of the telephone.

Black Pioneers of Science and Invention, by Louis Haber. A readable, perceptive account of the lives of 14 gifted innovators who have played important roles in scientific and industrial progress. The achievements of Benjamin Banneker, Granville T. Woods, George Washington Carver, and others have made jobs easier, saved countless lives, and in many cases, altered the course of history. (**E, M**) bit.ly/2PORrf2

Black Women in Science: A Black History Book for Kids, by Kimberly Brown Pellum. Fifteen powerful stories of fearless female scientists who advanced their STEM fields and fought to build a legacy. (**E, M**) bit.ly/3rJKg55

---

14 110th anniversary of the *Congreso Mexicanista*. *El Primer Congreso Mexicanista* met in Laredo, TX to address social, economic, and education issues affecting Mexicans and Mexican Americans. This convention aimed to discuss and formulate solutions to labor exploitation, segregation, economic disparities, and lynchings perpetrated by Anglo Texans against Mexicans and Mexican Americans. The convention was attended by hundreds of journalists, community activists, and citizens from Mexico and across Texas, forming the largest Mexican American civil rights forum of the time.

Sept. 14, 1911: El Primer Congreso Mexicanista Convenes in Laredo, by the Zinn Education Project. A short description of the first Mexicanist Congress meeting, along with related resources for teaching and learning. (**H**) www.zinnedproject.org/news/tdih/jovita-idar

Revolutionary Women of Texas and Mexico: Portraits of Soldaderas, Saints, and Subversives, edited by Ellen Riojas Clark, Kathy Sosa, and Jennifer Speed. This anthology embraces an expansive definition of the word revolutionary by looking at female role models and subversives from the last century and who stood up for their visions and ideals and continue to stand for them today. Eighteen portraits provide readers with a glimpse into each figure's life and place in history. (**H**) bit.ly/31DS51l

---

15 First day of Hispanic Heritage Month. Hispanic Heritage Month begins on September 15, the anniversary of independence for five Latin American countries: Costa Rica, El Salvador, Guatemala, Honduras, and Nicaragua.

Harvest of Empire: A History of Latinos in America, by Juan Gonzalez. Featuring family portraits of immigrants, as well as accounts of the events and conditions that compelled them to leave their homelands, this book is for anyone wishing to understand the history and legacy of this increasingly influential group. (**H**) bit.ly/3dxD2Mi

Dreams from Many Rivers: A Hispanic History of the United States Told in Poems, by Margarita Engle. From Juana Briones and Juan Ponce de León, to 18th century slaves and modern-day 6th graders, the many and varied people depicted in this moving narrative speak to the experiences and contributions of Latinos throughout the history of the United States, from the earliest known stories up to present day. It's a portrait of a great, enormously varied, and enduring heritage. (**E, M, H**) bit.ly/3dhGw73

Yom Kippur begins at sunset on 9/15/2021 and ends at sunset on 9/16/2021 (Judaism). Yom Kippur (the Day of Atonement) is one of two Jewish High Holy Days. It falls 10 days after Rosh Hashanah, the first High Holy Day.

Holiday Inclusion Guide, by Tanenbaum. A planning sheet for educators to think ahead about how to include diverse holidays in the classroom. (**TR**) bit.ly/2s3t4uS

Rethinking Holidays in Schools, a blog post by Alex Shevrin Venet. Reflection questions for educators that support schools in making intentional decisions about how to mark and celebrate holidays in classrooms. (**TR**) bit.ly/2PlSvaz

---

16 Mexican Independence Day. Otherwise known as *El Grito*, on this day Mexicans celebrate Mexico's independence from Spain.

El Grito: A Lesson Plan, by Patricia Schwarz. In this elementary-middle school lesson plan, students read a book written by students (*El Grito*) to learn the story of Mexico's fight for independence. Vocabulary activities, extension activities, links to build background information, and other resources are included. (**TR**) bit.ly/1cNPPpp

---

18 170th anniversary of Fort Defiance (AZ). Fort Defiance was established to create a military presence in Diné bikéyah (Navajo territory). Fort Defiance was built on valuable grazing land that the federal government then prohibited the Navajo from using. As a result, there was intense and ongoing fighting between the Diné and the US military.

Everything You Wanted to Know About Indians but Were Afraid to Ask: Young Readers Edition, by Anton Treuer. From the acclaimed Ojibwe author and professor Anton Treuer comes an essential book of questions and answers for Native and non-Native young readers alike. This expanded edition includes a new section on social activism. (**M, H**) bit.ly/31IlJTu

---

19 First Day of Banned Books Week. Banned Books Week was launched in 1982 in response to a sudden surge in the number of challenges to books in schools, bookstores, and libraries. More than 11,300 books have been challenged since 1982, according to the American Library Association.

Dear Banned Author, by the American Library Association's Office for Intellectual Freedom. During Banned Books Week, readers are encouraged to write to their favorite banned or challenged authors, sharing what their stories meant to them. (**E, M, H**) bit.ly/2SsnG0d

Celebrating the Freedom to Read, by the Banned Books Week Coalition. Information and resources, including links to videos, related to increasing awareness of the annual celebration of the freedom to read, and the movement against book censorship. (**TR**) bit.ly/2Sm6s4x

---

140th anniversary of Tuskegee Institute. In a bid to secure the Black vote in his race for re-election to the Alabama Senate, W.F. Foster agreed to get funding for a school for Black people. Legislation passed for the establishment of the "Negro Normal School of Tuskegee" with an appropriation of $2,000. Booker T. Washington was recruited as the Principal and only teacher. The school that began as a one-room shanty with 30 students has become a 3,000-student university on a sprawling campus.

A Teacher's Guide to The Souls of Black Folk, by Penguin USA. Several units of lesson plans ranging from DuBois's disagreements with Booker T. Washington to Jim Crow, to Emancipation and its aftermath. bit.ly/2mh3ajn

---

20 130th anniversary of the Cotton Pickers' strike. The strike was an attempt by Black sharecroppers to increase wages for picking cotton. At the time, many White landowners conspired to keep wages miserably low for their Black workers, and local law enforcement often rounded up the workers on vagrancy charges and forced them to work off their fines on select plantations. By the time a White mob put down the strike, at least 15 Black men and one White man had been killed.

Henry Stephens Salt, animal rights and social reform activist, born (1851-1939). Salt was an English writer, socialist, pacifist, naturalist, and ethical vegetarian whose book, *Animals' Rights: Considered in Relation to Social Progress*, influenced Mahatma Gandhi's study of vegetarianism and offered early and explicit concepts of animal rights.

Teaching Youth About Veganism, by Whitney Blomquist, The Vegetarian Resource Group. A brief lesson plan, resources and handouts, activities, and related PowerPoint slides to teach kids the basics of vegetarianism and veganism. (**E**) bit.ly/3nPFanw

---

40th anniversary of Solidarity Day. An estimated 400,000 people gathered in Washington, DC to protest President Reagan's budget cuts, tax policies, and his firing of air traffic controllers. The theme of "Jobs and Justice" acted as a point of solidarity among the AFL-CIO, other labor unions, civil rights groups, women's groups, and peace movements. Organizers were partly inspired by the Polish Solidarity movement, which was organized around workers' rights and social reform.

Teach Films with a Conscience, by Zinn Education Project. An annotated list of vetted films to support teaching and learning of social justice and critical political issues. The films are organized by themes, including Black Lives Matter, Colonialism, Criminal Justice, Labor Organizing, and many more. (**TR**) zinnedproject.org/materials/films-with-a-conscience

---

10th anniversary of repeal of "Don't Ask, Don't Tell". In 1994, the US adopted the discriminatory "Don't Ask, Don't Tell" policy for gay, lesbian, and bisexual people serving in the military. The Clinton administration seemed to think this was a reasonable compromise, though it prevented these service members from living their authentic lives while serving. By 2011, the tide of public opinion had turned, however, and President Obama rescinded the policy, enabling openly gay, lesbian, and bisexual service members to remain in the military.

On "Don't Ask, Don't Tell": Debating a Proposed Repeal, by Sarah Kavanagh and Holly Epstein Ojalvo for the Learning Network, *NYTimes*. From their description:

Should gays and lesbians be allowed to serve openly in the military? What issues are at stake in this issue? In this lesson, students consider the law and the arguments for and against repealing it, then engage in a "structured academic controversy" about whether or not the "Don't Ask, Don't Tell" policy should be repealed. (**H**) nyti.ms/3rMXXQT

Arsham Parsi, LGBTQI+ activist, born (1981). Parsi is an Iranian LGBTQ human rights activist living in exile in Canada after being forced to flee Iran where being gay is a crime punishable by death. He is the founder and Executive Director of the International Railroad for Queer Refugees, which helps queer Iranians with asylum applications, housing, and financial assistance. It also files petitions to governments on behalf of Iranian LGBTQ persons facing deportation back to Iran where they face a possible death sentence.

Am I Wrong to Love? by the UN Refugee Agency. A photo essay exhibit and collection featuring portraits and first-person stories of LGBTQI refugees and asylum seekers from around the world who are now living in Canada. (**M, H**) bit.ly/2PP2Mf6

The Power of Love: Meet the LGBTQI Refugees Finding Love Beyond Borders, by the UN Refugee Agency. Photos and stories of LGBTQI people finding and making home in new countries after forced displacement because of discrimination. (**M, H**) bit.ly/3oxa5VZ

---

21 International Day of Peace.

Initiated in 1981, the UN International Day of Peace is an annual commemoration aimed at encouraging all people to play a part in building a peace culture worldwide. Communities across the globe organize their own observances designed to bring people together for world peace.

Peace Tools for Teachers. This page on the peaceCENTER website offers a variety of peace teaching resources, including lessons, activities, dates, and quotes – all designed with teachers in mind. (**E, M, H, TR**) bit.ly/2HmWQSp

Painting for Peace: A Coloring Book for All Ages, by Carol Swartout Klein and Robert O'Neil. A journalist and marketing professional by training, Carol Swartout Klein grew up in Ferguson, MO, and was so inspired by witnessing the spirit of hundreds of volunteers coming together to bring hope to a community in shock that she wanted to capture the story and the art for posterity. *Painting for Peace* is a coloring book that helps begin conversations with children and inspires adults. (**E**) bit.ly/3clZHGw

---

First day of Sukkot begins at sunset 9/21/2021, ends at sunset 9/27 (Judaism). Sukkot is a 7-day harvest holiday that commemorates the 40-year period during which the Jews wandered the desert.

The Very Crowded Sukkah, by Leslie Kimmelman and Bob McMahon. This children's book tells the story of a family celebrating Sukkot by building a *sukkah* (a temporary hut) outdoors. When the weather doesn't cooperate, the family makes a decision about the celebration that includes some surprising guests. (**E**) bit.ly/2rZHvQR

40th anniversary of Belize's independence from Britain. A British Crown Colony since 1862, Belize was declared an independent nation on September 21, 1981. Though other Caribbean nations became independent in the early 1960s, Belize remained a British colony because Guatemala claimed a large part of Belize. After many years of diplomatic wrangling, made more difficult because the US took Guatemala's side, the small island nation finally got its independence.

The Night the Moon Fell: A Maya Myth, by Pat Mora. A whoosh from her grandfather's blowgun causes Luna, the moon, to tumble from the sky and fall to pieces in the dark ocean. To save herself, she enlists the help of little fish to glue her back together. At last she rises, beautiful and round again, taking her new friends with her to create the Milky Way. Pat Mora and artist Domi have taken the traditional Mopan Maya (Belize) myth in which the moon is a young weaver and the Milky Way a fish and transformed it into a magical story of friendship and imagination. (**E**) bit.ly/3dt4xqn

---

10th anniversary of the execution of Troy Davis. 42-year-old Black man, Troy Davis, was sentenced to death in 1989 for the fatal shooting of Mark McPhail, a White off-duty police officer. Despite new evidence proving Mr. Davis's innocence, Georgia's Board of Pardons and Paroles refused to grant him clemency, and he was executed the day after his hearing.

Death Penalty: What Is It? What Do We Think About It? by Marieke van Woerkom. This lesson was created in 2011 right after Troy Davis was executed. Still relevant today, the lesson involves studying Troy Davis's case and exploring different perspectives and facts about the death penalty. Resources include facts, readings, video links, and more. (**H, TR**) bit.ly/3cpIEb7

Just Mercy (Adapted for Young Adults): A True Story of the Fight for Justice, by Bryan Stevenson. Stevenson's story is one of working to protect basic human rights for the most vulnerable people in American society – the poor, the wrongly convicted, and those whose lives have been marked by discrimination and marginalization. Through this adaptation, young people will find themselves called to action and compassion in the pursuit of justice. (**H**) bit.ly/3sO6kg7

---

22 World Car-Free Day.

Each year, people around the world organize events to showcase alternatives to the automobile. The day was created in 2000 by Car Busters.

A People's Curriculum for the Earth: Teaching Climate Change and the Environmental Crisis, edited by Bill Bigelow and Tim Swinehart, *Rethinking Schools*. This book features some of the best articles from *Rethinking Schools* magazine, along with classroom-friendly readings on climate change, energy, water, food, and pollution, as well as on people who are working to improve the environment. (**E, M, H**) bit.ly/1VKElav

Buried Sunlight: How Fossil Fuels Have Changed the Earth, by Molly Bang and Penny Chisholm. Using simple language and breathtaking paintings, Bang and Chisholm present a clear, concise explanation of the fossil fuel energy cycle that began with the sun and now runs most of our transportation and energy use in our world. Readers will be mesmerized by this engaging fourth book in the award-winning Sunlight Series by Bang and Chisholm. (**E, M**) bit.ly/3ucdDia

---

23 George Jackson, Black Panther Party member, born (1941-1971).

At the age of 18, Jackson was sentenced to an indeterminate sentence of one year to life for stealing $70 from a gas station. While in prison, he became a communist and a member of the Black Panther Party. His book, *Soledad Brother*, is a collection of letters Jackson wrote while in prison. He was later accused of killing a prison guard. Three days before he was to go on trial, he was shot and killed by prison guards, which triggered riots in other prisons.

Soledad Brother: The Prison Letters of George Jackson. A collection of Jackson's letters from prison, *Soledad Brother* is a categorical condemnation of the racism of White America and a powerful appraisal of the prison system that eventually took his life but failed to break his spirit. (**H**) bit.ly/3qNNsfn

The Black Panthers: Vanguard of the Revolution, by Stanley Nelson. The first feature-length documentary to explore the Black Panther Party, its significance to the broader American culture, its cultural and political awakening for Black people, and the painful lessons wrought when a movement is derailed. Guide for educators included. (**H, TR**) pbs.org/1ol7BE6; bit.ly/1ooi5Zk

---

Amzie Moore, civil rights activist, born (1911-1982). Moore was a prominent figure in the Mississippi Civil Rights movement and voter registration campaign. He headed a local chapter of the NAACP and co-founded the Regional Council of Negro Leadership. Moore persuaded Bob Moses, a SNCC leader, to focus on voter registration rather than the usual sit-ins and other direct-action protests. He was instrumental in SNCC's recruiting campaign in Mississippi, and his grassroots strategies helped SNCC launch a major voter registration drive during Freedom Summer.

SNCC Digital Gateway, by the SNCC Legacy Project and the Duke Center for Documentary Studies. The SNCC Digital Gateway documentary website provides profiles, stories, a timeline, map, and much more about the Student Nonviolent Coordinating Committee. This is an invaluable classroom resource on the voting rights struggle and the overall fight for human rights and democracy in the United States. **(M, H, TR)** bit.ly/2FKYfmM

---

25 **50th anniversary of the repeal of the Emergency Detention Act of 1950**. The Japanese American Citizens League won its fight to repeal the Emergency Detention Act of 1950, which gave the government authority to detain suspected subversives without due process. Although the law was very personal to the JACL, they weren't its only opponents. Passed during the McCarthy era and vetoed by President Truman, it was designed to root out communists and was constitutionally problematic, both for the issues raised by the JACL and for glaring First Amendment violations.

Fish for Jimmy: Inspired by One Family's Experience in a Japanese American Internment Camp, by Katie Yamasaki. With the family forced to leave their home and go to an internment camp, Jimmy loses his appetite. Older brother Taro takes matters into his own hands and, night after night, sneaks out of the camp and catches fresh fish for Jimmy to help make him strong again. This affecting tale of courage and love is an adaptation of the author's true family story and includes a letter to readers with more information about the historical background and inspiration. (**E, M**) bit.ly/3mgFwTB

40th anniversary of swearing-in of Sandra Day O'Connor to Supreme Court. Sandra Day O'Connor was nominated by President Ronald Reagan to serve on the Supreme Court. Her appointment was unanimously approved by the Senate. Justice O'Connor was the first woman to serve on the highest court in the land. O'Connor, a conservative, had a record in which she sided with the other conservatives on the court on most cases, but mostly upheld women's rights to choose in the matter of abortion.

First: Sandra Day O'Connor, by Evan Thomas. A vivid and personal portrait of the life of Sandra Day O'Connor, the first woman to serve on the United States Supreme Court. (**H**) bit.ly/3cLpOMR

---

27 **200th anniversary of Mexico's independence from Spain**. The Mexican War of Independence, a revolutionary civil war, was fought over 14 years. The Treaty of Cordoba on August 24, 1821, officially ended Spanish rule in the territory. But it wasn't that straightforward. The road to independence was circuitous, involving mixed loyalties, upheavals in Spain, disagreements among the colonized Mexicans and among the Spanish military. Spain would later make attempts at recolonizing Mexico. Mexico finally became a republic in 1824.

Napí, by Antonio Ramirez. Napí is a young Mazateca girl who lives with her family in a little village on the bank of a river in the state of Oaxaca, Mexico. Each afternoon the family sits beneath the shade of a huge ceiba tree and listens to the grandfather's stories. As Napí listens dreamily, the afternoons take on different colors in her imagination. The ceiba tree sends Napí dreams every night, and in her favorite one, she becomes a heron, gliding freely along the river. Spanish language edition available. (**E**) amzn.to/39Ek6KV

---

28 **130th anniversary of Black longshoreman's strike**. 1,500 Black longshoremen walked off their jobs in Savannah, GA, demanding higher wages, guarantees of receiving the overtime pay they were due, and recognition of their union. The strike was well planned and orderly. A war chest of $5,000 had been accumulated, and a public relations blitz garnered full support from the Black community. Eventually, the companies brought in White scabs to replace the strikers, and the strike, ultimately unsuccessful, was called off after five days.

It's a Mystery – White Workers Against Black Workers, by Bill Bigelow and Norm Diamond. Teachers are provided with a unit plan depicting the history and social factors that contributed to the racial tensions between workers in the 1920s. (**H, TR**) bit.ly/1mFmfZV

---

30 **30th anniversary of the military coup in Haiti**. The military coup put an end to the government of Jean-Bertrand Aristide, Haiti's first democratically-elected president, only nine months after he took office. Aristide's election in December 1990, after nearly 30 years of dictatorship under "Papa Doc" and "Baby Doc" Duvalier, had brought hope to Haitians with promises of social, political, and economic improvements and an end to human rights abuses. The coup was strongly condemned by the international community.

Teaching About Haiti, by Teaching for Change. This page provides resources, lessons, and a link to an extensive booklist with insights into Haiti's strong history of resistance and serves as a critical tool in helping students gain an understanding of current issues. (**M, H**) bit.ly/5ONMaQ

October Resources

1 First day of Disability Employment Awareness Month. National Disability Employment Awareness Month aims to raise awareness about disability employment issues and celebrate the contributions of workers with disabilities.

Museum of disABILITY History. This site features an extensive virtual exhibition of images that help raise awareness of people with disabilities and their contributions to society. Lesson plans on disability-related topics for all grade levels are also provided. (**E, M, H**) bit.ly/1jDKHWi

Disability History Museum. This site was designed "to promote understanding about the historical experience of people with disabilities by recovering, chronicling, and interpreting their stories." This searchable collection offers documents and images related to disability history in the United States. (**M, H, TR**) bit.ly/JAD9r

---

World Vegetarian Day/First Day of Vegetarian Awareness Month. World Vegetarian Day is the annual kickoff for Vegetarian Awareness Month. The goal is to make a difference by raising awareness about the benefits of vegetarianism.

Meat.org: The Website the Meat Industry Doesn't Want You to See. A website with films and resources about animals killed for food. Free vegetarian starter kits and DVDs available. Warning: Explicit imagery that some may find hard to watch. (**H, TR**) bit.ly/17fyrKa

Decolonize Your Diet: Plant-Based Mexican-American Recipes for Health and Healing, by Luz Calvo and Catriona Rueda Esquibel. More than a cookbook, this book redefines what is meant by "traditional" Mexican food by reaching back through hundreds of years of history to reclaim heritage crops as a source of protection from modern diseases of development. (**M, H, TR**) bit.ly/3vfaYFE

First day of LGBT History Month. LGBT History Month celebrates the lives and achievements of LGBTQI+ people.

Gay, Lesbian, and Straight Education Network (GLSEN) Educator Resources. These resources help to ensure that LGBTQI+ students see themselves reflected in lessons and creates opportunities for all students to gain a more complex and authentic understanding of the world around them. **(E, M, H, TR)** bit.ly/2RZG9nF

Welcoming Schools. This is a guide for administrators, educators, parents and guardians who want to strengthen their schools' approaches to family diversity, gender stereotyping and bullying. It is specifically designed for use in K-5 learning environments and is inclusive of LGBTQI+ families and individuals in the broader context of diversity. (**E**) bit.ly/bN8CiT

170th anniversary of the Jerry Rescue. William Henry, an escaped slave from Missouri who went by the name of Jerry, was arrested in Syracuse, NY under the Fugitive Slave Law. The antislavery Liberty Party was holding its state convention in the city. When word of the arrest spread, several hundred abolitionists broke into the courthouse and set Jerry free. Jerry was taken into hiding and eventually transported to Canada. Nineteen of the rescuers were indicted, but only one was convicted.

I Lay My Stitches Down: Poems of American Slavery, by Cynthia Grady. This rich and intricate collection of poems chronicles the various experiences of enslaved people in America. Drawn together through imagery from quilting and fiber arts, each poem is spoken from a different perspective and supplemented by a historical note. (**E, M**) bit.ly/3fDkpt7

Anfesia Shapsnikoff, Aleut leader and educator, born (1901-1973). Shapsnikoff lived in Unalaska, where she served as a nurse, teacher, church member, and community leader. During WWII, Shapsnikoff supervised the burial of most of the Unalaska church treasures, fearing they would be looted or bombed. She spent years traveling throughout Alaska teaching basketry techniques. Shapsnikoff became a vocal critic of the continued presence of the US military in Unalaska, citing lack of respect and care for the land, waters, and people.

Seasons of Alaska Board Books, by Joni Spiess, Carla Snow, Yaari Toolie-Walker, and Angela Y. Gonzalez. Four board books about each of the seasons, all set in Alaska, written by Indigenous authors and including information about the Indigenous peoples of Alaska. (**E**) bit.ly/3s7ygdU

---

4 70th anniversary of Burglund HS walkout. In response to the murder of SNCC activist Herbert Lee by a Mississippi state legislator and the expulsion of their classmates from school for holding a sit-in at a Greyhound bus station, students at Burglund High School in McComb, MS organized a walkout. About 115 students participated, and in the weeks following the walkout, students kept up resistance and many were expelled. SNCC set up a temporary school for the expelled students.

Teaching SNCC: The Organization at the Heart of the Civil Rights Revolution, Teaching Activity by Adam Sanchez. In this series of role plays, students explore the history and evolution of the Student Nonviolent Coordinating Committee, including freedom rides and voter registration. Click "download to read in full" and register for a free account to access full lesson. (**H**) bit.ly/3bJnpC1

---

5 World Teachers' Day. World Teachers' Day was inaugurated in 1994 to commemorate the signing of the UNESCO/ ILO Recommendation Concerning the Status of Teachers in 1966.

Teaching When the World is On Fire, edited by Lisa Delpit. An energizing volume that speaks to our contentious world and the necessary conversations we all must have about it, *Teaching When the World Is On Fire* is sure to inspire teachers to support their students in navigating the current events, cultural shifts, and social dilemmas that shape our communities and our country. (**TR**) bit.ly/2z1VtYZ

Teachers Unions and Social Justice: Organizing for the Schools and Communities Our Students Deserve, edited by Michael Charney, Jesse Hagopian, and Bob Peterson. An anthology of more than 60 articles documenting the history and the methods of social justice unionism. Together, they describe the growing movement to forge multiracial alliances with communities to defend and transform public education. (**TR**) rethinkingschools.org/books/teacher-unions-and-social-justice

---

40th anniversary of *Seminole Tribe v. Butterworth*. In *Seminole Tribe v. Butterworth*, the 5th Circuit Court ruled that tribes have a right to create gambling enterprises on their land, a case that significantly influenced the development of modern Indian Gaming laws. Because of the decision, the Seminole Tribe was able to build and operate the nation's first tribally owned high-stakes bingo parlor on their reservation in Florida, even though bingo for profit was illegal under Florida law at the time.

She Sang Promise: The Story of Betty Mae Jumper, Seminole Tribe Leader, by Jan Godown Annino. The compelling and inspiring story of Betty Mae Tiger Jumper, one of modern America's first female elected tribal leaders. With its lyrical, poetic text, and rich, vibrant illustration, this biographical book will charm and amaze young readers. (**E, M**) bit.ly/2QVWKd6

---

6 First day of Navaratri (Hinduism). Navaratri is a 9-night festival of worship and dance that honors Mother Goddess in all her manifestations.

The Little Book of Hindu Deities: From the Goddess of Wealth to the Sacred Cow, by Sanjay Patel. Pixar animator and Academy Award-nominated director Sanjay Patel brings to life Hinduism's most important gods and goddesses (and one sacred stone) in fun, full-color illustrations, each accompanied by a short, lively profile. (**E**) bit.ly/2D23VXI

---

7 20th anniversary of the War in Afghanistan. A US-led coalition attacked Taliban-controlled Afghanistan with an intense bombing campaign. The invasion of Afghanistan was the opening salvo in the US "war on terror" and a response to the September 11, 2001 attacks in New York and Washington, DC by al-Qaida militants. "Operation Enduring Freedom" was intended to target terrorist mastermind Osama bin Laden's al-Qaida organization and the Taliban government that had ruled most of the country since 1996. The war continues today.

Winter Soldier: Iraq and Afghanistan - Eyewitness Accounts of the Occupations, Illustrated Edition, by Iraq Veterans Against the War. In spring 2008, inspired by the Vietnam-era Winter Soldier hearings, Iraq Veterans Against the War gathered veterans to expose war crimes in Afghanistan and Iraq. These are the powerful words, images, and documents of this historic gathering, which show the reality of life in Afghanistan and Iraq. (**H**) bit.ly/3ucc1oC

Teaching with the News: The United States in Afghanistan: Analyzing Political Cartoons, by The Choices Program. This lesson enables students to analyze a series of political cartoons to understand different viewpoints on US involvement in Afghanistan. (**M, H**) bit.ly/9EeGIe

---

8 Jesse Jackson, civil rights leader, Baptist minister, and politician, born (1941). Jesse Jackson is a prominent civil rights leader and minister, known for his partnership with Martin Luther King, Jr., his leadership in SCLC and Operation PUSH, as well as for running for President of the United States and popularizing the term African American. He was awarded the Presidential Medal of Freedom in 2000.

"I am Somebody," by Jesse Jackson. Full audio of Jesse Jackson's 1971 speech entitled, "I am Somebody," in which he affirms the dignity of Black people. (**E, M, H**) Original speech here: bit.ly/39Ftbmu; Version of the speech that he delivered on an episode of *Sesame Street* for young children here: bit.ly/3udW1lU

---

11 National Coming Out Day. National Coming Out Day is an annual event that celebrates coming out as gay, lesbian, bisexual, transgender, or queer. The goal is to promote a safe world for LGBTQI+ individuals to live their lives truthfully and openly.

When a Student Comes Out to You... Today or Any Day! by GLSEN. This blog post provides suggestions for how to respond when a student comes out to you. The post comes from GLSEN's Safe Space Kit available on their site. (**TR**) bit.ly/2Q1uwgl

King and The Dragonflies, by Kacen Callender. In a small but turbulent Louisiana town, one boy's grief takes him beyond the bayous of his backyard to learn that there is no right way to be yourself. (**M, H**) kacencallender.com/books

---

Indigenous Peoples Day (US). Indigenous Peoples Day, also known as Native American Day, began as a counter-celebration to Columbus Day in Berkeley, CA. The goal is to commemorate Native American history and promote Native American cultures.

All My Relations: A Podcast, by Matika Wilbur and Adrienne Keene. From the creators: "All My Relations is a podcast hosted by Matika Wilbur (Swinomish and Tulalip) and Adrienne Keene (Cherokee Nation) to explore our relationships – relationships to land, to our creatural relatives, and to one another. Each episode invites guests to delve into a different topic facing Native peoples today as we keep it real, play games, laugh a lot, and even cry sometimes." (**H**) allmyrelationspodcast.com

Reconsider Columbus Day, presented by Nu Heightz Cinema. This short PSA asks people to reconsider whether the crimes of Columbus should be celebrated. (**E, M, H**) bit.ly/9ILuXF

The People vs. Columbus, et al., by Bill Bigelow. This role play begins with the premise that a monstrous crime was committed in the years after 1492, when an estimated three million Taínos on the island of Hispaniola lost their lives. It's a free download excerpted from *Rethinking Columbus*. (**E, M, H**) bit.ly/hRdbSf

A Coyote Columbus Story, by Thomas King. Thomas King uses a bag of literary tricks to shatter the stereotypes surrounding Columbus's voyages. He invites children to laugh with him at the crazy antics of Coyote, who unwittingly causes Columbus to bring about the downfall of her human friends. He also makes the point that history is influenced by the culture of the storyteller. (**E**) bit.ly/1RyuKQl

An Indigenous Peoples' History of the United States for Young People, by Roxanne Dunbar-Ortiz, adapted by Jean Mendoza and Debbie Reese. The original academic text is fully adapted by renowned curriculum experts Debbie Reese and Jean Mendoza for middle-grade and young adult readers to include discussion topics, archival images, original maps, recommendations for further reading, and other materials to encourage students, teachers, and general readers to think critically about their own place in history. (**M, H**) bit.ly/2ULxJ5B

20th anniversary of California Senate Bill 828. Approved by Governor Gray Davis, the law required all offices within the California EPA to refine their environmental hazard strategies to identify and address gaps in existing programs, policies, and activities that impede the achievement of environmental justice. Protecting the health and property values of poor and minority neighborhoods has long been neglected. This law and other similar efforts at the federal level were meant to tackle those issues.

As Long as Grass Grows: The Indigenous Fight for Environmental Justice, from Colonization to Standing Rock, by Dina Gilio-Whitaker. Through the unique lens of "Indigenized environmental justice," Indigenous researcher and activist Dina Gilio-Whitaker explores the fraught history of treaty violations, struggles for food and water security, and protection of sacred sites, while highlighting the important leadership of Indigenous women in this centuries-long struggle. (**H**) bit.ly/3mlDxgF

---

12 110th anniversary of Society of American Indians. The Society of American Indians was formed by about 50 Native American men and women at Ohio State University. They chose this date – October 12 – because it is "Columbus Day," and this meeting was meant to represent a new start for American Indians. The

Society's goals were to raise awareness of the achievements of Native Americans and their contributions to society, as well as to discuss problems faced by Native Americans and possible solutions.

We Are Still Here: Native American Truths Everyone Should Know, by Traci Sorell. Twelve Native American kids present historical and contemporary laws, policies, struggles, and victories in Native life, each with a powerful refrain: *We are still here*! Precise, lyrical writing presents topics including forced assimilation, land allotment and Native tribal reorganization, termination, relocation, self-determination, Native civil rights, the Indian Child Welfare Act (ICWA), religious freedom, economic development, Native language revival efforts, cultural persistence, and nationhood. (**E, M**) tracisorell.com/we-are-still-here

---

13 100th anniversary of the founding of the Order of the Sons of America. The Order of the Sons of America was a civic organization formed by Mexican American citizens in San Antonio, TX. The organization spread to several other cities in Texas with the goal of protecting and promoting the interests of Mexican American US citizens and their communities and to fight discrimination against them. The group was primarily comprised of attorneys, teachers, and entrepreneurs.

They Call Me Guero: A Border Kid's Poems, by David Bowles. Twelve-year-old Guero is Mexican American, at home with Spanish or English and on both sides of the river. He's starting 7th grade with a woke English teacher who knows how to make poetry cool. (**E, M**) bit.ly/3rMhpNx

---

14 Dussehra (Hinduism). Dussehra is a Hindu festival that celebrates the victory of Lord Rama over Demon King Ravana, or good over evil.

Religions in My Neighborhood, by Tanenbaum. A collection of recommended readings, multimedia, and lesson plans to explore religious tolerance. (**E**) bit.ly/2GiZAC0

---

15 White Cane Safety Day. White Cane Safety Day celebrates the achievements of people who are blind or visually impaired and emphasizes the importance of the white cane as a symbol of independence.

The Sound of Colors: A Journey of the Imagination, by Jimmy Liao. This story follows the narrator, a woman who has lost her sight, through her journey around the city. She navigates the subway and the city she knows with language and descriptions that tap into her imagination as well as her innermost thoughts and feelings. (**E**) bit.ly/2s4hwaV

170th anniversary of The Second National Woman's Rights Convention. Held one year after the First National Woman's Rights Convention, the 1851 meeting drew a larger audience than the first. Although women's suffrage was a key element of the conference, many issues were raised, including education, job training, and women's place in the field of medicine. Citing the Declaration of Independence, the convention passed a resolution protesting the injustice done to women by depriving them of liberty and equality.

Lifting as We Climb: Black Women's Battle for the Ballot Box, by Evette Dionne. An eye-opening book that tells the important, overlooked story of Black women as a force in the Suffrage movement when fellow suffragists did not accept them as equal partners in the struggle. (**M, H**) bit.ly/2PY7Yx9

---

16 World Food Day. World Food Day is celebrated every year on October 16 to commemorate the founding of the United Nations Food and Agriculture Organization (FAO) in 1945.

The Omnivore's Dilemma, Young Readers Edition: The Secrets Behind What You Eat, by Michael Pollan. Based on Pollan's best-selling book of the same title, this version is written for teens, and challenges readers to consider the origin of the foods we eat and the broad ramifications of our eating habits. (**M, H, TR**) bit.ly/2s02Rxk

Multicultural Collection of Early Childhood Education Books About Food and Farming, by Ready to Grow. This list of recommended books, primarily featuring BIPOC characters and written by BIPOC authors, features stories about food and farming locally and internationally. (**E**) pareadysetgrow.org/book-list

---

130th anniversary of the death of Sarah Winnemucca, Paiute writer and activist (1844-1891). Known for her book *Life Among the Paiutes: Their Wrongs and Claims*, a memoir and ethnohistory of the first 40 years of Paiute contact with European Americans, Winnemucca worked as an interpreter and scout for the US Army but later became an outspoken advocate for Indigenous rights. Controversial for exaggerating her social status (daughter of a Paiute chief) and advocating assimilation of Natives to White culture, she is admired for her social work and activism.

How We Go Home: Voices from Indigenous North America, edited by Sara Sinclair. A collection of narrators' voices describing the ways in which their lives have been shaped by loss, injustice, and resilience, and by the struggle of how to share space with settler nations whose essential aim is to take all that is Indigenous. (**H**) bit.ly/2PW6SSI

---

17 International Day for the Eradication of Poverty. This day promotes the need to eradicate poverty worldwide, especially in the global South.

Finding Solutions to Hunger, by Kids Can Make a Difference. This educational program for middle and high school students focuses on the root causes of hunger and poverty, the people most affected, solutions, and how students can help. (**M, H**) bit.ly/cYEDNd

Teaching Economics As If People Mattered, by United for a Fair Economy. A collection of lesson plans about economics from a social justice perspective. bit.ly/6Aly7u

---

Vernon Bellecourt, American Indian Movement activist, born (1931-2007). Bellecourt, a member of the White Earth Band of Ojibwe, and a founding member of the American Indian Movement, was a leader in the fight for the human rights of Indigenous peoples, the restoration of Native American lands, and the preservation of Indigenous cultures and languages. He was especially noted for his ardent campaign against the use of Native names, images, and mascots by sports teams.

Interview with Vernon Bellecourt about the American Indian Movement. Bellecourt speaks about the state of nations and the demands being made in the American Indian Movement. **(H, TR)** bit.ly/9qBLCK

What's in a Mascot? by Pamela Gasway, Learning for Justice. A 9th grade English unit helps students analyze the legacy behind Native American mascots. (**H, TR**) bit.ly/3h3R5g8

150th anniversary of President Grant's declaring martial law over KKK violence in SC. The Ku Klux Klan formed in 1865 to resist Reconstruction in the South and to terrorize Black people. Despite warnings from the federal government, they continued to terrorize Black South Carolinians. President U.S. Grant declared martial law in nine counties and suspended the writ of habeas corpus so that KKK members could be arrested without going before a judge where they were not likely to be held accountable by White judges.

They Called Themselves the KKK: The Birth of an American Terrorist Group, by Susan Campbell Bartoletti. This is the story of how a secret terrorist group took root in America's democracy. Filled with chilling and vivid personal accounts unearthed from oral histories, congressional documents, and diaries, this account from Newbery Honor-winning author Susan Campbell Bartoletti is a book to read and remember. A YALSA Award for Excellence in Nonfiction for Young Adults Finalist. (**M, H**) bit.ly/3rN2DGk

---

22 National Day of Protest to Stop Police Brutality. The October 22nd Coalition to Stop Police Brutality, Repression, and the Criminalization of a Generation has been mobilizing annually to expose the epidemic of police brutality. The coalition asks that we wear black on this day to honor those whose lives have been stolen by police brutality. october22.org

The Day Tajon Got Shot, by T'Asia, J'yona, Reiyanna, Jonae, Makiya, Rose, Najae, Serenity, Jeanet, and Temil (the Teen Writers of Beacon House). In March 2015, 10 teenage girls from Beacon House in Washington, DC started writing a novel during the rise of the Black Lives Matter movement. They began with one central question: What really happens in a community when a Black youth is the victim of violence by police? How are those lives affected? Each writer takes on the perspective of a central character – the victim, the police officer, the witness, the parent, the friend, the officer's kids – and examines how it feels to be a human being on all sides of this event. Their stories thoughtfully explore issues of race, violence, loyalty, and justice in a community torn apart but seeking connection. (**E, M**) bit.ly/2PArMXC

We Still Here: Pandemic, Policing, Protest, and Possibility, by Marc Lamont Hill. In this urgent and incisive collection of new interviews bookended by two new essays, Marc Lamont Hill critically examines the "pre-existing conditions" that have led us to this moment of crisis and upheaval, guiding us through both the perils and possibilities, and helping us imagine an abolitionist future. (**H**) bit.ly/3sTMZua

Invisible No More: Police Violence Against Black Women and Women of Color, by Andrea Ritchie. A timely examination of how Black women, Indigenous women, and other Women of Color experience racial profiling, police brutality, and immigration enforcement. (**H**) bit.ly/3sUMYGr

---

24 150th anniversary of the Chinese Massacre of 1871. A mob of nearly 500 White people attacked and dragged Chinese Americans out of their homes while others built gallows to hang the victims. This happened after a police officer was shot and a civilian killed, allegedly by a Chinese American. The police stood by while the mob, including women and children, attacked innocent Chinese people. Eighteen of them were murdered in the largest mass lynching in US history. Only 10 people were tried; none went to jail.

Asian American Racial Justice Toolkit: From the organizers: "This toolkit represents the work and thinking of 15 grassroots organizations with Asian American bases living in the most precarious margins of power: low-income tenants, youth, undocumented immigrants, low-wage workers, refugees, women and girls, and queer and trans people. It reflects their experiences with criminalization, deportation, homophobia, xenophobia and Islamo-racism, war, gender violence, poverty, and worker exploitation. All of the modules are designed to begin with people's lived experiences, and to build structural awareness of why those experiences are happening, and how they are tied to the oppression of others." (**TR**) asianamtoolkit.org

Humanizing Asian Americans in the Classroom Through Children's Literature, by Monisha Bajaj, Learning for Justice. Too often, Asian American stories are absent from classroom libraries. In this article, one educator explains why this gap is so harmful and recommends ways to fix it. (**TR**) bit.ly/31Oas43

30th anniversary of the First National People of Color Environmental Leadership Conference. Black, Latinx, Native, and Asian Americans from all 50 states joined delegates from Puerto Rico, Canada, Central and South America, and the Marshall Islands for the first National People of Color Environmental Leadership Conference. The goal was to reaffirm their traditional connection to and respect for the natural world and to speak for themselves on some of the most critical issues of our times. Delegates adopted 17 "Principles of Environmental Justice" to outline core beliefs and guide their activism.

One Earth: People of Color Protecting the Planet, by Anuradha Rao. *One Earth* profiles Black, Indigenous and other People of Color who live and work as environmental defenders. Through their individual stories, the book shows that the intersection of environment and ethnicity is an asset to achieving environmental goals. The 20 short biographies introduce readers to diverse activists from all around the world. (**E, M**) bit.ly/2PPwP6q

---

25 40th anniversary of swearing-in of Sandra Day O'Connor to Supreme Court. Sandra Day O'Connor was nominated by President Ronald Reagan to serve on the Supreme Court. Her appointment was unanimously approved by the Senate. Justice O'Connor was the first woman to serve on the highest court in the land. O'Connor, a conservative, had a record in which she sided with the other conservatives on the court on most cases, but mostly upheld women's rights to choose in the matter of abortion.

First: Sandra Day O'Connor, by Evan Thomas. A vivid and personal portrait of the life of Sandra Day O'Connor, the first woman to serve on the United States Supreme Court. (**H**) bit.ly/3cLpOMR

---

26 Intersex Awareness Day. Intersex Awareness Day is the international day of grassroots action to end shame, secrecy, and unwanted genital cosmetic surgeries on intersex children.

InterACT, Advocates for Intersex Youth. A rich bibliography of resources, from academic papers and news articles to human rights rulings and policy statements related to intersex awareness and advocacy. (**M, H, TR**) bit.ly/1KUOkJN

Intersex Stories, Not Surgeries, by Pidgeon. A YouTube channel by non-binary, intersex youth, Pidgeon is a humorous and humanizing way to learn more about intersex experiences from their perspectives. (**M, H**) bit.ly/2s2tcLq

---

20th anniversary of the Patriot Act. Under the guise of national security, the Patriot Act was passed just 45 days after the 9/11 terrorist attacks. It was the first of many changes to surveillance laws, making it easier for the government to spy on American citizens by monitoring phone and electronic communications, collecting bank records, and tracking internet use. It also relaxed criteria for executing search warrants, violating Fourth Amendment protections.

Unconstitutional: The War on Our Civil Liberties, a film by Nonny de la Peña. A 70-minute documentary that investigates the ways in which the civil liberties of US citizens and immigrants have been rolled back since 9/11/2001 and the passage of the Patriot Act. (**H**) zinnedproject.org/materials/unconstitutional

27 Nawal El Saadawi (Arabic: نوال السعداوي) Egyptian feminist writer, activist, physician, and psychiatrist, born (1931-2021). Nawal El Saadawi graduated from medical school and worked as a psychiatrist and university lecturer. She published nearly 50 plays, novels, and short story collections over her long and distinguished career. Her writings focus on the subject of women in Egypt, refusing to shy away from controversial issues such as prostitution, domestic violence, and religious fundamentalism. She founded the Arab Women's Solidarity Association and co-founded the Arab Association for Human Rights.

An Interview with Nawal El Saadawi: "Do you Feel You Are Liberated? I Feel I Am Not." by Rachel Cooke for *The Guardian*. Video clips from a rich interview with Egyptian revolutionary Nawal El Saadawi with relevance to the issues of today. (**H**) bit.ly/3daNZ7J

---

31 130th anniversary of the Coal Creek War. The Coal Creek War was a protracted labor battle between miners and mining companies to stop the practice of convict leasing – bringing in primarily Black prisoners to replace White laborers in an effort to undermine labor organizing. On October 31, 1891, about 1,000 armed miners took control of the mine, set the convicts free, and burned down the stockades where the convicts were being kept. Eventually, convict leasing was outlawed.

Slavery by Another Name, directed by Sam Pollard. Based on the Pulitzer Prize-winning book, Douglas A. Blackmon's *Slavery by Another Name*, this 90-minute documentary challenges the view that slavery ended with the 13th Amendment in 1865. The PBS site includes video clips and links to other useful resources. (**M, H, TR**) to.pbs.org/zZnn6p

---

120th anniversary of Silas Esters' lynching. Silas Esters, a Black man awaiting trial on a charge of coercion, was kidnapped by a mob of White men from LaRue County Jail in Hodgenville, KY. The police officers handed over their keys to the mob, but Esters slipped free and ran 100 yards before he was shot dead. His corpse was hung at the courthouse, and nobody was charged with a crime following his murder.

The Legacy Museum and Curriculum. Opened in 2018, the Legacy Museum memorializes the enslavement of African Americans, the evolution of racial terror lynching, legalized racial segregation, and racial hierarchy in America. This museum explores the history of racial inequality and its relationship to a range of contemporary issues from mass incarceration to police violence. The 2nd link is to the museum's curriculum on the "Legacy of Lynching." (**H, TR**) bit.ly/3rP2l2t; bit.ly/3lgrQrd

---

***El Día de los Muertos* (Day of the Dead), begins on 10/31 and ends on 11/2**. *El Día de los Muertos* is a Mexican holiday during which ancient Aztec rituals honoring the dead are performed. The rituals have been practiced for at least 3,000 years.

Pablo Remembers, by George Ancona. This photodocumentary-style children's book follows Pablo and his family as they celebrate *Día de Los Muertos* by honoring his grandmother. (**E**) bit.ly/2LH9zBu

Funny Bones: Posada and His Day of the Dead Calaveras, by Duncan Tonatiuh. Funny Bones tells the story of how the amusing calaveras – skeletons performing various everyday or festive activities – came to be. They are the creation of Mexican artist José Guadalupe (Lupe) Posada (1852–1913). In a country that was not known for freedom of speech, he first drew political cartoons, much to the amusement of the local population but not the politicians. (**E**) bit.ly/2FKOXak

---

Halloween

What Do Halloween Costumes Say? by Learning for Justice. This lesson, adaptable across grades, can help students think critically about the ways Halloween costumes are marketed and how certain costumes perpetuate stereotypes. For school Halloween celebrations, the activity can be used to develop guidelines for acceptable costumes. (**E, M, H**) bit.ly/3mQOVBD

November Resources

1 First day of National American Indian Heritage Month. National American Indian Heritage Month recognizes the significant contributions of American Indians, also referred to as Native Americans.

We Shall Remain. This PBS miniseries and multimedia project establishes Native history as an essential part of American history. Five 90-minute documentaries, spanning 300 years, tell the story of pivotal moments in US history from the Native American perspective. Website includes teacher's guides. (**H**) to.pbs.org/2SvdUu2

Unlearning "Indian" Stereotypes, by Rethinking Schools. Narrated by Native American children, this DVD teaches about racial stereotypes and provides an introduction to Native American history through the eyes of children. Includes a teacher's guide and other resources. (**E, M, H**) bit.ly/2H64BOK

At the Mountain's Base, by Traci Sorell. A family, separated by duty and distance, waits for a loved one to return home in this lyrical picture book celebrating the bonds of a Cherokee family and the bravery of history-making women pilots. (**E, M**) bit.ly/2Xc7hSp

---

World Vegan Day. Veganism is a way of living that seeks to exclude, as far as possible and practicable, all forms of exploitation of and cruelty to animals for food, clothing, and any other purpose.

The Vegan Society. The Vegan Society is an educational charity that promotes and supports the vegan lifestyle. The Society was formed in 1944 by a group of vegetarians who recognized the ethical compromises of eating eggs and dairy products. (**M, H**) bit.ly/SY3Tx

Vegan Is Love: Having Heart and Taking Action, by Ruby Roth. Roth explores the many opportunities we have to make ethical decisions: refusing products tested on or made from animals; avoiding sea parks, circuses, animal races, and zoos; choosing to buy organic food; and more. Roth's message is direct but sensitive, bringing into sharp focus what it means to "put our love into action." (**E**) Book trailer by the author here: bit.ly/2OjlF8w

---

190th anniversary of the beginning of the Choctaw removal. The Choctaw began the long journey from their native lands in the Southeast to Oklahoma, forced by President Andrew Jackson's Indian Removal Act. About 13,000 would be relocated between 1831 and 1833. Thousands died on the journey. As they reached Little Rock, a Choctaw chief was quoted in the *Arkansas Gazette* that the removal thus far had been a "trail of tears and death," a phrase that would later become associated with the 1838 Cherokee Removal.

Mary and the Trail of Tears: A Cherokee Removal Survival Story, by Andrea Rogers. Twelve-year-old Mary and her Cherokee family are forced out of their home in Georgia by US soldiers in May 1838. Featuring nonfiction support material, a glossary, and reader response questions, this story explores the tragedy of forced removals following the Indian Removal Act of 1830. (**E, M**) bit.ly/3dEGJjl

---

40th anniversary of Antigua's and Barbuda's independence from Britain. Antigua was colonized by the British in 1632, followed in 1678 by nearby Barbuda. In 1967, Antigua became an "associated state" to Great Britain, meaning they controlled their own internal affairs, while the UK controlled external affairs and defense. By the 1970s, an independence movement began on the islands. Barbuda had been a dependency of Antigua but wanted to secede. Finally, both islands achieved independence as separate nations in November 1981.

---

2 Election Day

One Person, No Vote: How Not All Voters are Treated Equally (Young Adult Edition), by Carol Anderson. Complete with a discussion guide, photographs, and information about getting involved with elections in teens' own communities, this is an essential explanation of the history of voting rights and a call to action for a better future. (**H**) bit.ly/3fRMTjd

The Voting Booth, by Brandy Colbert. From the Zinn Ed Project: "*The Voting Booth*, a novel for ages 12+, lives up to its dedication to Fannie Lou Hamer. Two storylines sweep readers along – one about contemporary challenges of voting on election day and the other a budding love story." (**M, H**) brandycolbert.com/book-inner

---

4 Diwali (Deepavali), Indian Festival of Lights (Hinduism, Sikhism, Jainism, and Buddhism). Diwali (Festival of Lights) is an annual festival of lights that commemorates the return of Lord Rama from exile.

Lights for Gita, by Rachna Gilmore. This book introduces readers to Diwali, one of the most important holidays observed by Hindus all over the world, through the eyes of Gita, a young immigrant girl. (**E**) bit.ly/2rYz5Jm

Diwali: A Cultural Adventure, by Sana Sood. This book offers young readers a bright, beautiful introduction to Diwali and how and why it is celebrated. (**E**) bit.ly/2HY9NAU

---

7 90th anniversary of the deaths of Black women after Georgia hospital refused care. Dean Juliette Derricotte, of Fisk University, and three of her students were seriously injured in a hit-and-run accident. Hamilton Memorial Hospital in Dalton, GA refused to treat the women because they were Black. Ms. Derricotte and one of her students, Nina Johnson, were critically injured, and by the time they reached a hospital that would treat them, 35 miles away, both were dead.

A Black Women's History of the United States, by Daina Ramey Berry and Kali Nicole Gross. This book reaches far beyond a single narrative to showcase the complexity of Black women's lives throughout history. Berry and Gross prioritize many voices: enslaved women, freedwomen, religious leaders, artists, queer women, activists, and women who lived outside the law. (**H, TR**) bit.ly/3exil5r

---

180th anniversary of *The Creole* Revolt. *The Creole* was a ship transporting slaves between Virginia and New Orleans when some of the slaves revolted and ordered the ship be taken to the Bahamas, a British colony where slavery had been abolished. *The Creole* Revolt ignited a fierce debate about slavery in the US and a diplomatic crisis between the US and Britain. Most of the slaves were freed by the British government. The leaders of the rebellion were arrested and later freed.

Teaching A People's History of Abolition and the Civil War, by Adam Sanchez, Rethinking Schools. A collection of 10 classroom-tested lessons on one of the most transformative periods in US history. These lessons encourage students to take a critical look at the popular narrative that focuses on Abraham Lincoln as the Great Emancipator and ignores the resistance of abolitionists and enslaved people. (**TR**) bit.ly/2RrqHSG

60th anniversary of the first openly gay person to run for public office. Jose Sarria was a drag performer, politician, and community leader who ran for the San Francisco Board of Supervisors – the first openly LGBTQ+ person to run for public office in the US. Though unsuccessful, he garnered 6,000 votes and paved the way for future Board of Supervisors member Harvey Milk. Sarria was active in the Gay Rights movement, helping to establish the League of Civil Education and the Society for Individual Rights.

Queer History of the United States for Young People, by Michael Bronski and Richie Chevat. This book explores how LGBTQ people have always been a part of our national identity, contributing to the country and culture for more than 400 years. Through engrossing narratives, letters, drawings, poems, and more, the book encourages young readers of all identities to feel pride in the accomplishments of the LGBTQ people who came before them and to use history as a guide to the future. (**M, H**) bit.ly/3aVl0S3; teacher's guide: bit.ly/3br8hXB

210th anniversary of the Battle of Tippecanoe. Tecumseh was the leader of Native American allied resistance to US expansion. In his absence, his brother led an attack on a US military force led by William Henry Harrison near Prophetstown at the junction of the Wabash and Tippecanoe Rivers. The Natives were badly outnumbered and outgunned. After the battle, Harrison burned Prophetstown to the ground, a setback for Tecumseh and his allies, who subsequently sided with the British in the War of 1812.

Tecumseh's Speech to the Osages (Winter 1811-12). Tecumseh, a Shawnee leader, sought to persuade all Indian tribes to unify against the growing White incursion into Indian lands. Links lead to primary text and Brian Jones's video re-enactment of the speech. **(E, M, H, TR)** bit.ly/3tEIRht

Tecumseh, by James Laxer. Two hundred years after his death, the Shawnee Chief Tecumseh is still considered one of the greatest leaders of North America's First Peoples. This richly illustrated biography tells the story of his remarkable life, culminating in the War of 1812. The book includes an epilogue, a timeline, a glossary, and maps. (**M**) bit.ly/2R2K4RU

Daylight Saving Time Ends

10

Samuel Gridley Howe, abolitionist, and educator of blind people, born (1801-1876). Howe, a physician, had a novel approach to teaching blind people, treating them with confidence, not pity. He developed many innovative methods and helped establish the Perkins Institution in Massachusetts, one of the oldest schools for blind people in the US. He was also an ardent social reformer and was active in the antislavery movement, serving as chairman of a group opposed to the Fugitive Slave Law.

Resources from The Abolition and Disability Justice Coalition. Guiding principles, shareables, and other resources related to alternatives to policing based in disability justice. (**H, TR**) abolitionanddisabilityjustice.com

11

Veterans Day. Veterans Day (previously called Armistice Day) was originally intended to mark the end of World War I. Now it is a day to celebrate all those who have served in the US Armed Forces.

Voices in Wartime, by *YES!* Magazine and Voices in Wartime Education Project. This site seeks to enable students to engage deeply with the subject of war by hearing and re-telling the personal stories of witnesses to war, encouraging students to imagine and create a less violent world. The site includes the film's trailer, curriculum materials, and poetry. (**H, TR**) bit.ly/1uCgCMY

Project YANO – The Project on Youth and Non-Military Opportunities. Celebrate Veterans Day by helping students find alternatives to military service. Project YANO is a non-profit community organization that provides young people with an alternative point of view about military enlistment. (**H**) projectyano.org

190th anniversary of Nat Turner's execution. Nat Turner, an enslaved Black man, was convicted of leading a rebellion of about 75 enslaved people in Southampton, VA, which resulted in the deaths of 55 White people. White reaction was swift and brutal. At least 200 Black people were murdered, though Turner escaped. Six weeks later, he was captured and hanged, along with 16 other men, in a public show of strength by White authorities wanting to make an example of Turner.

Nat Turner: A Troublesome Property, by director/writer Charles Burnett, California Newsreel. This film chronicles the violent confrontation of Nat Turner's Rebellion and shows how the story has been continuously re-told since 1831. (**H**) bit.ly/d6B1Be

140th anniversary of George Frederick Keller's "A Statue for Our Harbor." Magazines and newspapers in the 19th century spread racist images of Chinese immigrants. An example is a disgusting cartoon captioned, "A Statue for Our Harbor," depicting a Chinese person standing in the middle of the harbor, wearing tattered clothes, and smoking an opium pipe, with rats around the pedestal. The rays of light around him say, "filth," "immorality," "diseases," and "ruin to White labor," suggesting that this is what Chinese immigrants bring.

Eyes that Kiss in the Corners, by Joanna Ho. A young Asian girl notices that her eyes look different from those of her peers. They have big, round eyes and long lashes. She realizes that her eyes are like her mother's, her grandmother's, and her little sister's. Drawing from the strength of these powerful women in her life, she recognizes her own beauty and discovers a path to self-love and empowerment. This powerful, poetic picture book will resonate with readers of all ages. (**E**) bit.ly/3fJq68X

After Atlanta: Teaching About Asian American Identity and History, by Elizabeth Kleinrock for Learning for Justice. One elementary classroom teacher shares the conversation she started with students the day after the attacks in Atlanta and recommends resources anyone can use to teach about Asian American history and identity. (**TR**) bit.ly/3dzuG77

Asian/Asian American Children's Books, Lee & Low Books. A collection of titles from Lee and Low publishers that highlight the diversity of Asian and Asian American identities. (**E, TR**) leeandlow.com/cultures/asian-asian-american-interest

Coolies, by Yin. Shek marvels at the new world as he and his brother, Little Wong, arrive in California. Along with hundreds of other workers, the brothers are going to build a great railroad across the West. Inspired by actual events, this story reveals the harsh truth about life for the Chinese railroad workers in 1865, while celebrating their perseverance and bravery. (**E, M**) bit.ly/2Rc5En1; lesson plans to accompany the book at yinauthorvisits.com

12

Sor Juana Ines de la Cruz, writer and advocate for women's rights, born (1651-1695). Cruz, a Catholic nun from Mexico, was a self-taught scholar and writer during the Latin American colonial period. She wrote masterful poetry, plays, and essays. Her works were controversial and revolutionary for their time, espousing the idea of the inherent rights of women.

Her book, *Respuesta a Sor Filotea*, defending women's right to education, is considered the first feminist publication in the New World.

500 Years of Chicana Women's History, by Elizabeth Martinez. This bilingual text, along with hundreds of photos and other images, ranges from female-centered stories of pre-Columbian Mexico to profiles of contemporary social justice activists, labor leaders, youth organizers, artists, and environmentalists, among others. (**H**) bit.ly/3ba7sEh

¡Viva la Causa! 500 Years of Chicano History, by the Southwest Organizing Project and Collision Course Video Productions. Based on the book *500 Years of Chicano History in Pictures*, edited by Elizabeth Martínez, this two-part video in English offers a compelling introduction to the history of Mexican American people. (**M, H**) amzn.to/XhUqfa

---

13 30th anniversary of Audre Lorde's being named Poet Laureate of New York. Lorde described herself as a "Black, lesbian, mother, warrior, poet." She dedicated her life and talent to confronting and addressing the injustices of racism, sexism, classism, and homophobia. She was highly respected for her contributions to feminist theory, critical race studies, and queer theory, as articulated in both prose and poetry form. She was a co-founder of The Kitchen Table Women of Color Press and an editor of the lesbian journal *Chrysalis*.

A Litany for Survival: The Life and Work of Audre Lorde, a film by Ada Gay Griffin and Michelle Parkerson. This documentary explores the life of an activist whose work was entrenched in the Civil Rights movement, the Feminist/Womanist movement, and the Lesbian and Gay Rights movement. (**H, TR**) to.pbs.org/3ezleBN

---

15 140th anniversary of the Federation of Organized Trades and Labor Unions. The Federation of Organized Trades and Labor Unions was a precursor to the American Federation of Labor. It combined several different unions representing a variety of trades. The FOTLU worked to educate the public on labor issues and lobbied the US Congress to pass laws supporting the rights of workers.

The US Labor Movement Mixer, by Rethinking Schools. A "mixer" activity designed to engage students in playing the part of a worker during a particular period in US labor history. Includes role sheets with descriptions, clear instructions for the teacher, and pages of additional books and resources for teaching about US labor history. **(E, M, H**) bit.ly/2BBthKU

---

17 International Students' Day. An international observance and celebration of student community, multiculturalism, and inclusivity. Originally intended to commemorate the Nazi Germany storming of Czech universities, colleges and universities now mark it as a celebration of their international students.

We Came to America, by Faith Ringgold. A timely and beautiful look at America's rich historical diversity, with an appropriate complication of the "nation of immigrants" narrative that includes recognition of Indigenous peoples and the forced migration of the slave trade. (**E**) bit.ly/2llxdp8

60th anniversary of the Albany Movement. The Albany Movement was a coalition in Albany, GA fighting all forms of racial discrimination. They succeeded in mobilizing the majority of the Black community in the city to participate in boycotts and demonstrations. Although the movement achieved few of its goals, it is credited with helping refine tactics and strategies for the Civil Rights movement, including peaceful demonstrations, jail-ins, sit-ins, boycotts, and legal fights.

The Albany Movement: A Collection of Papers and Resources, from the MLK, Jr. Research and Education Institute, Stanford University. Shining light on the lesser known Albany Movement coalition, this collection of information, resources, and primary source documents includes Dr. King's diary entries from an Albany jail, an "Albany Manifesto," and other key documents. (**H, TR**) kinginstitute.stanford.edu/mlk-topic/albany-movement

---

20 Transgender Day of Remembrance. This day is set aside to memorialize those who were killed because of anti-transgender hatred.

A Trans* and Gender Non-conforming Reading List for All Ages, by The Booklist Reader. The list highlights books by and about the trans*/GNC community for all ages. For non-trans readers with family members, friends, or colleagues who are trans*/GNC – actually, for all readers with open minds and hearts – these books can lead the way toward becoming well-informed allies. (**E, M, H, TR**) bit.ly/2oxQCnU

Just Like You: A 60 Second Text, by Ki Gross, Woke Kindergarten. In 1-minute narrated images, Ki Gross translates "big concepts for little people." Designed for early childhood, this particular 60-second text features the important and beautiful lives of Black transgender people, and the ways in which these human beings are "just like you." (**E**) wokekindergarten.org/60secondtexts

Schools in Transition: A Guide for Supporting Transgender Students in K-12 Schools, by the ACLU. This guide highlights best practices while offering strategies for building upon and aligning them with each school's culture. (**TR**) bit.ly/3dwMEak

The Trans Educators Network (TEN) is a support and community-building focused organization for trans and other PK-12 educators who don't always fit neatly into systems of gender at school. The Network is open to trans educators or anyone whose gender exists outside prescribed lines of male and female, and who works with youth in PK-12 schools. TEN is firmly committed to trans justice, racial justice, and anti-oppression work in education. (**TR**) transeducators.com

---

23 Mamie Till Mobley, educator, activist, and mother of Emmett Till, born (1921-2003). Mamie was born in Mississippi, moving to Chicago at an early age. It was here that her son Emmett was born. After Emmett's brutal murder in Mississippi by White supremacists in 1955, Mamie chose to hold an open-casket funeral for her son to let the world know how he had been brutalized. After the acquittal of two of Emmet's murderers, she continued to fight for justice and civil rights for Black people.

Getting Away with Murder: The True Story of the Emmett Till Case, by Chris Crowe. Although the two White men who murdered Emmett Till were tried and acquitted by an all-White jury, they later bragged publicly about the crime. It was a galvanizing moment for Black leaders and ordinary citizens, including activists such as Rosa Parks. In clear, vivid detail accessible to high school students, Chris Crowe investigates the before-and-aftermath of the crime, as well as the dramatic court trial, and places it in the context of the nascent Civil Rights movement. (**H**) zinnedproject.org/materials/getting-away-with-murder

---

24 Arundhati Roy, Indian author and activist, born (1961). An award-winning writer and activist, Roy has written novels, screenplays, and essays covering topics including war, imperialism, nuclear weapons, environmental issues, democracy, race, genocide, and capitalism. She was awarded the 1997 Man Booker Prize for *The God of Small Things*, which has been translated into dozens of languages worldwide. She has also written several nonfiction books. In 2002, she received the Lannan Foundation Cultural Freedom Prize.

Arundhati Roy: A Digital Collection of Interviews and Conversations, assembled by Alternative Radio: Audio Energy for Democracy. An amazing audio collection of interviews and other conversations with Roy, all linked for easy access. The first program linked is a conversation between Arundhati Roy and Howard Zinn recorded in 2002. Other topics include "Confronting Empire," "A Writer's Place in Politics," "Surviving the Future," and many more. (**H**) alternativeradio.org/speaker/arundhati-roy

---

25 Thanksgiving/Day of Mourning

A Racial Justice Guide to Thanksgiving for Educators and Families, by Border Crossers. This guide includes a wealth of teaching approaches, lesson plans, study guides, resources for families, a reading list, and more. All vetted resources are categorized and hyperlinked. (**E, M, H, TR**) bit.ly/2o3fJAp

---

110th anniversary of the *Plan de Ayala*. Emiliano Zapata's *Plan de Ayala* called for the return to Mexicans land that had been lost through expropriation by the Spanish hacienda system. This document represents the basis for the Mexican Revolution. The *Plan de Ayala* was designed to explain Zapata's philosophy and generate support from other peasant groups. After its publication, disenfranchised peons from southern Mexico flocked to join Zapata's army and movement.

An Educator's Guide to the Mexican Revolution, by University of New Mexico's Latin American & Iberian Institute (LAII). This curriculum guide is inspired by, although it stands apart from, an exhibit of photos of the Mexican Revolution – many never published before. This guide provides K-12 educators resources for exploring the Mexican Revolution and offers suggestions for how to incorporate the topic into their classrooms. (**M, H**) bit.ly/3bIodHe

---

26 Buy Nothing Day

Buy Nothing Day. Buy Nothing Day (BND) is an international day of protest against consumerism, strategically celebrated on "Black Friday," the busiest shopping day of the year in the US.

The Story of Stuff, by Annie Leonard. *A* 20-minute, free downloadable video that explores consumption and exposes the connections between various environmental and social issues, while providing suggestions for action. (**E, M, H**) Website: bit.ly/vXj7EC; Reading Guide: bit.ly/1TQdXO0

The Story of Change, by Annie Leonard. A follow-up video to *The Story of Stuff*, *The Story of Change* asks if shopping can save the world, urging viewers to put down their credit cards and start exercising their civic muscles to build a more sustainable, just, and fulfilling world. (**M, H**) bit.ly/Vo6GIQ

Fur-Free Friday. This annual national protest against the wearing of fur is held on the day after Thanksgiving with the aim of educating shoppers and spreading awareness about the horrors of the fur industry.

Amos's Sweater, by Janet Lunn. Amos the sheep is old and cold and tired of giving up all his wool. But, despite his noisy objections, Aunt Hattie shears Amos once again and knits his wool into a brightly colored sweater for Uncle Henry. Poor Amos decides that this time he has had enough, and he sets out to reclaim what is rightfully his. (**E**) bit.ly/1nuzw9i

---

160th anniversary of the state of West Virginia. After Virginia joined the Confederacy in the Civil War, western delegates who disagreed with the decision formed West Virginia. Although it didn't immediately abolish slavery, the state authorized gradual abolition, meaning most enslaved children would be freed when they turned 21, and others immediately if born after July 4th, 1863. West Virginia ultimately abolished slavery in 1865, shortly before passage of the 13th Amendment.

How the Word Is Passed: A Reckoning with the History of Slavery Across America, by Clint Smith. Beginning in his own hometown of New Orleans, Clint Smith leads the reader through an unforgettable tour of monuments and landmarks – those that are honest about the past and those that are not – that offer an intergenerational story of how slavery has been central in shaping our nation's collective history and ourselves. (**H**) bit.ly/3sS7448

Mahalia Jackson, gospel singer and civil rights activist, born (1911-1972). Jackson's first major hit, "Move On Up a Little Higher," was released in 1948 and became the biggest selling gospel single at the time. Jackson quickly became well known in the US and abroad. She was also a strong supporter of the Civil Rights movement and was friends with Dr. Martin Luther King, Jr. She performed at the March on Washington as well as at King's funeral.

Mahalia, a film produced by Robin Roberts. A Lifetime Channel biopic featuring the life and accomplishments of Mahalia Jackson, starring Danielle Brooks. (**M, H**) bit.ly/3rL2OTr

Mahalia Jackson: Walking with Kings and Queens, by Nina Nolan. Accompanied by John Holyfield's gorgeous illustrations, debut author Nina Nolan's narrative wonderfully captures the amazing story of how Mahalia Jackson became the Queen of Gospel in this fascinating picture book biography for young children. (**E**) bit.ly/3wyo2XA

---

28 First day of Hanukkah begins at sunset on 11/28/2021 (Judaism).

Hanukkah is an 8-day Jewish holiday also known as the Festival of Lights.

Holidays Around the World: Celebrate Hanukkah: With Lights, Latkes, and Dreidels, by Deborah Heiligman. This children's book features *National Geographic* photography to illustrate how Jewish people around the world celebrate Hanukkah. (**E**) bit.ly/2U0xkr3

---

29 Wendell Phillips, abolitionist and activist, born (1811-1884).

Wendell Phillips, a White lawyer from Boston, was the foremost orator in the Abolitionist movement and a passionate advocate for the rights of Native Americans. He was horrified to learn that many of his friends and acquaintances supported slavery, so he quit his law practice and devoted all his energy to abolition. After passage of the 15th Amendment, he worked on behalf of women's rights, universal suffrage, and the Labor movement.

White Anti-Racist Biographies: Early Grades, by Learning for Justice. For young White students, explorations of fair and unfair, just and unjust can go a long way in advancing anti-racist White identity. Purposeful use of literature and basic study of White anti-racists are among the ways educators can advance such aims. Learning for Justice presents four short biographies for early grades classrooms, with activity ideas. (**E**) bit.ly/3rSpLn0

December Resources

1 World AIDS Day. The United Nations has designated this day to honor AIDS victims, focus attention on issues surrounding HIV/AIDS, and organize anti-discrimination activities.

How To Survive a Plague, a documentary film by David France. From ZinnEd Project's Films with a Conscience collection: "The riveting and heartbreaking story of the founding and growth of ACT UP (AIDS Coalition to Unleash Power), a central player in the struggle to pressure drug companies and the U.S. government to aggressively pursue a treatment and cure for AIDS. Through rich and intimate archival material, viewers learn about the people who comprised ACT UP... and see, in real time, how their bold civil disobedience was mobilized at key moments in the struggle. (**H**) zinnedproject.org/materials/films-with-a-conscience/#lgbtq

AVERT: Averting HIV and AIDS. A variety of resources and information, including quizzes, handouts, videos, and lessons for teachers and teens about living with and preventing HIV/AIDS. (**M, H**) bit.ly/uq5WS7

---

3 International Day of Persons with Disabilities. Launched by the UN in 1992, International Day of Persons with Disabilities aims to promote an understanding of issues faced by people with disabilities, with a view toward ensuring the dignity, rights, and well-being of this often-marginalized group.

10 Quick Ways to Analyze Children's Books for Ableism, by Chloë Myers and Hank Bersani, Jr. This article from Rethinking Schools gives teachers the tools to become aware of the omission of persons with disabilities in children's literature. This exclusion decreases the likelihood that the histories, experiences, or feelings of people with disabilities will be discussed in our classrooms. (**TR**) bit.ly/2qk6Nb2

Being Heumann: An Unrepentant Memoir of a Disability Rights Activist, by Judith Heumann with Kristen Joiner. One of the most influential disability rights activists in US history tells her personal story of fighting for the right to receive an education, have a job, and just be human. (**H**) beacon.org/Being-Heumann-P1691.aspx

---

7 80th anniversary of the attack on Pearl Harbor. The Japanese attack on the American naval base at Pearl Harbor, HI catapulted the US into World War II. The attack left more than 2,400 dead and 1,000 wounded in addition to destroying more than 300 planes and 20 ships. The Japanese were attempting to pressure the US into dropping economic sanctions against them, but it had the opposite effect. Another effect of the attack was rampant anti-Asian racism, resulting in the internment of thousands of Japanese Americans.

Righting a Wrong: Japanese Americans and World War II, by the National Museum of American History. Based on an exhibition that was on view at the National Museum of American History, this website offers artifacts and primary resources on Japanese immigration, executive order 9066, and life in internment camps and beyond. (**E, M, H**) s.si.edu/3r9LW7v

We Are Not Free, a book of Young Adult Fiction by Traci Chee. For 14-year-old budding artist Minoru Ito, her two brothers, her friends, and the other members of the Japanese American community in southern California, the three months since Pearl Harbor was attacked have become a waking nightmare: attacked, spat on, and abused with no way to retaliate – and now things are about to get worse, their lives forever changed by the mass incarcerations in the relocation camps. (**M, H**) tracichee.com/we-are-not-free

Write to Me: Letters from Japanese American Children to the Librarian They Left Behind, by Cynthia Grady. Through the three years of their internment, the children correspond with Miss Breed, sharing their stories, providing feedback on books, and creating a record of their experiences. Using excerpts from children's letters held at the Japanese American National Museum, author Cynthia Grady presents a difficult subject with honesty and hope. (**E, M**) bit.ly/3d8XLY9

---

9 60th anniversary of Tanganyika's (now Tanzania) independence from Britain. Tanganyika had been part of German East Africa since the mid-1880s, following a swap meet among European colonial powers. After Germany's defeat in World War I, Britain was awarded the Tanganyika territory, which became a protectorate rather than a full-fledged colony, meaning they could get out of Tanganyika what they wanted without putting much in. An independence movement in the '50s eventually led to independence in 1961, with African Socialist Julius Nyerere the first president.

---

10 International Human Rights Day. This day celebrates the UN's adoption of the Universal Declaration of Human Rights in 1948.

Human Rights and Service-Learning: Lesson Plans and Projects, by Kristine Belisle and Elizabeth Sullivan, Amnesty International-USA and Human Rights Education Associates (HREA). This manual contains lessons and service-learning projects. The lesson plans are divided into five human rights topics: Environment; Poverty; Discrimination; Children's Rights to Education and Health; and Law and Justice. (**E, M, H, TR**) bit.ly/2mObd9C

Toolkit for Schools to Become Human Rights-Friendly, by Amnesty International. Human rights-friendly schools are founded on the principles of equality, dignity, respect, non-discrimination, and participation. They are communities where human rights are learned, taught, practiced, respected, protected, and promoted. The *Human Rights-Friendly Schools* package contains a toolkit, pamphlets for students, schools, teachers, communities, and families, as well as a poster. (**E, M, H, TR**) bit.ly/2AkWpYp

---

International Animal Rights Day. International Animal Rights Day began in 1997 when a group of animal rights activists declared that all animals are sentient beings and deserve to be treated with respect. The group picked December 10 because it is also Human Rights Day and the anniversary of the signing of the Universal Declaration of Human Rights.

Animal Protection Activities, by the Institute for Humane Education. Activity topics include the connections between animal and human oppression, the inconsistencies in how we make choices about how we treat others, and more. (**E, M, H**) bit.ly/2m0xO49

Grace Thorpe, Native American and environmental activist, born (1921-2008). Thorpe served in the Women's Army Corps (WAC) during World War II and was a tribal judge and anti-nuclear activist, shaping a remarkable legacy as a steward for the rights of Indigenous peoples and the environment. She took an active role in the 1969 Native American occupation of Alcatraz, demanding the abandoned prison be turned into an Indian cultural center and school, and remained active in Native American economic development programs.

Life Story: Grace Thorpe, from Women & The American Story. The story of a Native American woman who served her country on the Pacific front during World War II and became an advocate for Native rights and the Anti-Nuclear movement, told through primary source multimedia resources, teaching materials, and suggested activities. (**M, H**) bit.ly/3dWMdXb

---

10th anniversary of Tawakkol Karman's Nobel Peace Prize. Tawakkol Karman was awarded the Nobel Peace Prize for her contributions as a leader in the Yemeni uprising. She was known as the "Iron Woman" and "Mother of the Revolution." She was the first Yemeni and Arab woman to win the Nobel Peace Prize and the second Muslim woman to win any Nobel Prize.

Our Women on the Ground: Essays by Arab Women Reporting from the Arab World, edited by Zahra Hankir. A growing number of intrepid Arab and Middle Eastern *sahafiyat* – female journalists – are working tirelessly to shape nuanced narratives about their changing homelands, often risking their lives on the front lines of war. Nineteen of these women tell us, in their own words, about what it's like to report on conflicts. (**H**) bit.ly/3fZrkwV

The Arab Spring: One Year On, by the CHOICES Program. In this unit plan, students learn about various Arab Spring protest movements in the Middle East and North Africa. There are additional general resources included, as well as country-specific resources and materials. (**H, TR**) bit.ly/3dTPPco

---

15 **230th anniversary of the adoption of the Bill of Rights**. Written by James Madison, the Bill of Rights comprises the first 10 amendments to the Constitution, designed to protect the rights of citizens by limiting the power of the Federal government. Madison had written 17 amendments and submitted them for approval. The Senate approved 12 of them, which were then sent to the states for ratification. They approved 10 of the submitted amendments. Virginia became the last state to ratify them on December 15, 1791.

"That's Your Right," by Annenberg Classroom. An interactive online card game that helps students learn about their rights under the Bill of Rights, the first 10 amendments to the Constitution. The game offers three levels of play: Easy, Normal, and Difficult. (**E, M**) bit.ly/3t9UQ6S

Gun Violence in Schools, by Learning for Justice. Use these resources to help navigate conversations about gun violence, school safety, mental health, and how to take action after a school shooting. (**TR**) learningforjustice.org/magazine/gun-violence-in-schools

---

10th anniversary of National Institutes of Health's (NIH) ending funding for new experiments on chimps. In response to animal rights activists, the NIH accepted guidelines requiring that new research on chimpanzees be necessary for human health and that there were no other options available to accomplish the desired results. In 2015, the US Fish and Wildlife Service finalized a rule listing all chimpanzees as endangered under the Endangered Species Act, effectively ending biomedical studies on our closest human relatives.

Becoming a Solutionary, by the Institute for Humane Education. This activity explores skills and processes needed to address problems of concern to students and develop meaningful solutions. In this activity, students practice critical-, creative-, strategic-, and systems-thinking skills in order to brainstorm potential solutions to a problem that concerns them. (**M, H**) bit.ly/3vnvJz6

---

18 **International Migrants Day**. There are an estimated 200 million migrant workers in the world. The UN marks this date to recognize this diverse group of workers and the economic, social, and political contexts that affect their rights and livelihoods.

Things Are Good Now, by Djamila Ibrahim. In the pages of this collection of short stories, men, women, and children who have crossed continents in search of a better life find themselves struggling with the chaos of displacement and the religious and cultural clashes they face in their new homes. (**H**) bit.ly/2EH3WzP

50th anniversary of Alaska Native Claims Settlement Act. In response to a lawsuit alleging violation of Alaska Native land rights by opening their lands for lease to private oil companies, Congress passed the Alaska Native Claims Settlement Act, which created 12 regional and 220 village for-profit corporations to own and manage 44 million acres of land, one tenth of their previous holdings. The Act mandated that both regional and village corporations be owned by enrolled Alaska Native shareholders.

As We Have Always Done: Indigenous Freedom Through Radical Resistance, by Leanne Betasamosake Simpson. Across North America, Indigenous acts of resistance have in recent years opposed the removal of federal protections for forests and waterways in Indigenous lands, halted the expansion of tar sands extraction and the pipeline construction at Standing Rock, and demanded justice for murdered and missing Indigenous women. In *As We Have Always Done*, Simpson identifies Indigenous political resurgence as a practice rooted in uniquely Indigenous theorizing, writing, organizing, and thinking. (**H**) akpress.org/aswehavealwaysdone

Standing with Standing Rock: Voices from the #NoDAPL Movement, edited by Nick Estes and Jaskiran Dhillon. Amid the Standing Rock movement to protect the land and the water that millions depend on for life, the Oceti Sakowin (the Dakota, Nakota, and Lakota people) reunited. Through poetry and prose, essays, photography, interviews, and polemical interventions, the contributors reflect on Indigenous history and politics and on the movement's significance. Their work challenges our understanding of colonial history not simply as "lessons learned" but as essential guideposts for activism. (**H**) bit.ly/3fZbtys

---

20 **50th anniversary of UN Declaration on the Rights of "Mentally Retarded" People**. This declaration asserts that the "mentally retarded" person (an antiquated term no longer used to describe people with cognitive challenges) has, to the maximum degree of feasibility, the same rights as other human beings. It encouraged participation in community life and mandated protection from exploitation. Essentially, the Declaration paved the way for future comprehensive sets of principles, which would eventually seek to integrate persons with disabilities into society.

Skin, Tooth, and Bone: The Basis of Movement Is Our People: A Disability Justice Primer, by Sins Invalid. Provides an overview of what disability justice is, and more important, what it can become, through the use of art, quotes, conversation, poetry, and more. Sins Invalid published this guide as a resource for activists and disabled and D/deaf communities to reclaim the term "disability justice" for queer and gender nonconforming disabled people of color, who originated the movement. (**H, TR**) bit.ly/2Gmsi4U

Classroom Resources on Disability, by the Nora Project. Free, linked resources for both classrooms and families to support the work of disability awareness and inclusion. (**E, TR**) bit.ly/3uFkLDP

10th anniversary of largest women's demonstration in modern Egyptian history. Egyptian women marched through the streets of Cairo demanding an end to military rule and the brutal treatment of demonstrators by Egypt's security services. The women rallied outside a government office complex in Tahrir Square, the scene of violent clashes between police and demonstrators, leaving at least four dead. Dozens of men joined the protest out of solidarity and to serve as protection for the women who were frequently degraded and sexually assaulted by security forces.

The Egyptian Revolution: An Interactive Timeline, by the CHOICES Program. Lesson plan and multimedia resources that engage young people in identifying core themes of Egyptian protest movements. (**H**) bit.ly/3fJqt3n

Can Egyptian Women Start a Revolution Against Sexual Violence?, by Nick Schifrin. In Tahrir Square, the center of the Egyptian revolution, women safely joined men to demonstrate for a new future. But that moment soon ended; hundreds, even thousands of female protesters were sexually assaulted. In some cases, activists believe the government used violence as a political weapon. Special correspondent Nick Schifrin examines how women have fought back through activism in this 10-minute video and interview with activists conducted for PBS NewsHour. (**H**) to.pbs.org/3wu7yzA

21 Winter Solstice (Northern Hemisphere). The Winter Solstice marks the beginning of winter. It is the shortest day and longest night of the year.

A Coyote Solstice Tale, by Thomas King. Trickster Coyote is having his friends over for a festive solstice get-together in the woods when a little girl comes by unexpectedly. She leads the partygoers through the snowy woods to a shopping mall – a place they have never seen before. Winner of the American Indian Library Association Youth Literature Awards, Best Picture Book. (**E**) bit.ly/1TIeAtW

22 Soyal, the New Year's celebration of the Hopi and Zuni. Among the Hopi and Zuni people, a ritual is performed to honor the return of the sun after winter and to celebrate a time of renewal and purification.

Celebrate My Hopi Corn, by Anita Poleahla. This board book, written in Hopi and English, is the story of how corn is planted, cultivated, harvested, and prepared for use in the Hopi home. The colorful illustrations by Hopi artist Emmett Navakuku depict the changing seasons and daily activities in a Hopi village. (**E**) bit.ly/2n7lqep

24 70th anniversary of Libya's independence. Prior to independence in 1951, the territory comprising present-day Libya had been a semi-independent province of the Ottoman Empire from 1711 to 1835, an Italian colony from 1912 until 1947, and was under British and French occupation from 1943 to 1951. It attained full independence in 1951 as the Kingdom of Libya under the rule of King Idriss I.

25 Christmas. Christmas is a Christian holiday that celebrates the birth of Jesus, who is believed by Christians to be the son of God.

The Christmas Gift/El Regalo de Navidad, by Francisco Jiménez. With honesty and grace, Jiménez shares his most poignant Christmas memory in this beautifully illustrated picture book. As Christmas approaches, Panchito can't wait to see what present he gets. But on Christmas Day, he is disappointed when all he gets is a bag of candy, until he sees the gift his father gives his mother. Panchito then realizes that gifts of the heart are the most precious of all. (**E**) bit.ly/2Veahtj

Let the Faithful Come, by Zetta Elliott. This lyrical retelling of the traditional Christmas story serves as a plea for greater compassion and unity in our contemporary world. Peace and goodwill are values celebrated during the holidays, but they should also be applied to the daily struggle of those traveling over land and sea in search of hope and sanctuary. This simple nativity narrative urges readers to recognize the value of every child, and to respect our shared responsibility for all the members of our global community. (**E, M**) bit.ly/2VZUGim

The Women Who Gave Us Christmas, by William Loren Katz. Article about how women organized Christmas bazaars to finance the abolition cause and used the fundraisers as an opportunity to spread anti-slavery messages. (**M, H, TR**) bit.ly/1QvQJe8

70th anniversary of Harry T. Moore's murder. Moore, an African American teacher, was the state secretary of the Florida NAACP. He organized voter registration activities, investigated lynchings, and fought for equal pay for Black teachers. On Christmas night 1951, his home was bombed, killing him and his wife. He is considered the first martyr of the Civil Rights movement.

Lynching in America: Confronting the Legacy of Racial Terror, by Equal Justice Initiative. EJI's report is based on investigation of thousands of racial terror lynchings. In addition to this comprehensive report, EJI opened the Memorial for Peace and Justice in Montgomery, AL, a 6-acre site using sculpture, art, and design to contextualize the history of racial terror. (**H, TR**) Report: bit.ly/3eDnvNu; Memorial: bit.ly/3eBGrvS

Clara Barton, nurse and humanitarian, born (1821-1912). Barton, who began her lifetime of service as a nurse during the Civil War, founded the American Red Cross, as part of an independent and protected international movement to provide medical aid to wounded soldiers during war. The Red Cross has expanded its mission to provide aid during natural disasters as well as individual tragedies such as fires.

Gender and Jobs – Women in the Workforce, by Learning for Justice. This lesson plan from Teaching Tolerance will guide students in exploring gender equity, reflecting on how gender-based injustice might affect them and exploring ways in which they can fight this injustice. (**M, H, TR**) bit.ly/1eNtNSW

26 First day of Kwanzaa (Umoja = Unity). Kwanzaa is a 7-day celebration honoring African American culture and heritage in which each of the seven days is dedicated to a specific life principle.

The Sound of Kwanzaa, by Dimitrea Tokunbo. Hear the words, sing the songs, dance to the beat, and shout "Harambee!" as you jump into this joyful celebration of the sounds of Kwanzaa! The sound is Umoja – bringing us together. The sound is Kuumba – the songs of our ancestors. The sound is Kwanzaa! Lively verse and colorful illustrations guide you through the seven principles of this festive holiday. (**E**) bit.ly/2AMDX9l

27 Second day of Kwanzaa (Kujichagulia = Self-determination)

The Story of Kwanzaa, by Donna Washington. Light the candles on the *kinara* (candelabrum)! Fly the *bendera* (flag or banner) and tell stories from Africa! The festival of Kwanzaa was originated by Dr. Maulana Karenga to honor the customs and history of African Americans. (**E**) This site includes an author essay: bit.ly/2DjGv0a

190th anniversary of the Baptist War (aka Christmas Rebellion). In Jamaica, Baptist preacher Samuel Sharpe organized a nonviolent general strike of slaves on Christmas Day. When their demands for emancipation were not met, the strike turned into a rebellion on Dec. 27. The rebellion, the largest slave uprising in the West Indies, was eventually defeated, but is credited with accelerating emancipation in Jamaica.

Wake: The Hidden History of Women-Led Slave Revolts, by Rebecca Hall. Part graphic novel, part memoir, this book tells the story of Dr. Rebecca Hall, a historian, granddaughter of slaves, and a woman haunted by the legacy of slavery. The accepted history of slave revolts had always told her that enslaved women took a back seat. But Dr. Hall decided to look deeper, and her journey takes her through old court records, slave ship captain's logs, crumbling correspondence, and even the forensic evidence from the bones of enslaved women from the "Negro burying ground" uncovered in Manhattan. She found women warriors everywhere. (**M, H**) bit.ly/3s2TAB7

30th anniversary of Minnesota's ruling for same-sex guardianship. The Minnesota Court of Appeals ruled in favor of Karen Thompson, allowing her to become legal guardian of her partner Sharon Kowalski. Kowalski was in a car accident that left her paralyzed and speech impaired. Kowalski's family had refused to recognize the pair's relationship, so this ruling was a huge win for them and all same-sex couples.

My Footprints, by Bao Phi. Every child feels different in some way, but Thuy feels "double different." She is Vietnamese American and she has two moms. Thuy walks home one winter afternoon, angry and lonely after a bully's taunts. Then a bird catches her attention and sets Thuy on an imaginary exploration. What if she could fly away like a bird? What if she could sprint like a deer, or roar like a bear? Mimicking the footprints of each creature in the snow, she makes her way home to the arms of her moms. (**E**) bit.ly/3wJBsjm

---

28 Third day of Kwanzaa (Ujima = Collective Work and Responsibility)

Mutual Aid Toolbox, by Big Door Brigade. We cannot rely on the government to provide what people need, especially when vulnerable people are under attack by government agencies and agents. This toolbox is a list of models and tools for starting mutual aid projects – projects that help materially support people facing eviction, deportation, criminalization, poverty, isolation, and violence. (**M, H, TR**) bit.ly/2kL2cup

---

29 Fourth day of Kwanzaa (Ujamaa = Cooperative Economics)

Cultivate.Coop. Cultivate.Coop is an online hub for pooling knowledge and resources on cooperatives. It is a space to collect free information for those interested in cooperatives, and where people can build useful educational tools for the co-op community. (**H, TR**) bit.ly/ekaidO

---

30 Fifth day of Kwanzaa (Nia = Purpose)

Seven Principles, by Sweet Honey in the Rock. This is a song that teaches the seven principles of Kwanzaa. (**E, M, H**) bit.ly/vNc77L

30th anniversary of *El Pueblo para el Aire y Agua Limpio v. Kings County Board of Supervisors*. The court ruled that the environmental impact report that resulted in issuance of a permit for the construction and operation of a hazardous waste incinerator was inadequate under the California Environmental Quality Act (CEQA). The incinerator could burn hundreds of millions of pounds of toxic waste each year in addition to that produced by an existing plant in a town whose population is predominately Latinx. In addition, the report should have been translated into Spanish.

Editorial Cartoons: Poverty/ Environmental Justice, by Learning for Justice. The fourth lesson in the series "Using Editorial Cartoons to Teach Social Justice," this lesson plan engages students in analyzing editorial cartoons about environmental injustice. The cartoons help students understand the disproportionate share of environmental problems people in poverty face, too often living near environmentally undesirable and dangerous places. (**M, H**) bit.ly/3fYPvvo

---

31 New Year's Eve

Freedom Soup, by Tami Charles. Every year, Haitians all over the world ring in the new year by eating a special soup, a tradition dating back to the Haitian Revolution. This year, Ti Gran is teaching Belle how to make the soup – Freedom Soup – just like she was taught when she was a little girl. Together, they dance and clap as they prepare the holiday feast, and Ti Gran tells Belle about the history of the soup, the history of Belle's family, and the history of Haiti, where Belle's family is from. (**E**) bit.ly/3mCzUTI

Sixth day of Kwanzaa (Kuumba = Creativity)

What Do You Do with an Idea? by Kobi Yamada. This story is about a child who one day discovers he has an idea. He wonders where the idea came from, but he is afraid to tell others about it because they might think it's silly. Instead of giving up, the child decides to nurture and feed the idea. Something magical happens – the idea bursts out into the world, bringing with it a miraculous change. (**E**) Find a read-aloud video and guidelines for a philosophical discussion from the Prindle Institute here: bit.ly/39YUmJg

January Resources

1 130th anniversary of Ellis Island Immigration Center. Ellis Island opened in 1892 as an immigration station and continued to serve this purpose until it closed in 1954. At its peak, from 1900 to 1914, an average of 1,900 people passed through every day. American isolationism and racist objections to foreign immigrants resulted in the Immigrant Quota Act of 1921 and the National Origins Act of 1924, effectively ending the era of mass immigration. From 1925 to its closing in 1954, only 2.3 million immigrants passed through Ellis Island.

Explore Ellis Island: Stories of Yesterday and Today, by Scholastic Teachers. An interactive tour of and virtual field trip to Ellis Island, along with stories from young immigrants, immigration data, book lists, interactive maps of immigrant settlement patterns, and more. (**E, M**) bit.ly/3d8TbJ6

60th anniversary of Illinois becoming the first state to repeal anti-sodomy laws. Illinois became the first state to legalize consensual adult same-sex relationships, but the change in the state's criminal code had few practical benefits for the state's LGBTQ population. Police raids and harassment on other pretexts continued for another two decades. Illinois was the only state to legalize consensual adult same-sex relationships until 1971, after which several states followed suit. In 2003, the Supreme Court, in *Lawrence v. Texas*, struck down anti-sodomy laws nationwide.

Supporting LGBTQIA Youth: A Resource List, by the Harvard Graduate School of Education's "Making Caring Common" Project. How can educators support LGBTQIA-identifying middle and high school students and create more inclusive school communities? The list at this site offers a sample of resources and links to websites for teachers and students. (**TR**) bit.ly/3dtRkOh

---

40th anniversary of the publication of Lois Marie Gibbs' *Love Canal: My Story*. In 1978, Gibbs discovered that her child's school was built over a toxic-chemical dump in Niagara Falls, NY. Facing fierce opposition from Occidental Petroleum and local, state, and federal officials, Gibbs organized the Love Canal Homeowners' Association, demanding to be relocated. In 1980, President Carter delivered an Emergency Declaration, moving 900 families from this hazardous area. Gibbs went on to become a leading advocate for environmental justice, assisting more than 10,000 grassroots groups nationwide.

A Fierce Green Fire: Love Canal: Children and Toxic Waste, a film by American Masters. The one-hour documentary chronicles one of the largest movements of the 20th century. *A Fierce Green Fire* spans 50 years of grassroots and global activism from the 1960s to 2009 and connects the major causes of environmentalism, from conservation to climate change. First link includes clips from the film; the second link is to teacher resources. (**H**) to.pbs.org/2Omdq9l; bit.ly/2u1FHvk

---

Seventh day of Kwanzaa (Imani = Faith)

A Question of Faith: Books and Resources to Help Us Talk to Our Kids About Religion and Spirituality, by Olugbemisola Rhuday-Perkovich. How do we help our children process the messages they receive from media sources about religion and faith, its connections to conflict, history, and culture? Helpful tips, books, and other resources to support educators and families in talking to kids about multicultural faiths and spirituality. (**E, M**) bit.ly/3dRplTo

---

3 230th anniversary of Mary Wollstonecraft's *A Vindication of the Rights of Women*. This was a groundbreaking work of literature, which still resonates in feminism and human rights movements today. Wollstonecraft was the first to argue for equal rights for women, a revolutionary position at the time, calling for coeducational schools, as well as opportunities for women to earn a living, support themselves, and vote. The book was met with derision from all but the most liberal intellectuals but has become a cornerstone of human rights in modern times.

Let It Shine: Stories of Black Women Freedom Fighters, by Andrea Davis Pinkney. Beautifully illustrated by Stephen Alcorn, Pinkney's short biographies emphasize one common theme: These 10 African American women spoke out fearlessly in the fight for racial justice. (**E, M**) bit.ly/3dYjmBQ

170th anniversary of the arrival of the first Chinese laborers in Hawaii. Seeking cheap labor for the growing sugar industry, the Royal Hawaiian Agricultural Society brought 195 Chinese laborers to work on sugarcane plantations. They were the first foreign contract workers in the islands. Under the 1850 Masters and Servants Act, plantation overseers could exploit these workers with impunity, paying them $36 per year for grueling work under unspeakable conditions.

We Are Not a Stereotype: Breaking Down Asian Pacific Islander Bias, a video series by The Smithsonian Asian Pacific American Center. This series explores and challenges the complexity surrounding the term Asian Pacific American, breaking it down into topics that span multiple timelines, geographies, and identities. (**H**) bit.ly/3r2sObD

---

6 190th anniversary of the founding of New England Anti-Slavery Society. William Lloyd Garrison, co-founder of the anti-slavery newspaper, *The Liberator*, helped organize a meeting of Massachusetts abolitionists in Boston at a Black Baptist church, introducing the idea of the New England Anti-Slavery Society. The Society advocated for immediate, uncompensated abolition of slavery and stated categorically that slavery was immoral. There were 12 members at its start; within two years, their number exceeded 2,000.

The Abolitionists, by PBS American Experience. Bringing to life the intertwined stories of Frederick Douglass, William Lloyd Garrison, Angelina Grimké, Harriet Beecher Stowe, and John Brown, *The Abolitionists* takes place during some of the most violent and contentious decades in American history, shining a light on the debates of the era. (**M, H**) to.pbs.org/1fgdrWn

---

110th anniversary of New Mexico's becoming 47th state. After Mexico's independence from Spain in 1821, New Mexico became a province of Mexico, opening trade with the US. In 1846, the Mexican-American War erupted, ending with the Treaty of Guadalupe Hidalgo, in which Mexico ceded the territory to the US. In 1853, the territory was expanded to its present size through the Gadsden Purchase. Native American resistance to US colonial expansion continued until 1886, but after three decades of bloodshed, they finally conceded.

---

8 110th anniversary of the founding of the African National Congress (ANC). The Union of South Africa recognized only the rights of White people, denying basic rights to the majority Black population. On January 8, 1912, chiefs, local leaders, church organizations, and other prominent individuals gathered in Bloemfontein and formed the African National Congress. The ANC declared its aim to bring all Africans together as one people to defend their rights and freedoms. After decades of resistance, the ANC became South Africa's governing party, with Nelson Mandela as the country's first Black president.

The Legacy of Nelson Mandela, a lesson plan by AFT Human Rights. In this lesson, students explore the life and career of Nelson Mandela. With videos and other multimedia resources, students consider what it means to be a leader in difficult times. (**M, H**) bit.ly/3s5gVSH

20th anniversary of "No Child Left Behind." NCLB, a reauthorization of President Johnson's landmark Elementary and Secondary Education Act (1965), was signed into law by President George W. Bush. The stated goal was to provide equal access to high quality education to all students regardless of socioeconomic status. However, the policy has been roundly criticized by teachers and other educators for its overemphasis on standardized testing and accountability without regard to schools' and students' specific needs and challenges.

More Than a Score: The New Uprising Against High-Stakes Testing, edited by Jesse Hagopian. A collection of essays, poems, speeches, interviews, and accounts of personal courage, and trenchant insights from frontline fighters who are defying the corporate education reformers, often at great personal and professional risk, and fueling a national movement to reclaim and transform public education. (**TR**) haymarketbooks.org/books/618-more-than-a-score

---

10 Bodhi Day (Buddhism). Bodhi Day commemorates the day that Buddha reached enlightenment.

Under the Bodhi Tree, by Shi Jin Rou, Dharma Realm Buddhist Association. This book tells the story of the Buddha's life, from his birth as a pampered prince, through his cultivation and enlightenment, to his founding of the Buddhist *sangha* and his final *Nirvana*. (**E, M**) bit.ly/2MhVfQh

---

11 National Human Trafficking Awareness Day. The goal of this day is to raise awareness of and vigilance for the millions of human trafficking victims around the globe, with the aim of eradicating this insidious crime.

What Is Modern Slavery? Investigating Human Trafficking, by Holly Epstein Ojalvo. In this lesson, students learn about human trafficking, also known as modern slavery. Using coverage of human trafficking by Nicholas D. Kristof, a *New York Times* columnist, they explore the causes of trafficking and the consequences for victims and traffickers, the role of globalization, and ways to respond effectively. (**M, H**) nyti.ms/XG0Z3n

The Dark Side of Chocolate, by Miki Mistrati and U. Roberto Romano. A team of journalists investigate how human trafficking and child labor in the Ivory Coast fuels the worldwide chocolate industry. The crew interview both participants and opponents of these alleged practices and use hidden camera techniques to delve into the gritty world of cocoa plantations. (**H**) bit.ly/2HogD3E

110th anniversary of the Bread and Roses Strike. Thousands of largely immigrant and female textile workers walked off the job at the American Woolen Company Mills in Lawrence, MA in protest of wage cuts and subpar working conditions. The Industrial Workers of the World (IWW) helped organize community support services during the strike, including medical clinics and soup kitchens. On March 12, 1912, the strike ended when management agreed to wage increases, overtime pay, and the acquittal of strike leaders.

Bread and Roses, Too, by Katherine Paterson. With two teenagers as the protagonists of this historical fiction novel, Paterson introduces the reader to the Industrial Workers of the World, major figures such as Big Bill Haywood and Elizabeth Gurley Flynn, worker solidarity, the role of labor songs, and the various tactics used by the company to undermine the strike. (**M, H**) bit.ly/Lhb8PS

"Bread and Roses," by James Oppenheim. Oppenheim's poem is closely associated with the Strike of 1912. This site has the words of the poem, "Bread and Roses," as well as a song version recorded by Mimi Fariña, which has become an anthem for women's and workers' rights. (**E, M, H**) bit.ly/a4iuHP

The Real Bread and Roses Story Missing from Textbooks, by Robert Forrant. The author challenges the myth that the Bread and Roses Strike was spontaneous and provides a counternarrative of the events. Additional resources for teaching the strike are available from Zinn Education Project at the end of the article. (**H, TR**) bit.ly/3wJYKpv

---

16 190th anniversary of Alabama's declaring sovereignty over Creek and Cherokee peoples. The General Assembly of Alabama enacted provisions that prohibited the Creek and Cherokee peoples from doing anything that violated Alabama law. They could not practice their customs, make laws, or hold meetings of tribal leaders, and were prohibited from testifying in court when suits did not involve other Cherokee or Creek people.

Jingle Dancer, by Cynthia Leitich Smith. Jenna, a contemporary Muscogee (Creek) girl in Oklahoma, wants to honor a family tradition by jingle dancing at the next powwow. But where will she find enough jingles for her dress? (**E**) cynthialeitichsmith.com/kidbooks

Tips for Teachers: Developing Instructional Materials About American Indians, compiled by Debbie Reese and Jean Mendoza. A helpful list of guiding information and principles for educators working to develop and choose instructional resources about American Indians. (**TR**) bit.ly/328xT8g

---

Religious Freedom Day. Religious Freedom Day commemorates the 1786 passage of the Virginia Statute for Religious Freedom, which declared that government-mandated religion was a violation of one's natural rights. In doing so, Virginia became the first state to officially separate church and state.

Maintain Neutrality, by Teaching Tolerance. This link provides a collection of lessons designed to help teachers maintain the distinction between "teaching religion" and "teaching *about* religion." The site has a wide array of other lessons and resources on the topic. (**E, M, H**) bit.ly/2IIR7Wp

Taking a Closer Look at Religions Around the World, by Teaching Tolerance. This lesson offers a starting point for exploring religions and faith traditions, creating an ongoing respectful dialogue about religious tolerance. (**M, H**) bit.ly/d0WqIg

Respecting Atheists and Nonreligious People, by Teaching Tolerance. Students often learn the importance of respecting people of different religions, but what about people who do not hold religious beliefs at all? This lesson introduces students to people who choose not to follow a religion. (**E, M, H**) bit.ly/nonrelig

17 Martin Luther King, Jr. Day (Observed). Martin Luther King, Jr. Day is a US federal holiday marking the birth of Rev. Dr. Martin Luther King, Jr., a prominent leader in the Civil Rights movement. It is observed on the third Monday of January, around the time of King's birthday (January 15th).

Liberation Curriculum, by the Martin Luther King, Jr. Research and Education Institute. Lesson plans, primary resources, and articles based on the Martin Luther King, Jr. Archives at Stanford University. (**H**) stanford.io/1DNVv1M

Putting the Movement Back into Civil Rights Teaching, by Deborah Menkart, Alana Murray, and Jenice L. View. The book includes interactive and interdisciplinary lessons, readings, writings, photographs, graphics, and interviews, with sections on education, labor, citizenship, and culture, and reflections on teaching about the Civil Rights movement. (**E, M, H**) bit.ly/1iv4HhU

Muhammad Ali, champion boxer and human rights activist, born (1942-2016). Muhammad Ali was a three-time World Heavyweight boxing champion. He was a philanthropist and social activist, taking unwavering stands against racism and American imperialism. Ali won an Olympic gold medal in 1960 and the World Heavyweight Boxing Championship in 1964. As a conscientious objector, he refused to serve in the military after being drafted in 1967, for which he was stripped of his world title and prosecuted by the US government. His conviction was later overturned by the US Supreme Court.

The Greatest: Muhammad Ali, by Walter Dean Myers. This book follows the extraordinary career and accomplishments of Muhammad Ali, focusing on Ali's impact on race relations inside and outside the sports world. (**M, H**) bit.ly/38xQfmR

What's My Name, Fool?: Sports and Resistance in the United States, by Dave Zirin. This book examines US history with a focus on racism, sexism, and homophobia in sports, along with the profound connection between sports and patriotic nationalism. Chapter 3 focuses on Muhammad Ali, his critical consciousness and activist spirit. (**H, TR**) bit.ly/3ciCvNG

Muhammad Ali, a film by Ken Burns, Sarah Burns, and David McMahon for PBS. In total, an 8-hour documentary series on the life of Muhammad Ali. (**H**) to.pbs.org/3ymU3Tn

---

60th anniversary of Executive Order 10988. President John F. Kennedy's executive order, "Employee-Management Cooperation in the Federal Sector," was a landmark in federal employee labor rights, establishing for the first time the collective bargaining rights of Federal Government employees. The order has been reviewed periodically by subsequent presidents and has been further broadened and strengthened by later executive orders. It also led to comprehensive reform of the Federal Civil Service in 1979, the first such reform since 1883.

Labor Matters, a lesson plan by Learning for Justice. In recent decades, the right to collective bargaining, ensured by the National Labor Relations Act, has been called into question. This lesson, from the Southern Poverty Law Center, draws on prior knowledge and uses primary source documents to help students understand the origins of union goals and tactics in the US. (**M, H**) bit.ly/185DPul

---

18 60th anniversary of the temporary closing of Southern University. As a reaction to student protests that had been going on for several years in support of integration and against racism and discrimination, the president of Southern University, a Historically Black University in Baton Rouge, LA, ordered the campus temporarily closed. Under pressure from Louisiana's governor, the university expelled at least 18 student protesters and barred the Congress of Racial Equality (CORE) from campus.

Congress of Racial Equality (CORE), by Digital SNCC Gateway. Background information with hyperlinked additional information throughout, and multimedia primary sources related to the Student Nonviolent Coordinating Committee (SNCC) and CORE, and their work together in the South. (**M, H**) bit.ly/3dvMph7

---

19 10th anniversary of Ava DuVernay's Sundance Film Festival Best Director Award. Ava DuVernay is a Black woman screenwriter, director, producer, and independent film distributor. She produced the film *Middle of Nowhere*, which focuses on the work of People of Color and women, which was screened at the Sundance Film Festival in 2012. DuVernay won Best Director for the film, becoming the first Black woman to do so. She is also known for directing *Selma* (2014), *13th* (2016), and *A Wrinkle in Time* (2018), among others.

13th Critical Viewing Guide, by Graduate Students at the Lynch School of Education of Boston College and Dr. Leigh Patel. Ava DuVernay's film, *13th*, provides a history of the establishment and maintenance of the prison industrial complex as an extension of chattel slavery in a racist, profit-driven society. This guide seeks to further elucidate several important themes not sufficiently covered in the documentary, but that undergird the structure of racist capitalism. The guide provides questions for reflection, readings, videos, infographics, and other materials, and aims to facilitate a more critical engagement with the film. (**H, TR**) bit.ly/2n1BZt8

Ava DuVernay on Her Journey to Become the First Black Woman to Direct an Oscar-Nominated Film, by *Time* Magazine. In this short interview, DuVernay talks about growing up in a matriarchy and breaking down barriers in the patriarchal film industry. (**M, H**) youtube.com/watch?v=J4Gh4WYvaDs

---

22 90th anniversary of the peasant uprising in El Salvador. A peasant uprising in response to land seizures by the ruling class and deplorable working conditions was quickly suppressed by the government, which slaughtered an estimated 30,000 people, most of whom were Indigenous. The event became known as "La Matanza" (The Massacre). The US responded by sending a cruiser and two destroyers to stand by in support of the government.

Talking with Mother Earth/Hablando con Madre Tierra, by Jorge Argueta. Tetl's skin is brown, his eyes are black, and his hair is long. He's different from the other children, whose taunts wound him deeply, leaving him confused and afraid. But Tetl's grandmother knows the ancient teachings of their Aztec ancestors and how they viewed the earth as alive with sacred meaning. Tetl's journey from self-doubt to proud acceptance of his Nahuatl heritage is told in a series of powerful poems, beautifully expressed in both English and Spanish. (**E**) bit.ly/3d7dg2B

110th anniversary of lynching in Hamilton, GA. Three Black men and a Black woman (John Moore, Eugene Harrington, Burrell Hardaway, and Dusky Crutchfield) were lynched when they were forcibly removed from jail after being arrested, with no evidence, for the murder of White planter Norman Hadley. Hadley was known to sexually assault Black women and girls. Hardaway was a minister who had spoken out about Hadley's behavior. Crutchfield, the lone woman in the group, was told to testify against the men, but she refused.

Say Her Name, by Zetta Elliott. Inspired by the #SayHerName campaign, these poems pay tribute to Black women who are victims of police brutality, as well as Black Lives Matter activists. Elliott draws on the work of poets from the past two centuries to create a chorus of voices celebrating the creativity, resilience, and courage of Black women and girls. (**M, H**) bit.ly/3tcSQun

---

25 50th anniversary of Shirley Chisholm's announcing her candidacy for President. Chisholm was the first Black woman elected to Congress (D-NY) and the first woman and first African American to seek the nomination for the office of President. She lost the nomination and returned to Congress where she served until 1981. Chisholm said, "I want history to remember me... not as the first Black woman to have made a bid for the presidency, but as a Black woman who lived in the 20th century and who dared to be herself."

She Was the First!: The Trailblazing Life of Shirley Chisholm, by Katheryn Russell-Brown. This book highlights the accomplishments of Shirley Chisholm, a woman of many firsts, who was a political trailblazer, a candidate of the people, and catalyst of change who opened the door for women in the political arena. (**E**) bit.ly/3laM7yj

Chisolm '72: Unbought and Unbossed, a POV documentary. This site includes lesson plans and resources for using Chisholm '72. Also provides access to a lending library where teachers can borrow the video for free. The film is available with Amazon Prime and is streaming for under $4 from a variety of sites such as YouTube. (**M, H, TR**) bit.ly/2RW7q8z

---

80th anniversary of the lynching of Cleo Wright in Sikeston, MO. Cleo Wright, a Black man accused of assaulting a White woman, was shot multiple times when he was arrested. The hospital refused to admit him, and he ended up in the city jail, where a White mob abducted him. They lynched him in front of two local Black churches and hundreds of churchgoers. This was the first lynching investigated by the Department of Justice, but no one was ever convicted.

We Are Not Yet Equal: Understanding Our Racial Divide, by Carol Anderson and Tonya Bolden. Adapted from Anderson's bestselling *White Rage* (2016), this book summons young people to bear witness to the devastatingly expansive strategies White citizens have taken up to preserve the racialized violence that emerged from the founding of the nation. (**M, H**) bit.ly/2w1AiVE

40th anniversary of *Merrion v. Jicarilla Apache Tribe*. Writing for the majority, Supreme Court Justice Thurgood Marshall held that an Indian tribe not only has the authority to impose taxes on non-Indians who are conducting business on the reservation, it is an inherent power necessary to tribal self-government and territorial management. The *Merrion v. Jicarilla Apache Tribe* decision is a landmark case in Native American law, having been cited in more than 400 subsequent law review articles.

American Indian Law: When Two Sovereigns Collide, by Reasonably Speaking Podcast. In this episode, American Indian law and policy experts, Matthew Fletcher and Wenona Singel, discuss the nuanced and highly complex field of American Indian Law. They begin by exploring the history of tribal sovereignty and discuss the rights of American Indians as both tribal citizens and US citizens. They explore jurisdiction across border lines, particularly in a criminal context and discuss the history of violence against native women, and why, until recently, prosecution has been so difficult. Court challenges, both past and present, to the Indian Child Welfare Act are also examined. (**H**) bit.ly/3mDNmqv

---

26 Bessie Coleman, first Black and first Native American woman pilot, born (1892-1926). Coleman's dream of becoming a pilot was thwarted when every flight school she applied to in the US rejected her because of her race and gender. She was accepted to a school in France, where she earned her license in 1921. The following year, she completed the first flight by a Black woman pilot. Throughout her career, she refused to fly at venues that didn't allow Black spectators, and openly encouraged Black women to learn to fly.

Black Women in Science: A Black History Book for Kids, by Kimberly Brown Pellum. Throughout history, Black women have blazed trails across the fields of science, technology, engineering, and mathematics. Features 15 pioneering Black women including Bessie Coleman. (**E**) bit.ly/30D5Qx0

Bessie Coleman Read-Alouds, from *Women and Girls are Changemakers*, created by Shay InLak'Ech. An exceptional collection of picture books on powerful women throughout history, each linked to a YouTube read-aloud of the book. The link on this page includes three read-alouds about Bessie Coleman. (**E**) bit.ly/2Qlav4N

---

28 Margo Tamez, scholar, poet, and Indigenous rights advocate, born (1962). Tamez's poetry reflects a keen awareness of the culture of Indigenous people, social inequities, colonization, sexual violence, women's labor, and the land. She rejects the notion of the romanticized Indigenous life and speaks of spiritual and physical pain that's deeply rooted in memory. Her poem "Raven's Eye" was nominated for a Pulitzer Prize. In 2004, she co-organized the Symposium on Globalism and the Environmental Justice and Toxics Movement in Tucson, AZ.

Margo Tamez, from the Poetry Foundation Information page, with select poems from and about Margo Tamez. (**M, H**) poetryfoundation.org/poets/margo-tamez

---

29 20th anniversary of Mee Moua's election to the Minnesota State Senate. After graduating from Brown University with a public policy degree, Moua studied law at the University of Minnesota. In 2002, she ran for an open seat in the Minnesota State Senate, becoming the first Hmong American to hold legislative office. She held the seat for three terms and was an outspoken advocate for civil rights, education, housing, and economic development. After retiring in 2010, she became president and executive director of Asian Americans Advancing Justice.

A Map into the World, by Kao Kalia Yang. As the seasons change, so too does a young Hmong girl's world. She moves into a new home with her family and encounters both birth and death. As this curious girl explores life inside her house and beyond, she collects bits of the natural world. But who are her treasures for? (**E, M**) lernerbooks.com/shop/show/17915; link to author video: bit.ly/324DeO2

---

30 50th anniversary of Northern Ireland's Bloody Sunday. In Londonderry, Northern Ireland, 14 unarmed demonstrators were shot dead by British Army paratroopers in an event that became known as "Bloody Sunday." The peaceful demonstration was in protest of the British policy of internment without trial of suspected Irish nationalists. British soldiers fired indiscriminately into the crowd, killing 14 and wounding 17. The killings brought worldwide attention to the crisis in Northern Ireland and sparked protests across the Republic of Ireland.

February Resources

1 First day of African American History Month. Since 1976, February has been designated African American (or Black) History Month. The idea dates back to 1915 with the establishment of the Association for the Study of Negro Life and History. Headed by historian Carter Woodson and minister Jesse E. Moorland, the organization sponsored the first Negro History Week in 1926 with the goal of celebrating the contributions of Black people to American history, society, and culture.

The HistoryMakers: The Nation's Largest African American Video Oral History Collection. An easy-to-use online database of video oral history interviews with thousands of African Americans from a broad range of backgrounds and experiences. The HistoryMakers Digital Archive provides high-quality video content and fully searchable transcripts. Interviews are separated into 15 categories – Art, Civics, Education, STEM, etc. – and the corpus is searchable by subject and keyword. (**E, M, H, TR**) bit.ly/2HZSrsg

Tell All the Children Our Story, by Tonya Bolden. From the first recorded birth of a Black child in Jamestown all the way up to the present day, this is African American history from the perspective of the children who lived through it. A scrapbook of letters, photos, artwork, testimonials, and more, this is the history that didn't make it into the original history books – the agonies and the sweet victories of African American children. (**M**) Discussion guide included here: bit.ly/2US1hKv

The Undefeated, by Kwame Alexander. Originally performed for ESPN's *The Undefeated*, this poem (in the form of a picture book illustrated by Kadir Nelson) is a love letter to Black life in the United States. (**E**) bit.ly/2PNXDEB

The Black Radical Tradition: A Compilation of Essential Texts. A free PDF of 500+ pages of the most essential critical texts about Black Power, African American history, and civil rights. (**H, TR**) bit.ly/1O0CvTj

---

First day of the annual Black Lives Matter at School Week of Action. During this national week of action, educators throughout the US commit to teaching lessons about structural racism, intersectional Black identities, Black history, and anti-racist movements to affirm the lives of Black students, teachers, and families.

Teaching for Black Lives, by Rethinking Schools. From the editors' introduction: "*Teaching for Black Lives* grows directly out of the Movement for Black Lives. We recognize that anti-Black racism constructs Black people, and Blackness generally, as not counting as human life. The chapters here push back directly against this construct by providing educators with critical perspectives on the role of schools in perpetuating anti-Blackness, and by offering educators concrete examples of what it looks like to humanize Black people in curriculum, teaching, and policy." (**TR**) teachingforblacklives.org

Black Lives Matter at School: An Uprising for Educational Justice, by Denisha Jones and Jesse Hagopian. This book succinctly generalizes lessons from successful challenges to institutional racism that have been won through the Black Lives Matter at School movement. (**TR**) bit.ly/3qJs773

What We Believe: A Black Lives Matter Principles Activity Book, by Laleña Garcia and Caryn Davidson. Created by two teacher activists, the book presents the 13 guiding principles of BLM Week of Action in down-to-earth, child-friendly language, with each principle accompanied by writing prompts, space for children or adults to create their own reflections, and a coloring page. Supporting materials guide adults in sharing the principles with children and encourage kids to dream big and take action within their communities. (**E**) bit.ly/3vnbiCg

Black Lives Matter at School Website, by a national coalition of organizers. A comprehensive website for #BLMatSchool that includes the demands, the principles, and a ton of lesson plans, posters, and classroom resources to support your planning for this annual week of action affirming the lives of Black students and Black people in general. (**TR**) blacklivesmatteratschool.com

---

Lunar New Year. Lunar New Year is the beginning of the year according to the Lunar Calendar. It is celebrated throughout the world, particularly in Asia.

Bringing in the New Year!, by Grace Lin. This exuberant story follows a Chinese American family as they prepare for the Lunar New Year. Each member of the family lends a hand as they sweep out the dust of the old year, hang decorations, and make dumplings. (**E**) bit.ly/2SkTYJp

---

Tet (Vietnamese New Year). Tet, the Vietnamese New Year, is the most popular holiday in Vietnam. Tet marks the arrival of spring, based on the Chinese lunisolar calendar. Celebrations last at least three days and include people visiting friends and family and cooking special holiday foods.

Vietnamese Americans: Lessons in American History, by Learning for Justice. This curriculum guide sheds light on the complexities of the Vietnamese American experience. (**M, H**) bit.ly/9Q1L0r

Going Home, Coming Home, by Truong Tran. This summer, Ami Chi is taking a trip to Vietnam, where the streets are crowded with zipping scooters and fruit is shaped like dragons and stars. To her parents, Vietnam is still home – a home they haven't seen since they left during the war. But all this talk of going back home leaves Ami Chi confused. How can you go back home to a place you've never been? (**E**) bit.ly/3g8fiS3

Langston Hughes, poet, author, playwright, born (1902-1967). Langston Hughes was a central figure in the Harlem Renaissance. In his writing, he portrayed both the joys and hardships of Black life in America. Some of his harshest critics at the time were Black intellectuals who felt Hughes depicted Black people in a negative light at a time when White acceptance was paramount. Over time, Hughes came to be regarded as one of the leading American writers of all time.

Love to Langston, by Tony Medina. This biography in poems was published in 2002 in honor of American poet and author Langston Hughes (1902–1967) on the anniversary of his 100th birthday. Each poem explores a significant event or theme in the life of Hughes. Young readers learn about his lonely childhood, the racism he faced, his decision to become a writer, his years of travel, his love of New York's Harlem neighborhood, and his success as a poet. (**E, M**) Teacher's guide here: bit.ly/3ti1nMO

---

2 510th anniversary of Taíno leader Hatuey's execution in Cuba. Hatuey was the first prominent freedom fighter in the Americas. On Hispaniola (now Haiti and the Dominican Republic), Hatuey united Indigenous people and runaway enslaved Africans to resist European colonizers. They headed to Cuba to mobilize other Caribbean islanders to resist, but Spaniards, led by Diego Velásquez, overwhelmed them, and Hatuey was publicly executed.

Black Indians: A Hidden Heritage, by William Loren Katz. This startling and readable work of people's history chronicles the attempts to keep Black people and Indians divided in the Americas and the two groups' efforts to unite. This expanded and updated edition includes additional research and documentary and photographic evidence illustrating the Native American and African American alliance that for four centuries challenged European conquest and slavery. (**M, H**) zinnedproject.org/materials/black-indians

---

6 120th anniversary of Thomas Brown's lynching. Before he could stand trial for allegedly assaulting a White woman, Black teenager Thomas Brown was taken from his jail cell by a mob of 200 White men and hanged from a tree in front of the Jessamine County Courthouse in Nicholasville, KY. No one was ever prosecuted for Brown's lynching even though the leader of the mob had been identified.

Lynching in America, by The Equal Justice Initiative. Two units that total 13 lesson plans exploring lynching and racial terror historically and its ongoing legacy today. (**H, TR**) bit.ly/2JsovSt

---

7 National Black HIV/AIDS Awareness Day. According to the CDC, in 2016, African Americans accounted for 44% of HIV diagnoses, despite comprising only 12% of the US population. National Black HIV/AIDS Awareness Day is an HIV testing and treatment community mobilization initiative designed to increase the awareness of HIV/AIDS prevention, care, and treatment among Black people in the US. HIV diagnoses among African Americans have declined in recent years. However, more work is needed to reduce and eradicate HIV.

Don't Call Us Dead: Poems, by Danez Smith. These poems by nonbinary poet Danez Smith come from a place of too many funerals and too few miracles. Touching on topics from police brutality toward African Americans to the realities of an HIV diagnosis, this is a heartrending collection. (**H**) bit.ly/2ARmRHa

---

8 110th anniversary of the San Diego Free Speech Fight. In a move aimed at limiting labor activism and agitation, San Diego passed a city ordinance banning public speaking and singing in a 49-block area of the city. The Industrial Workers of the World (IWW) and other unions organized a demonstration to demand the right of individuals to exercise free speech as protected by the First Amendment. Police arrested 41 of the participants for violating this unconstitutional ordinance.

For the Win, by Cory Doctorow. *For the Win* introduces the reader to the global economy and the history of organizing, with a focus on the Industrial Workers of the World (IWW). The characters in *For the Win* make a living in virtual gaming all over the world. They connect and organize online (forming the Webblies), and after initial skepticism convince the traditional labor unions to join them. (**H**) bit.ly/123xmA6

---

11 Lydia Maria Child, abolitionist and author, born (1802-1880). Lydia Maria Child was a White American abolitionist, women's rights activist, opponent of American expansionism, Native American rights activist, novelist, and journalist. Child published many works protesting slavery and demanding equality for marginalized groups, especially Native Americans, slaves, and women. One of her best-known works, *An Appeal in Favor of that Class of Americans Called Africans*, was published in 1833 and inspired many people to join the Abolition movement.

IntersectionAllies: We Make Room for All, by Latoya Council, Carolyn Choi, and Chelsea Johnson. Written by three Women of Color sociologists, *IntersectionAllies* introduces children to intersectional feminism. The nine interconnected characters describe themselves and their backgrounds, offering an opportunity to take pride in a personal story and connect to a collective struggle for justice. (**E**) bit.ly/2Q2iVOs

---

14 Valentine's Day. Valentine's Day began as a celebration of one or more early saints named Valentinus and became associated with romantic love several centuries later during the Middle Ages in England.

Flower Workers Lesson Plans, International Labor Rights Forum. This lesson plan explores workers' rights in the cut flower industry and how consumerism on Valentine's Day in the US affects workers abroad. (**E, M**) bit.ly/tFAlAq

---

15 Parinirvana (Nirvana) Day (Buddhism). Parinirvana Day is a Mahayana Buddhist holiday that marks the day when the Buddha is said to have achieved Parinirvana, or complete Nirvana, upon the death of his physical body.

Becoming Buddha: The Story of Siddhartha, by Whitney Stewart. This book follows Buddha from pre-birth prophecies through his pampered youth, his break with royal life, and his quest for enlightenment. (**E**) bit.ly/2IlILOC

---

17 Huey Newton, civil rights activist and Black Panther Party co-founder, born (1942-1989). Huey Newton was a civil rights activist who co-founded and led the Black Panther Party. The group set forth its political goals in a document entitled the "Ten-Point Program," which called for better housing, jobs, and education for Black Americans. Under his leadership, the Panthers founded more than 60 community support programs, the most famous of which was Free Breakfast for Children, which fed thousands of poor children in the 1970s before it was sabotaged by the federal government.

What We Don't Learn About the Black Panther Party — but Should, a teaching activity By Adam Sanchez and Jesse Hagopian for Zinn Education Project. This mixer role play introduces students to the pivotal and largely untold history of the Black Panthers. Students are given a role with a thumbnail sketch of that person's biography along with details that help illuminate aspects of the party. (**H**) bit.ly/3ctdBuX

'What We Want, What We Believe': Teaching with the Black Panthers' Ten Point Program, Teaching Activity, by Wayne Au. This lesson leads students to study the Black Panthers' Ten Point Program to help assess issues in their own communities and to develop Ten Point Programs of their own. **(H)** bit.ly/KbuoS7

The Huey P. Newton Reader, edited by David Hilliard and Donald Weise. The first comprehensive collection of writings by the Black Panther Party founder and revolutionary icon of the Black Liberation era, this reader combines now-classic texts with previously unpublished writings from the Black Panther Party archives and Newton's private collection. (**H**) bit.ly/2Q3UzUJ

---

19 80th anniversary of President Franklin D. Roosevelt's order to intern Japanese Americans. Following the attack on Pearl Harbor, discrimination against Japanese Americans deepened. After the US entered World War II, President Franklin D. Roosevelt signed an executive order authorizing the military to intern Japanese Americans in camps, despite reports from the FNI, Office of Naval Intelligence, and his own investigators who said mass incarceration was unnecessary. The order was suspended in December 1944 after the Supreme Court ruling in *Ex parte Mitsuye Endo*.

In the Shadow of My Country: A Japanese American Artist Remembers, by Densho. One Japanese American family's memories of living behind barbed wire during World War II are captured in this bilingual multimedia website. The acclaimed artist Roger Shimomura, who was held at Minidoka, Idaho as a 3-year-old, found inspiration in his grandmother's journals. A virtual exhibition, *In the Shadow of My Country* displays the artist's sharply ironic paintings tempered by the grandmother's patient, hopeful words. Complementing the central images are photos of daily life in the detention camps, an interview with the artist, and quotations of Japanese Americans incarcerated as children. Teacher's guide to the exhibit included here: densho.org/in-the-shadow-of-my-country

---

160th anniversary of the Anti-Coolie Act. The racist term "coolie" referred to Asian contract laborers from China and India who were recruited to fulfill the US economy's need for cheap labor after the abolition of slavery. The Anti-Coolie Act sought to appease growing xenophobic sentiments and anti-immigration campaigns led by White laborers and politicians. These xenophobic campaigns influenced later immigration exclusion acts, such as the Chinese Exclusion Act of 1882.

Landed, by Milly Lee. *Landed* tells the story of Sun, a young Chinese man who emigrates to America during the age of the Chinese Exclusion Act. Lee based the story on that of her father-in-law and provides useful historical background information. (**E**) bit.ly/2qne0rv

---

21 **Presidents Day**. Presidents Day began as an official holiday to honor George Washington's birthday, and is still officially called Washington's Birthday by the federal government. Today, the holiday honors all those who have served as President of the United States.

Brick by Brick, by Charles R. Smith, Jr. This story opens with America becoming a new country and our first president, George Washington, needing a home. It then describes how enslaved Africans were put to work to build the White House. Through text and illustrations, *Brick by Brick* tells the story of enslaved people working under the blistering sun for hours a day under grueling conditions. (**E**) bit.ly/2l9NTSD

Write the Truth, by Bob Peterson, Rethinking Schools. Peterson describes an inquiry project in which his 5th graders investigated which US presidents owned slaves, and then wrote letters to textbook publishers to demand that this information be included. (**E, M**) bit.ly/svqysP

International Mother Language Day. International Mother Language Day is observed yearly to promote linguistic and cultural diversity and multilingualism

Rethinking Bilingual Education, by Rethinking Schools. A new, edited collection of articles about bringing students' home languages into our classrooms. The stories offer powerful examples of social justice curricula taught by bilingual teachers. The volume also includes ideas and strategies for how to honor students' home languages in schools with no bilingual programming. (**TR**) bit.ly/2njKRdr

En Comunidad: Lessons for Centering the Voices and Experiences of Bilingual Latinx Students, by Carla España and Luz Yadira Herrera. *En Comunidad* brings bilingual Latinx students' perspectives to the center of our classrooms and offers classroom-ready lessons that amplify the varied stories and identities of Latinx children. (**TR**) bit.ly/2Vyy22c

---

22 **190th anniversary of the Female Anti-Slavery Society**. The Female Anti-Slavery Society, founded in Salem, MA, was established by and for Black women, though White women were invited to join two years later. In addition to abolition, the Society got involved in issues such as education for Black children, segregation and discrimination in the North, and assisting freed or runaway slaves. The movement spread and female-led anti-slavery societies became key components in the campaign to abolish slavery and later in the Women's Rights movement.

Teaching at the Intersections: Honor and Teach About Your Students' Multiple Identities, by Monita K. Bell for Learning for Justice. This article provides definitions and examples of intersectionality and videos and lesson plans for teaching intersectionality in school. It also provides links to resources on how to apply an intersectional lens to student data and school policies, as well as a teaching toolkit. (**E, M, H, TR**) bit.ly/2Rv2ZCz

---

20th anniversary of Monsanto PCB verdict. In a landmark environmental lawsuit, Monsanto and its corporate successors were found liable on six counts pertaining to the production and release of highly toxic PCBs (polychlorinated biphenyls) in Anniston, AL. Anniston residents, many of whom worked for Monsanto, knew nothing of the dangers of PCB, though it was shown that the company had known about it for decades but deliberately and consciously suppressed the information.

The World According to Monsanto. A French documentary that looks at the domination of the agricultural industry by one of the world's most powerful companies. (**H, TR**) bit.ly/37hc1Zi

---

25 **40th anniversary of Wisconsin's civil rights protections for LGBT people**. Wisconsin became the first state to protect lesbians and gay men from discrimination in employment, housing, and public accommodations. One year later, the legislature legalized all sexual relations between consenting adults, including those between same-sex lovers. These landmark achievements were the result of a 15-year struggle carried out by progressive lawmakers and LGBT activists. Despite strong opposition from the religious right, the 1982 bill passed with bipartisan support.

They, She, He, Me: Free to Be!, by Maya & Matthew. The authors have succeeded in creating a gorgeous and much-needed picture book about pronouns and gender fluidity. (**E**) bit.ly/3uSs4lB

---

26 **60th anniversary of *Bailey v. Patterson***. In *Bailey v. Patterson*, the Supreme Court, in a unanimous decision, found that no group of people could be discriminated against on the basis of race during use of interstate and intrastate transportation. This included buses, trains, planes, and other forms of public transportation.

Mighty Justice: The Untold Story of Civil Rights Trailblazer Dovey Johnson Roundtree, by Katie McCabe, adapted for young readers by Jabari Asim. A young reader's adaptation of the memoir of activist and trailblazer Dovey Johnson Roundtree. She was one of the first Black women to break the racial and gender barriers in the US Army; a fierce attorney in the segregated courtrooms of Washington, DC; and a minister in the AME church, where women had never before been ordained as clergy. In 1955, Roundtree won a landmark bus desegregation case that eventually helped end "separate but equal" and dismantle Jim Crow laws across the South. (**E, M**) bit.ly/32dGdDG

50th anniversary of the Buffalo Creek Disaster. Pittston Coal Company's poorly constructed "dam," made of heaps of slag that separated a sludge pond and all the strip-mining waste from Buffalo Creek and the people of the town of Saunders, was overwhelmed after heavy rains on the night of February 25. The following morning the dam burst, and an estimated 132 million gallons of water flooded Saunders, killing 125, injuring more than 1,100, and leaving more than 4,000 people homeless.

Got Coal? Teaching About the Most Dangerous Rock in America, by Bill Bigelow. This teaching activity gives students the opportunity to play and analyze a game created by The American Coal Foundation. Students will also write from different perspectives and watch excerpts from films to expand their knowledge of coal mining and think critically about the industry's motives and goals. (**H, TR**) bit.ly/2n9WMxu

---

10th anniversary of Trayvon Martin's murder. Trayvon Martin, a Black 17-year-old, was walking home from a convenience store in Sanford, FL. Neighborhood Watch member George Zimmerman called 911 and was told not to confront the teen. Zimmerman subsequently shot and killed the unarmed Trayvon. Zimmerman was acquitted of murder on the basis of Florida's "Stand Your Ground" statute. Protests broke out nationwide, serving as a precursor to the Black Lives Matter movement.

Thirteen Ways of Looking at a Black Boy, by Tony Medina and 13 artists. This book offers a counternarrative of Black boyhood by depicting 13 views of everyday life: young boys dressed in their Sunday best, running to catch a bus, and growing up to be teachers, all while emphasizing intergenerational, community love. (**E, M**) bit.ly/3tdfLWc

When They Call You a Terrorist (Newly Adapted Young Adult Edition): A Story of Black Lives Matter and the Power to Change the World, by Patrisse Cullors and Asha Bandele. From one of the co-founders of the Black Lives Matter movement comes a poetic memoir and reflection on humanity that reminds us that protest in the interest of the most vulnerable comes from love; that love is the push to search for justice for those victimized by the powerful. With journal entries, photos, and notes that show the formation of an activist from a very young age, this meaningful, empowering account of survival, strength, and resilience seeks to change the culture that declares innocent Black life expendable. (**M, H**) bit.ly/2Q6vOHr

---

28 **Mahashivaratri (Hinduism)**.

Mahashivaratri (Night of the Shiva) is an annual Hindu festival that celebrates Lord Shiva. Devotees observe day and night fasting and perform ritual worship of Shiva Lingam to appease Lord Shiva.

Hinduism, by The Pluralism Project, Harvard University. A comprehensive collection of essays and resources related to topics such as Introduction to Hinduism; The Hindu Experience; and Current Issues for Hindus in America. The site also includes resources for "America's Many Religions." (**H, TR**) bit.ly/2TQIG17

80th anniversary of White mobs rioting against racial integration in Detroit. In the Great Northern Migration, many African Americans settled in Detroit, where housing was limited. The federal government and the Detroit Housing Commission created the Sojourner Truth Homes as public housing for Black people in a predominantly White neighborhood. When Black families began to move in, they were met with violent resistance from an angry White mob. Police responded by stopping the Black people from moving in and arresting 200 Black victims and only three White rioters.

White Rage: The Unspoken Truth of Our Racial Divide, by Carol Anderson. In this video, Anderson discusses her book in which she chronicles where Black progress in history has been met by what she calls "White rage." (**H**) bit.ly/36ey6Xj

March Resources

1 First day of Women's History Month. Women's History Month, which grew out of a week-long celebration in California, is designed to highlight women's contributions to history, society, and culture.

Let Her Learn: A Toolkit to Stop School Push Out for Girls of Color, by the National Women's Law Center. This toolkit will help you determine if your school's discipline policy treats girls of Color fairly. Use this guide to learn your rights, ways in which you can change your school policy, and where to find help. (**TR**) bit.ly/2i1PIRG

Little Leaders: Bold Women in Black History, by Vashti Harrison. This 96-page book features 40 biographies, accompanied by charming illustrations, of African American women who helped shape history. It was an instant *New York Times* bestseller when it debuted in December 2017. (**E**) bit.ly/2p5UijE

Women and Girls Are Changemakers, created by Shay InLak'Ech. An exceptional collection of picture books on powerful women throughout history, each linked to a YouTube read-aloud of the book. (**E**) bit.ly/390Wz6C

The Women Who Caught the Babies: A Story of African American Midwives, by Eloise Greenfield. This book for children highlights important aspects of the training and work of African American midwives and the ways in which they have helped, and continue to help, so many families by "catching" their babies at birth. (**E, M**) bit.ly/3wMGICZ

180th anniversary of *Commonwealth v. Hunt*. The Massachusetts State Supreme Court ruling in *Commonwealth v. Hunt* was the first US court case to find that labor unions could exist legally if they were organized for a legal purpose and used legal means to achieve their goals.

Fannie Never Flinched: One Woman's Courage in the Struggle for American Labor Rights, by Mary Cronk Farrell. This beautiful book about early 20th century labor organizer Fannie Sellins begins with her murder by sheriff's deputies, in broad daylight, at the age of 47. No one is prosecuted. The author then jumps back 20 years to trace Sellins' life organizing garment and mine workers. Full of photos and primary documents, *Fannie Never Flinched* puts Sellins' story in the context of the struggles of workers and the Labor movement during the "Gilded Age." (**E, M**) bit.ly/328Y6nn

---

150th anniversary of Yellowstone National Park. Congress passed the Yellowstone Act of 1872, setting aside 2 million acres of land believed to be of no economic value. It was the first national park in the world. In establishing this popular tourist attraction, Yellowstone displaced a group of Eastern Shoshone people who agreed to move in exchange for hunting rights in the park. The US government reneged on the treaty, building a fort to prevent Indigenous people from using the park as they had been promised.

What is a National Park? A lesson plan from the National Park Service. Students analyze the arrowhead logo as an introduction to the National Park Service. They learn how the design of the National Park Service arrowhead is made up of symbols, and then have a chance to create their own designs specific to their own states. They then learn ways that we can help care for our parks through the seven "Leave No Trace" principles, helping students to understand that the National Parks are our collective responsibility. (**E**) bit.ly/2QpNzkP

80th anniversary of the Japanese internment proclamation. General John DeWitt issued the first public proclamation notifying all "persons of Japanese ancestry" that they were to be removed from the western parts of Washington State, California, Oregon, and parts of Arizona. A curfew was imposed and other exclusion orders followed. In all, 108 exclusion orders carried the same instructions: that Japanese Americans had one week to prepare themselves for removal, taking with them only what they could carry.

They Called Us Enemy, by George Takai. In this autobiographical graphic novel, actor, author, and activist George Takei recounts his childhood imprisoned in American concentration camps during World War II. (**M, H**) bit.ly/3eElaSf

---

2 Ash Wednesday/first day of Lent (Christianity). Ash Wednesday is the first day of Lent, a 40-day period of penitence and reflection in preparation for Easter for most Western Christians.

BBC Schools: Guide to Christianity. This site includes basic information about Christianity, including Lent and Easter, as well as links to classroom activities intended to help students understand the beliefs and practices of Christians. (**M, H, TR**) bbc.in/ROXVFb

---

10th anniversary of Iowa's "Ag-Gag" law. Iowa's passage of an "Ag-Gag" law made it illegal for journalists and animal rights groups to engage in undercover investigations at factory farms. This was prompted by a whistleblower's report on the cruel treatment of pigs on an Iowa farm that led to public outrage over animal abuse in agribusinesses. Struck down as unconstitutional in 2019, the Iowa legislature passed another similar law months later.

Teaching About Farmed Animals in Elementary School, by TeachHeart. A free resource guide containing age-appropriate lessons about the treatment of animals on factory farms, aimed at grades 3-8. (**E, M**) bit.ly/3ddKRb3

Debate Kit: Is Animal Agriculture Harmful to the Environment? by PETA. "Here at PETA, our core belief is that animals are not ours to use. We know that many schools assign debates on topical issues to help their students learn to speak and write persuasively, develop research skills, and recognize multiple sides of a controversial or multifaceted issue. The impact of various industries on the environment is certainly one such topic. This student debate kit lists a variety of resources that can be shared with students to support the argument that animal agriculture is harmful to the environment and that eating vegan is one solution." (**H**) bit.ly/3mKugyR

130th anniversary of People's Grocery lynching. Thomas Moss was a Black man who owned People's Grocery, a successful grocery store in Memphis, TN. He, along with Calvin McDowell and Will Stewart, two of his employees, were hanged by a White mob who resented the power and economic success of Moss. The event led to investigations by social activists exposing the racism and injustice behind the lynching of Black men, yet little was done to acknowledge and stop these murders.

Ida B. The Queen: The Extraordinary Life and Legacy of Ida B. Wells, by Michelle Duster. The awe-inspiring story of a pioneering woman who was often overlooked and underestimated – a woman who refused to exit a train car meant for White passengers; a woman who brought to light the horrors of lynching in America; a woman who co-founded the NAACP. Written by Wells' great-granddaughter Michelle Duster, this "warm remembrance of a civil rights icon" (Kirkus Reviews) is a unique visual celebration of Wells' life, and of the Black experience. (**M, H**) bit.ly/3wUMI1O

110th anniversary of HR 409 hearings on Lawrence Strike. Victor Berger, a congressman from Milwaukee, introduced a resolution in the House of Representatives to conduct hearings about the Lawrence Textile/Bread and Roses/Singing Strike because the American Woolen Company was the beneficiary of a tariff designed to protect labor, yet its workers were some of the lowest paid in America.

Lawrence, 1912: The Singing Strike, a teaching activity by Bill Bigelow and Norm Diamond for Zinn Education Project. Through role play, students in this lesson explore some of the actual dilemmas faced by strikers in Lawrence, MA in 1912. The teaching methodology is designed to match the history itself, as students portray Industrial Workers of the World (I.W.W.) organizers deciding how – and for what cause – to conduct a massive strike. (**H**) bit.ly/3hkL4f1

---

3 180th anniversary of first US child labor law regulating working hours. Massachusetts passed the first child labor law in the US limiting workdays to 10 hours a day. The state had passed an earlier law (1836) that required children under 15 to attend school at least three months a year. Other states passed their own laws governing child labor, but it wasn't until 1938 that the US enacted a comprehensive law (the Fair Labor Standards Act) regulating child labor nationwide.

The Bobbin Girl, by Emily Arnold McCully. Rebecca is a "bobbin girl," trying to help her struggling family by working all day in a hot, noisy cotton mill. Working conditions at the mill are abysmal, and there is talk of lowering the workers' wages. Rebecca's friend Judith wants to protest the pay cut, but the organizers at the mill are dismissed. Does Rebecca have the courage to join the protest? The story is followed by a note from the author about the historical context. (**E, M**) zinnedproject.org/materials/bobbin-girl

Migrant, by Maxine Trottier. Each spring Anna leaves her home in Mexico and travels north with her family where they work on farms. Sometimes she feels like a bird, flying north in the spring and south in the fall. She wonders what it would be like to stay in one place. The Low German-speaking Mennonites from Mexico are a unique group of migrants who moved from Canada to Mexico in the 1920s and became an important part of the farming community. But it has become increasingly difficult for them to earn a livelihood, so they come back to Canada each year as migrant workers. (**E**) bit.ly/32baKIB

50th anniversary of the Center for Independent Living. This Berkeley, CA center was the world's first community-based independent living facility. It was established by a group of disabled students from the University of California at Berkeley, a key moment in the broader movement for independent living.

Crip Camp, a film by Nicole Newnham and James LeBrecht. A powerful documentary about a summer camp for children with disabilities in the 1970s, which traces how the independence and experience of the campers helped them create a loose network that contributed to the Disability Rights movement. Website includes lesson plans. (**M, H**) cripcamp.com

---

4 140th anniversary of Anti-Chinese Demonstration Day. Anti-Chinese sentiment was so widespread that California Governor Perkins declared March 4, 1882 a legal holiday for anti-Chinese demonstrations in the run-up to an impending vote in Congress on the Chinese Exclusion Act. An estimated 30,000 people attended a demonstration in San Francisco, where the crowd was entertained by a band playing patriotic music. Newspaper headlines screamed of the need to save the US from the "vile hordes" coming from Asia.

Us vs. Them – The Chinese Exclusion Act of 1882, by The National Museum of American History. This lesson plan is a case study that establishes what "exclusion" in immigration law looked like, particularly in the late 19th and early 20th centuries. Students will explore the selective and racist nature of quotas and their impact on the US population. Reading arguments made in Congress and reflected in political cartoons, students analyze the attitudes and beliefs about "others" undergirding restrictive immigration policies. (**M, H**) s.si.edu/3eYohog

---

Miriam Makeba, South African singer and activist, born (1932-2008). Makeba, a singer popularly known as "Mama Afrika," used her music and activism as a way to draw the world's attention to Apartheid. As a result, her South African citizenship was revoked while she was abroad, and she lived in exile, mainly in the US, until the end of Apartheid. She always insisted that her songs were not political; they simply reflected the realities of her life in South Africa.

Movers and Movements: Fighting for Social Justice in South Africa, by Brenda Randolph, published in *Putting the Movement Back into Civil Rights Teaching: A Resource Guide for Classrooms and Communities*. Teaching lesson that highlights both unsung activists and well-known people such as Miriam Makeba, associated with the Anti-Apartheid movement in South Africa. (**M, H**) bit.ly/1ziLORr

Mama Africa!: How Miriam Makeba Spread Hope with Her Song, by Kathryn Erskine. Set defiantly in the present tense, this biography offers readers an intimate view of Makeba's fight for equality. Kathryn Erskine's call-and-response-style text and Charly Palmer's bold illustrations come together in a raw, riveting duet of protest song and praise poem. A testament to how a single voice helped to shake up the world – and can continue to do so. (**E, M**) kathrynerskine.com/book/title/mama_africa

---

7 80th anniversary of the death of Lucy Parsons. Parsons was a leading figure in American anarchism and the Radical Labor movement. Born a slave, she married Albert R. Parsons, a White radical Republican. They continued their labor organizing activities in Chicago where Albert was tried and executed for participating in the Haymarket Square Bombing. After his execution, Lucy founded the newspaper *Freedom*, addressing issues such as labor organizing, women's rights, lynching, and Black forced labor in the South.

Haymarket: A Novel, by Martin Duberman. This moving work of historical fiction makes working-class life and organizing come alive. The detail and drama of the struggle for an 8-hour workday, as seen through the lives of labor activists Lucy and Albert Parsons, hold the reader's attention. The author deftly weaves together critical themes of race and gender. (**H**) bit.ly/2mgA17U

---

8 240th anniversary of the Gnadenhutten Massacre of Lenape (Ohio). British-affiliated Native Americans forced a group of Lenape from Gnadenhutten to the mouth of the Sandusky River to prevent them from aiding the American Revolutionaries. About 100 nearly starving Lenape returned to Gnadenhutten to retrieve their belongings and feed their families. A band of Pennsylvania militia attacked the group, accused them of participating in recent raids in PA, and murdered and scalped 28 men, 29 women, and 39 children.

When the Shadbush Blooms, by Carla Messinger and Susan Katz. Today when a Lenape Indian girl ventures to the stream to fish for shad, she knows that another girl did the same thing generations before.

Through the cycle of the seasons, what is important has remained: being with family, knowing when berries are ripe for picking, and listening to stories in a warm home. (**E, M**) Teacher's guide from Lee & Low Books here: bit.ly/3mKxHWh

---

9 Walter Mercado, television personality, born (1932-2019). Mercado was a wildly popular Puerto Rican entertainer and TV astrologer with a multinational Spanish-language audience estimated at 120 million. Ironically, the thing he was best known for was astrology, but he got into that field by accident when he was asked to fill in for the regular astrologer who had failed to show up for a TV appearance. A 2020 Netflix documentary, *Mucho Mucho Amor: The Legend of Walter Mercado*, chronicles Mercado's fascinating life.

Mucho Mucho Amor: The Legend of Walter Mercado, directed by Cristina Costantini and Kareem Tabsch. This 2020 documentary film chronicles the life and career of Walter Mercado, one of the most influential and important astrologists in Latin America and the world. (**H**) bit.ly/3bL5NFM

---

10 100th anniversary of the arrest of Mahatma Gandhi for sedition. In an effort to end British colonial rule in India, Mahatma Gandhi encouraged Indians to boycott British goods. Following Gandhi's boycott, protesters in Chauri Chaura picketed a local liquor shop, but the protest turned violent. Gandhi ended the boycott but was arrested and tried for sedition. He was sentenced to six years in prison.

Ahimsa, by Supriya Kelkar. In 1942, after Mahatma Gandhi asked Indians to give one family member to the Freedom movement, 10-year-old Anjali is devastated to think of her father risking his life for the freedom struggle. But it turns out he isn't the one joining. Anjali's mother is. And with this change comes many more adjustments designed to improve their country and use "ahimsa" – non-violent resistance – to stand up to the British government. (**M, H**) Teacher's guide from Lee & Low Books here: leeandlow.com/books/ahimsa

---

50th anniversary of the first National Black Political Convention. Thousands of Black activists, including Jesse Jackson, Louis Farrakhan, Julian Bond, and the widows of Dr. King and Malcolm X, attended this convention in Gary, IN. Delegates created a National Black Political Agenda, which included the election of a proportionate number of Black representatives to Congress, community control of schools, national health insurance, and the recognition of a Palestinian homeland. In later years, leaders of the Black Lives Matter movement said the convention served as a model for them.

The Colored Conventions Movement: Black Organizing in the Nineteenth Century, edited by P. Gabrielle Foreman, Jim Casey, and Sarah Lynn Patterson. This volume of essays is the first to focus on the Colored Conventions movement, the 19th century's longest campaign for Black civil rights. Well before the founding of the NAACP and other 20th century pillars of the Civil Rights movement, tens of thousands of Black leaders organized state and national conventions across North America. (**H**) bit.ly/3tikshU

---

13 Daylight Saving Time begins

First Day of Deaf History Month. Deaf History Month celebrates the contributions of deaf Americans to US society and culture and promotes awareness of Deaf culture in America.

Observing Deaf History Month, by Alexandra Gomez. This article provides information about milestones in Deaf history, as well as links to fiction and nonfiction books about deaf people. (**M, H, TR**) on.nypl.org/VDs76u

History Through Deaf Eyes, by Gallaudet University. The DEAF EYES project at Gallaudet University was established to bring Deaf history to the public and expand our understanding of the Deaf community in the US. It includes an online exhibition, a book, and a documentary film. (**M, H**) bit.ly/U73AW2

Raising Deaf Kids: A Book List. A compilation of children's books about hearing loss and deafness. (**E, M**) bit.ly/2ds3xCR

All He Knew, by Helen Frost. A novel in verse about a young deaf boy during World War II, the sister who loves him, and the conscientious objector who helps him. Inspired by true events. (**M, H**) bit.ly/39HC4vZ

---

15 International Day Against Police Brutality. Police brutality is not limited to the US. Police worldwide have abused their power for centuries and continue to this day. In 1997, a joint effort by the Montreal-based Collective Opposed to Police Brutality and the Switzerland-based Black Flag group established March 15 as International Day Against Police Brutality. It is marked by protests worldwide – which are often met with a brutal police response.

Every Mother's Son, by P.O.V. This film presents three primary examples of police brutality and what is being done about it. The lesson accompanying the video addresses actions that students can take. (**H**) to.pbs.org/1cNyCMD

80th anniversary of Norwegian teachers resisting Nazi curriculum. When 12,000 out of 14,000 teachers in Norway resisted the Nazi school curriculum and refused to join a new Nazi teachers' association put in place by the Nazi-controlled government, 1,300 of them were arrested. Half of them were sent to concentration camps and the other half were exiled to the Arctic to work in forced labor camps.

The Teachers' Protest: How Norwegian Teachers Defeated Nazi Education, a film by Jon Seal. In 1942 Nazi-occupied Norway, teachers were forced to join the Nazi Teachers' League and teach Nazi ideas in their classrooms. 8,000 of them wrote protest letters. They were threatened with salary withdrawal and dismissal, but they refused. In a desperate attempt to break them, the Nazi government arrested 1,000 male teachers and sent them to prison camps, 300 miles above the Arctic Circle. This 75-min documentary weaves together archive footage, first-hand testimony, and the skillful animation of Herlov Åmland's poignant drawings to tell this gripping story to an international audience for the first time. (**H**) Film available for free here: theteachersprotest.com

---

16 Purim begins at sunset on 3/16 (Judaism). Purim celebrates the defeat of a plot to exterminate Jews living in Persia (estimated to have occurred in the 4th century BCE). It is one of the most joyous holidays of the Jewish faith.

Cakes and Miracles: A Purim Tale, by Barbara Diamond Goldin. Purim is approaching and Hershel, the only blind boy in the village, wishes he could help his mother prepare *hamantashen* (a traditional pastry) for the holiday. With new courage, Hershel creates something more beautiful than anyone in the village can imagine. An Author's Note about Purim is also included. Reading guide included at this site. (**E**) bit.ly/2DCZ7XS

230th anniversary of Denmark's abolition of the slave trade. A law to abolish the slave trade was passed in 1792, but that isn't the same as abolishing slavery. That didn't come about until 1847, when a law was passed to phase out slavery over a 12-year period. An 1848 revolt by slaves on the island of St. Croix, led by John Gottlieb (also written Gottliff), also known as General Buddhoe, demanding an immediate end to slavery, finally ended the practice in Denmark's territories.

Routes of Passage: Rethinking the African Diaspora, by Ruth Simms Hamilton. A conceptual, substantive, and empirical orientation to the study of African people worldwide. The book addresses issues of geographical mobility and geosocial displacement; changing cultural, political, and economic relationships between Africa and its diaspora; inter-diaspora relations; political and economic agency and social mobilization, including cultural production and psychocultural transformation; existence in hostile and oppressive political and territorial space; and confronting interconnected relations of social inequality, especially class, gender, nationality, and race. (**H**) bit.ly/3deMc1u

---

17 Bayard Rustin, civil rights and LGBTQ+ rights activist, born (1912-1987). Bayard Rustin, an openly gay, Black man, was a civil rights activist and one of the chief organizers of the 1963 March on Washington for Jobs and Freedom. He also helped coordinate the Freedom Rides and the founding of the Southern Christian Leadership Conference. Despite his many achievements, Rustin was silenced, arrested, imprisoned, and fired from important leadership positions, largely because he was gay. He was posthumously awarded the Presidential Medal of Freedom in 2013.

Troublemaker for Justice: The Story of Bayard Rustin, the Man Behind the March on Washington, by Jacqueline Houtman, Walter Naegle, and Michael G. Long. A biography for young adult readers about one of the most influential activists of our time, who was an early advocate for both African American and gay rights. (**E, M**) bit.ly/2Q0nSHA

---

18 First Day of Holi (Hinduism). Holi is a 2-day Hindu festival celebrating the triumph of good over evil, as well as the arrival of Spring. It is also known as the "Festival of Colors" for the ritual throwing of colored water and powder on friends and family.

Festival of Colors, by Kabir Sehgal and Surishtha Sehgal. Learn all about Holi, the Indian Festival of Colors, in this lush picture book from the bestselling mother/son duo. (**E**) bit.ly/2KO5lpt

---

Fred Shuttlesworth, civil rights activist, born (1922-2011). Fred Shuttlesworth co-founded the Southern Christian Leadership Conference and was one of the "Big Three" of the Civil Rights movement, along with Dr. Martin Luther King, Jr. and Ralph Abernathy. King referred to Shuttlesworth as "the most courageous civil rights fighter in the South." He survived the bombing of his home as well as countless other brutal attacks throughout his decades-long fight for equal rights for Black Americans.

Civil Rights Martyrs, by the Civil Rights Memorial. Chronology briefly describing the lives of martyrs of the Civil Rights movement – activists who were targeted for death because of their civil rights work, random victims of vigilantes determined to halt the movement, and individuals who, in the sacrifice of their own lives, brought new awareness to the struggle. (**M, H, TR**) bit.ly/1oWUxuX

30th anniversary of White South Africans voting to negotiate an end to Apartheid. In 1990, the South African government began negotiations with the African National Congress to end Apartheid and establish a multiracial democracy. When the negotiations inspired a right-wing backlash, then-President F.W. De Klerk called a Whites-only referendum on continuing negotiations. 68 percent of White South Africans voted yes.

Movers and Movements: Fighting for Social Justice in South Africa, by Brenda Randolph, published in *Putting the Movement Back into Civil Rights Teaching: A Resource Guide for Classrooms and Communities*. Teaching lesson that highlights unsung activists associated with the Anti-Apartheid movement in South Africa. (**M, H, TR**) bit.ly/1ziLORr

---

19 60th anniversary of Algerian independence. After a bloody 7-year war, the Algerian Liberation Front (FLN) succeeded in ending 130 years of French colonial rule in the North African country. The small guerilla force, made up of young Algerian Muslims, overcame 500,000 French troops. The war had polarized public opinion in France. Charles de Gaulle returned to power as Prime Minister and initiated peace talks with the FLN, which resulted in an end to the fighting and independence for Algeria.

Lesson of the Day: "A Continent Remade," by *NYTimes* Learning Network. In this lesson, students will learn about the Year of Africa in 1960, when 17 African countries declared their independence. (**H**) nyti.ms/3u1jJCj

---

20 170th anniversary of the publication of *Uncle Tom's Cabin*. Originally published as a 40-part serial in an abolitionist newspaper, *Uncle Tom's Cabin*, by Harriet Beecher Stowe, became a hugely popular novel that fueled the debate over slavery and raised the consciousness of White America and Europe. Stowe's vivid characters and portrayal of their struggles opened reader's eyes to the realities of slavery and the humanity of enslaved people, bringing a new level of empathy for enslaved individuals.

Annotated Bibliography for Young Readers of Harriet Beecher Stowe Biographies, by the Harriet Beecher Stowe Center. A list of books for young readers interested in learning more about Harriet Beecher Stowe and her social justice work. (**E, M, H, TR**) bit.ly/3ecm32y

---

21 World Down Syndrome Day. This day is dedicated to raising public awareness and advocating for the rights, inclusion, and well-being of people with Down Syndrome. It has been officially recognized by the UN since 2012.

My Friend Isabelle, by Eliza Woloson. This is a story about Charlie and Isabelle's friendship. At first, Charlie sees only the differences between him and Isabelle, who has Down Syndrome, but in the end, he recognizes all the similarities they share. Book description is on 6 Elements of Social Justice Ed. Book Blog, which offers a summary of this book and other social justice children's literature titles. (**E**) bit.ly/154hueW

International Day for the Elimination of Racial Discrimination. The United Nations International Day for the Elimination of Racial Discrimination commemorates the lives of the anti-apartheid demonstrators killed on March 21, 1960 in Sharpeville, South Africa.

The White Supremacy and Me Workbook, by Layla Saad. A text and a process for those holding White privilege to examine and dismantle their complicity in White supremacy. (**TR**) bit.ly/2Agvf2C

Zackie Achmat, South African LGBTQ and AIDS activist, born (1962). Zackie Achmat is a South African AIDS activist who helped form and lead Treatment Action Campaign (TAC), an organization that aims to ensure AIDS patients have access to antiviral drug therapies at affordable prices. He went from anti-apartheid activist to AIDS activist in response to then-president Thabo Mbeki's outlandish views on the causes of AIDS and his refusal to provide conventional treatment through the public health service.

An Interview with Zackie Achmat: AIDS Activism in South Africa, by amfAR: Making AIDS History. A 2004 interview with Zackie Achmat about his activist work, the state of global politics related to HIV/AIDS, and more. (**H**) bit.ly/2OVcZqa

---

10th anniversary of Juan Felipe Herrera's being named California Poet Laureate. Son of Mexican migrants, Juan Felipe Herrera was named California Poet Laureate. He later went on to be elected to the Board of Chancellors for the Academy of American Poets in 2011, was awarded the Guggenheim Fellowship in Poetry in 2010, and won the National Book Critics Circle Award in Poetry in 2009.

Resistencia: Poems of Protest and Revolution, edited by Mark Eisner and Tina Escaja, with an introduction by Julia Alvarez. An extraordinary collection, rooted in a strong tradition of protest poetry and voiced by icons of the movement and some of the most exciting writers today. The poets of *Resistencia* explore feminist, queer, Indigenous, and ecological themes alongside historically prominent protests against imperialism, dictatorships, and economic inequality. Within this momentous collection, poets representing every Latin American country grapple with identity, place, and belonging, resisting easy definitions to render a nuanced and complex portrait of language in rebellion. (**H**) bit.ly/3cTJKgw

---

22 World Water Day. This observance is held annually to highlight water issues and to advocate for universal access to sustainable freshwater resources.

Poisoned Water: How the Citizens of Flint, Michigan Fought for Their Lives and Warned the Nation, by Candy Cooper and Marc Aronson. Based on original reporting by a Pulitzer Prize finalist and an industry veteran, this is the first book for young adults about the Flint water crisis. The book shows not just how the crisis unfolded in 2014, but also the history of racism and segregation that led up to it, the beliefs and attitudes that fueled it, and how the people of Flint fought – and are still fighting – for clean water and healthy lives. (**M, H**) bit.ly/3fDy8QT

A Tale of Two Cities, by The Story of Stuff Project. This film tells the story of citizens from two very different Michigan communities – picturesque, small town Evart, and gritty, industrial Flint – that have found their futures inextricably linked by a threat to the one thing that all life requires: water. This short documentary explores the growing threat of water privatization and what happens when government runs a critical function, like providing clean drinking water, as if it were a business. (**M, H**) bit.ly/2LJg0nr

We Are Water Protectors, by Carole Lindstrom. Inspired by the many Indigenous-led movements across North America, *We Are Water Protectors* issues an urgent rallying cry to safeguard the Earth's water from harm and corruption. A bold and lyrical picture book written by Carole Lindstrom and vibrantly illustrated by Michaela Goade. (**E**) bit.ly/2AeJ2tH

50th anniversary of *Eisenstadt v. Baird*. The US Supreme Court struck down a Massachusetts statute that banned the distribution of contraceptives to unmarried people in *Eisenstadt v. Baird*. The Court, citing the Equal Protection Clause of the 14th Amendment, ruled the Massachusetts law was unconstitutional. The decision meant that anyone, married or single, could get contraceptives.

What Is Sex Education? For Educators, by Planned Parenthood. Sex education helps people gain the information, skills, and motivation to make healthy decisions about sex and sexuality. Planned Parenthood provides guidelines, resources, standards, and more for K-12 educators to share with young people. (**H**) bit.ly/2vb0Cao

---

23 90th anniversary of the Norris-LaGuardia Act. Co-sponsored in Congress by George Norris and Fiorello La Guardia, this Act prohibited federal courts from using "yellow dog contracts," agreements between employers and employees in which the employee is forced to agree not to join a union as a condition of employment. It disallowed federal courts from issuing injunctions against activities by labor organizations when attempting to prevent strikes or boycotts.

Ella Jenkins and a Union of Friends Pulling Together, by Ella Jenkins. Legendary children's performer Ella Jenkins and a group of young and older musical friends introduce children to the ideas of unity, cooperation, and labor unions through songs, recitation, and poetry. Recorded in 1999, this CD features harmonica, piano, percussion, banjo, guitar, vocals, and chorus. The recording reminds us how unity and strength are part of family ties as well as adult life and work. (**E**) s.si.edu/3wXuk3d

---

24 190th anniversary of the Treaty of Cusseta. The Creek Tribe signed the Treaty of Cusseta, surrendering 5.2 million acres of their land in Alabama in return for five years of government protection while they decided if they wanted to sell their remaining land to White landowners. However, White intruders started taking over Creek land while the government did nothing, leading to the Second Creek War. Eventually, the US forcibly removed the rest of the Creek people from Alabama.

Creek Trail of Tears: Historic Sites and Points of Interest, by Explore Southern History. Linked images and informational text about sites and events associated with the Creek Trail of Tears. (**E, M, H**) exploresouthernhistory.com/creektrail

---

Dorothy Height, educator and civil rights activist, born (1912-2010). Dorothy Height was an important figure in the Civil Rights movement. She worked with the National Council of Negro Women and eventually became the fourth president of the Council. She focused on ending the lynching of Black Americans and making improvements in the criminal justice system. She helped many presidents, including Roosevelt, Eisenhower, and Johnson, on issues important to the Black community. Height was a key organizer of the 1963 March on Washington.

Open Wide the Freedom Gates: A Memoir, by Dorothy Height. In her memoir, Dr. Height, at the age of 91, reflects on a life of service and leadership. We witness her childhood encounters with racism and the thrill of New York college life during the Harlem Renaissance. We see her protest the lynching of Black people. We sit with her onstage as Martin Luther King, Jr. delivers his "I Have a Dream" speech. And we watch as she leads the National Council of Negro Women for 41 years during which her diplomatic counsel was sought by presidents from Eisenhower to Clinton. (**H**) https://n.pr/3diUnd0

40th anniversary of the Sanctuary Movement (also called the Overground Railroad). The Sanctuary Movement was formed to offer protection to undocumented refugees fleeing Central American wars. After the assassination of Archbishop Oscar Romero in El Salvador, John Fife, a Minister in Tucson, declared his congregation a sanctuary for refugees from civil wars in Guatemala and El Salvador, catalyzing a nationwide movement of religious institutions. The US government, which supported the Guatemalan and Salvadoran governments, denied refugee status to most people fleeing violence in Central America.

Caravan to the North: Misael's Long Walk, by Jorge Argueta. This short novel in verse follows Misael and his family as they join the caravan from El Salvador to the Mexico/US border. Misael details the violence he is fleeing and the beauty of his country that he will miss. (**M, H**) bit.ly/3qHrwTr

---

28 50th anniversary of Barbara Jordan's election as President of the Texas Senate. Barbara Jordan was elected President of the Texas Senate six years after winning a seat in the Texas Legislature in 1966. She was the first Black woman to have power over a legislative body. Later that year, she served as Acting Governor because both the governor and lieutenant governor were out of the state. In doing so, she became the first Black governor in the nation.

What Do You Do with a Voice Like That?: The Story of Extraordinary Congresswoman Barbara Jordan, by Chris Barton. Even as a child growing up in the 5th Ward of Houston, Texas, Barbara Jordan stood out for her big, bold, booming, crisp, clear, confident voice. It was a voice that made people sit up, stand up, and take notice. So, what do you do with a voice like that? This is a remarkable picture book biography about a woman whose struggles and mission continue to inspire today. (**E, M**) bit.ly/3gd1qpt

---

80th anniversary of the arrest of Minoru Yasui for breaking Japanese American curfew. Yasui, a lawyer, deliberately broke a curfew imposed by the US government on Japanese Americans during World War II to test its legality. His case went to the Supreme Court, which upheld his conviction. That conviction was overturned 40 years later. After the war, Yasui practiced law and worked with the Japanese American Citizens League, which sought redress for Japanese Americans interned during the war. He posthumously received the Presidential Medal of Freedom in 2015.

Never Give Up!: Minoru Yasui and the Fight for Justice, a documentary film by Holly Yasui and Will Doolittle. This award-winning documentary explores the life of Minoru (Min) Yasui, born in Hood River, Oregon in 1916 of immigrant parents. He was the first Japanese American attorney in Oregon. During World War II, he initiated a legal test case by deliberately violating military orders that led to the incarceration of more than 110,000 persons of Japanese ancestry in concentration camps. He spent nine months in solitary confinement awaiting his appeal to the US Supreme Court, which ruled against him. The film depicts his family's wartime experiences in the temporary detention centers and the Tule Lake and Minidoka concentration camps. (**M, H**) minoruyasuifilm.org

---

30 220th anniversary of Indian Intercourse Act of 1802. The stated purpose of the six Indian Intercourse Acts was to protect Native Americans from exploitation and illegal seizure of their lands. That's not how it turned out, however. Although the trading posts installed as a proviso of the 1802 Act provided animals, farm equipment, and other goods, it also pushed many into debt, which was used as leverage to force Native Americans off their land. It didn't take long before the government engaged in wholesale land theft and mass murder.

An Indigenous People's History of the United States for Young People, by Roxanne Dunbar-Ortiz. A history of the United States told from the perspective of Indigenous peoples, revealing how Native Americans actively resisted expansion of the US empire for centuries. (**M, H**) bit.ly/31EZLQA; Link to teacher's guide: bit.ly/2UzuFYZ

---

31 César Chávez Day. This day marks the birthday of César Chávez, an American farmworker, labor leader, and civil rights activist. Chávez co-founded the National Farm Workers Association (later known as United Farm Workers of America), which achieved unprecedented gains for farmworkers.

Harvesting Hope: The Story of César Chávez, by Kathleen Krull. This picture book chronicles Chávez's youth and the struggles he endured on his journey to becoming a leader. The second link is to a teacher's guide. (**E**) bit.ly/2qkxOfj; link to Teacher's Guide: bit.ly/1Qd1FZx

Model Curriculum and Resources for Teachers. This curriculum on the life and work of César Chávez, from the California Department of Education, includes biographies, pictures, and other resources to help teachers prepare lessons for this holiday. (**E, M, H**) bit.ly/1mFT0W3

60th anniversary of the National Farmworkers of America (NFWA). César Chávez, the son of farmworkers, had worked with the grassroots Community Service Organization (CSO), eventually becoming national director. He left CSO to focus on the specific plight of farmworkers, co-founding the National Farm Workers Association (NFWA) with Dolores Huerta, an experienced union organizer. They met with workers in towns throughout California, building an organization that would ultimately become the United Farm Workers, one of the most effective unions in the country.

Side by Side/Lado a Lado: The Story of Dolores Huerta and César Chávez, by Monica Brown and Joe Cepeda. This picture book pairs the stories of Huerta and Chávez. Each double-page spread features text in both Spanish and English, with Huerta's story on the left and Chávez's on the right. (**E**) bit.ly/2NcFlao

April Resources

1 First day of Arab American Heritage Month. The US Department of State published a proclamation on April 1, 2021 recognizing April as National Arab Heritage Month. The month offers the opportunity to celebrate the richness and complexity of Arab American heritage and culture. Previous attempts by various Members of Congress to designate a month as Arab American Heritage Month have not been successful.

Celebrating Arab American Heritage Month, by Learning for Justice. A rich collection of resources, articles, lesson plans, and more to help educators celebrate Arab identity, counter negative stereotypes, teach about Arab history and cultures, and ensure an inclusive environment that supports Arab American students this month and throughout the year. (**TR**) bit.ly/3aO9wkX

Celebrate Arab American Heritage Month, by Beatrice Alvarez for PBS. A collection of short films representing some of the millions of voices and diverse experiences of Arab Americans.

First day of Sexual Assault Awareness Month. Inaugurated in 2001, Sexual Assault Awareness Month seeks to raise awareness about sexual violence and to educate the public, including law enforcement, about the true causes of sexual assault – primarily male entitlement and lack of respect for women. It also promotes bystander involvement and encourages victims to report assaults without fear or shame.

How My Third-Graders and I Address Consent, by Elizabeth Kleinrock. In the wake of #MeToo and the Kavanaugh hearings, Ms. Kleinrock shares her strategies for addressing consent with elementary students. (**E, TR**) bit.ly/2RQL8XV

The Reckoning: Teaching About the #MeToo Moment and Sexual Harassment with Resources from The New York Times, by the *NYTimes* Learning Network. In this unit, *NYTimes* staff pull together a wealth of *Times* reporting, opinions, and videos to suggest several ways to begin confronting the questions and issues the #MeToo movement raises. Christopher Pepper, a health educator in the San Francisco Unified School District, who helped design the district's high school sex education curriculum, co-wrote this piece with the Learning Network staff. (**H**) nyti.ms/2DD6eyi

Rights, Respect, Responsibility: A K-12 Sexuality Curriculum, by Advocates for Youth. This website offers an education resource center, which includes K-12 lesson plans, curricula, national standards, and state legislation about sex education. (**H**) bit.ly/2HnHGjv

NO! The Rape Documentary. This documentary explores the impact of sexual violence on Black women and girls. As incidents of violence and sexual assault increase in number, this film can be used to support people as they learn to navigate the challenging terrain of sexuality without violence. (**H**) bit.ly/2RXJUKi

---

First day of National Poetry Month. The largest literary celebration in the world, National Poetry Month is an annual celebration of poetry and its place in American culture.

40 Books to Celebrate National Poetry Month, by Black Children's Books and Authors. Forty powerful poetry books by Black writers, which can be used during National Poetry Month and year-round. (**E**) bit.ly/2Ei0lXa

Woke: A Young Poet's Call to Justice, by Mahogany Browne with Elizabeth Acevedo and Olivia Gatwood. Historically, poets have been on the forefront of social movements. *Woke* is a collection of poems by women that reflect the joy and passion in the fight for social justice, tackling topics from discrimination to empathy, and acceptance to speaking out. (**E, M, H**) bit.ly/3gnx3Kl

Thanku: Poems of Gratitude, edited by Miranda Paul. An anthology exploring themes of thankfulness and gratitude through poetry written mostly by Black, Indigenous, and poets of Color. (**E, M**) bit.ly/2Fh30CM

90th anniversary of the Chicago School Children's Strike. During the Depression, 500 school children, living in poverty and close to starvation, marched through downtown Chicago to the Board of Education demanding that the school system provide them with food.

Kids on the March: 15 Stories of Speaking Out, Protesting, and Fighting for Justice, by Michael Long. From the March on Washington to March for Our Lives to Black Lives Matter, the powerful stories of kid-led protest in America. Kids have always been activists. This book shows that no one is too young to make a difference. (**E, M**) bit.ly/3lhzHVu

---

2 First Day of the month of Ramadan (Islam). Ramadan is a holy month of fasting and prayer in the Islam faith. It is the 9th month of the 12-month Islamic calendar and commemorates the month during which Mohammed received the revelations that became the *Koran* (Quran). It begins the evening of April 2.

How Teachers Can Support Students During Ramadan, by Rusul Alrubail. Ramadan is a month in the Islamic calendar when Muslims observe fasting from sunrise to sunset. It can be a difficult month for many to get through, especially students who have to go through a normal school day without eating or drinking. For schools, it's important to provide an environment for students where they feel safe to practice their religion, but maybe more important, one that ensures their well-being during the school day. (**TR**) to.pbs.org/3ujLfuC

Lailah's Lunchbox: A Ramadan Story, by Reem Faruqi. Lailah's hesitation about her faith and traditions is explained from a child's point of view. Though she is excited to begin fasting during Ramadan, she is unsure about how to explain this practice to her classmates or deal with the temptations of lunchtime. Eventually, with the help of her librarian and teacher, she gains confidence among her peers. (**E**) bit.ly/2kFmPLM; Interview with author: bit.ly/2kzsP6e

Drummer Girl, by Hiba Masood. Young Najma loved Ramadan and had a secret dream. She longed to beat the drum that traditional male *musaharati* drummers use during the wakeup call for the pre-dawn meal. Supported by her loving family, Najma realizes her long-cherished dream and pushes the boundaries of what girls can accomplish. (**E**) bit.ly/2pDcQHq

Halal If You Hear Me, edited by Fatimah Asghar and Safia Elhillo. A BreakBeat Poets anthology of writings by Muslims who are women, queer, genderqueer, nonbinary, or trans. The collected poems dispel the notion that there is only one correct way to be a Muslim by holding space for multiple, intersecting identities while celebrating and protecting those identities. (**H**) bit.ly/2vdWYym

Ramadan Moon, by Na'ima Bint Robert. This lyrical and inspiring picture book captures the wonder and joy of Ramadan from the perspective of a child. Written and illustrated by Muslim people, this is a book for all children who celebrate Ramadan and those in the wider communities who want to understand why this is such a special experience for Muslim people. (**E**) bit.ly/39F2vCA

---

4 Dorothea Dix, social reformer, mental health activist, and advocate for women nurses, born (1802-1877). Dix championed causes for both the mentally ill and Indigenous populations, challenging 19th century notions of reform and illness. Dix was appointed Superintendent of Army Nurses during the Civil War, advancing the role of nurses in the war and in the medical field. During a period when male doctors openly expressed disdain for female nurses, she continued to push for formal training and more opportunities for women nurses.

Mad in America: Bad Science, Bad Medicine, and the Enduring Mistreatment of the Mentally Ill, by Robert Whitaker. A haunting, deeply compassionate book, updated with a new introduction and prologue, bringing in the latest medical treatments and trends, this book raises important questions about our obligations to the mad, the meaning of "insanity," and what we value most about the human mind. (**H, TR**) bit.ly/2PAvcto

---

5 190th anniversary of the Black Hawk War. Black Hawk was a Sauk warrior who resisted the growing presence of White settlers on tribal lands. The Sauk and Fox tribes had signed a treaty in 1804 ceding all their land east of the Mississippi to the US. Black Hawk claimed the treaty was invalid. In 1832 a large army of US soldiers cornered Black Hawk and his followers, and a protracted war ensued. Black Hawk's people were vastly outnumbered and eventually surrendered.

Teaching Critically About Lewis and Clark: Challenging Dominant Narratives in K-12 Curriculum, by Alison Schmitke, Leilani Sabzalian, and Jeff Edmundson. The Lewis and Clark Corps of Discovery is often presented as an exciting adventure story of discovery, friendship, and patriotism. However, this same period in US history can be understood quite differently when viewed through an anticolonial lens and the Doctrine of Discovery. This book challenges dominant narratives and packaged curricula about Lewis and Clark to support more responsible social studies instruction. The authors provide a conceptual framework, ready-to-use lesson plans, and teaching resources to address oversimplified versions of the Lewis and Clark expedition. (**TR**) bit.ly/3drvmMR

---

6 310th anniversary of slave revolt in New York. In New York City, more than 25 enslaved Africans and possibly two Native Americans set fire to a building and killed nine White men who came to fight the fire. The rebels were captured and those who didn't commit suicide were brutally executed. This set the stage for severe punishments for rebellions that followed.

No More! Stories and Songs of Slave Resistance, by Doreen Rappaport. Using true accounts, author Doreen Rappaport puts readers in the shoes of 11 extraordinary individuals and documents the many forms of slave resistance: subversion, uprisings, escape, poetry, religion, and song. (**E, M**) bit.ly/2ufG7xj

Poetry of Defiance: How the Enslaved Resisted, a teaching activity by Adam Sanchez for Rethinking Schools. Through a mixer activity, students are introduced to the various ways that enslaved people resisted the brutal exploitation of slavery. The lesson culminates in a collective class poem highlighting the defiance of the enslaved. (**M, H**) bit.ly/2O5TEPu

---

Rose Schneiderman, union organizer and women's rights activist, born (1882-1972). Schneiderman spent 50 years working to improve working conditions for women. As president of the New York Women's Trade Union League (NYWTUL) and the National WTUL, Schneiderman served as liaison between presidents and governors and organized women workers. She was the only woman on FDR's Labor Advisory Board and played a key role in shaping the landmark legislation of the New Deal: the National Labor Relations Act, the Social Security Act, and the Fair Labor Standards Act.

Jewish Women: A Comprehensive Historical Encyclopedia, by the Jewish Women's Archive. Organized by categories such as activism, art, science, and sports, this online encyclopedia cataloguing the accomplishments of hundreds of Jewish women throughout history is a rich biographical resource. (**E, M, H**) jwa.org/encyclopedia

---

7 World Health Day. World Health Day is observed annually to commemorate the establishment of the World Health Organization (WHO) and to bring awareness to the importance of global health. This year marks the 70th anniversary of the organization, which works to guarantee universal healthcare and prevent, treat, and reduce the spread of diseases. President Trump decided unilaterally to withdraw the US from the WHO, but President Biden rescinded that order in 2021.

Critical Condition and other films about healthcare. Films about healthcare from P.O.V. and Media That Matters. (**H**) to.pbs.org/sGen3S

Harry Hay, LGBTQ activist and labor organizer, born (1912-2002). Hay is considered the founder of the Gay Rights movement. He was a founding member of the Mattachine Society, one of the first Gay Rights organizations in the US, and the Radical Faeries. He was also a union organizer and was active in fighting for the rights of Native Americans and against Jim Crow. Hay was the first person to publicly define the gay community as an oppressed group, a radical idea at the time.

Hope Along the Wind: The Life of Harry Hay, directed by Eric Slade and produced by Jack Walsh. This documentary follows the life of one of the founders of the Mattachine Society, a highly successful gay rights organization. The website provides information regarding Hay's life and information on purchasing the film. (**H**) vimeo.com/48114440

---

8 National Day of Silence. During the National Day of Silence, a project of the Gay, Lesbian and Straight Education Network (GLSEN), students organize protests against LGBTQ+ harassment in schools.

Day of Silence Website. This site includes information about the history of the Day of Silence, as well as FAQs, reproducible materials, an organizing manual for students, and more. (**M, H**) bit.ly/3SF54f

---

Vesak (Buddhism). Vesak (Wesak/Vesakha) is the most important holiday in the Buddhist calendar, celebrating Buddha's birth, enlightenment, death, and his passing into *Nirvana*. The exact date of Vesak varies according to the lunar calendars used in different traditions.

Celebrations: Wesak, by Anita Ganeri. This children's book, part of the *Celebrations* series, explores the history behind Wesak (Vesak) and how it is celebrated today with special foods, clothing, songs, and rituals. (**E**) amzn.to/VAg7CL

---

9 70th anniversary of the Bolivian National Revolution. After the annulment of a Bolivian presidential election in which the Nationalist Revolutionary Movement (MNR) candidate won in a landslide, a serious popular uprising emerged. Out of that came a series of radical reforms. This historic event, in which workers and peasants overthrew an entrenched oligarchy of tin barons and landholders, was the first successful revolution in

Latin America after Mexico and is viewed by most contemporary scholars as a transformative moment for Bolivia and Latin America as a whole.

Indigenous Struggle and the Bolivian National Revolution: Land and Liberty! by James Kohl. In a critical revision of conventional works, the author reappraises and reconfigures the tortuous history of insurrection and revolution, counterrevolution and resurrection, and overthrow and aftermath in Bolivia. Underlying the history of Creole conflict between dictatorship and democracy lies another conflict – the unrelenting 500-year struggle of the conquered Indigenous peoples to reclaim usurped lands, resist White supremacist dominion, and seize autonomous political agency. (**H, TR**) bit.ly/3tn1XZT

---

10 **50th anniversary of the United Nations Biological Weapons Convention**. This UN treaty was the first multilateral disarmament treaty banning an entire category of weapons. Signatories to the convention agreed to never develop, produce, stockpile, or otherwise acquire or retain several categories of disease-causing and toxin-based chemical and biological weapons. It is a key element in the international community's efforts to address the proliferation of weapons of mass destruction.

Weapons of Mass Destruction: A Resource Unit, by the Morningside Center for Teaching Social Responsibility. A substantive reader and activity guide on chemical, biological, and nuclear weapons. (**H**) bit.ly/3tsKDml

---

130th anniversary of the Cuban Revolutionary Party (PRC). José Martí founded the *Partido Revolucionario Cubano* (The Cuban Revolutionary Party), which sought to organize and prepare for the invasion of Cuba. The plan was to fight against the foreign governments and colonial constitution that held power within Cuba and oppressed the Cuban citizens. Martí didn't live to see his dream fulfilled, dying in battle one month after the invasion of Cuba began in 1895.

Martí's Song for Freedom/Martí y sus versos por la libertad, by Emma Otheguy. As a boy, José Martí found freedom in the river that rushed to the sea and peace in the *palmas reales* that swayed in the wind. Freedom, he believed, was the inherent right of all people. But his home island of Cuba was colonized by Spain, and some of the people were enslaved by rich landowners. Enraged, Martí took up his pen and fought against this oppression through his writings. By age 17, he was declared an enemy of Spain and forced to leave his beloved island. Written in verse, with excerpts from Martí's seminal *Versos sencillos*, this bilingual book is a beautiful tribute. (**E, M**) Teacher's guide from Lee & Low Books here: bit.ly/3dsPAFW

---

14 **70th anniversary of Ralph Ellison's *Invisible Man***. Ralph Ellison's groundbreaking novel chronicles the journey of a Black man moving from the segregated South to New York City, which was on the brink of social upheaval. *Invisible Man* confronts the complex social, psychological, and political assumptions and beliefs of the time and the damage inflicted on those in society's shadows. *Invisible Man* became an instant classic, earning Ellison the 1953 National Book Award.

An Interview with Ralph Ellison, by Alfred Chester and Vilma Howard for the *Paris Review*. A rich and beautiful interview with Ralph Ellison about his work, his life, and his views on "the American Negro writer." (**H**) bit.ly/2P1liRw

---

Vaisakhi (Sikhism). Vaisakhi is a festival that celebrates the founding of the Sikh community.

8 Ways to Include Vaisakhi in Classrooms, by Navjot Kaur and Saffron Press. Background information on the holiday, as well as eight meaningful activities for children, are included on this site. (**E, M**) bit.ly/2AqVjen

A Lion's Mane, by Navjot Kaur. This is a picture book that helps young readers journey to cultures around the world to explore the meaning of the *dastaar*, the Sikh turban. The second link is to a teacher's guide for the book. (**E, TR**) bit.ly/3cgyvvp; Teacher's Guide: bit.ly/V1oNIK

Guru Nanak, by Rina Singh. The Sikh faith, the world's 5th largest religion, began with the teachings of Guru Nanak in the 15th century and evolved with the nine gurus who followed him. He grew up to be a great spiritual teacher, revolutionary for his time, declaring that there is no difference between Hindus and Muslims, that men and women are equal, and that caste is irrelevant. This biography, exquisitely illustrated in the Indian miniature-painting tradition, tells the story of his life. (**E**) amzn.to/1qMWw5Q

---

15 **First day of Passover begins at sunset on 4/15 (Judaism)**. Passover is an 8-day festival that commemorates the deliverance of the Israelites from slavery in Egypt.

The Story of Passover, by David Adler. One of the most significant holidays in Jewish tradition, Passover commemorates Moses leading his people out of slavery in Egypt. *The Story of Passover* recounts the major events of the story in dramatic but accessible language, from Jacob settling in Egypt to the miraculous parting of the Red Sea. The text and images have been vetted for accuracy by a rabbinical authority, and the book includes an author's note about the modern Passover celebration, the seder, and how the different parts of the meal symbolize elements of the story. (**E, M**) bit.ly/3e8UtTS

Good Friday (Christianity). Good Friday occurs 2 days before Easter and commemorates the death of Jesus.

130th anniversary of the founding of *Kawkab America*. *Kawkab America* was an Arabic-language weekly (later daily) newspaper published in New York City, the first Arabic-language newspaper in North America. *Kawkab*'s core readers were the residents of Little Syria, or the "Syrian Colony." The paper was the first of more than 50 US-based Arabic publications affiliated with Little Syria, which soon became a global literary and cultural center for the greater Syrian diaspora coming from what today is Syria and Lebanon.

The Map of Salt and Stars: A Novel, by Zeyn Joukhadar. The story of two girls living 800 years apart – a modern-day Syrian refugee seeking safety and a medieval adventurer apprenticed to a legendary mapmaker – places today's headlines about Syria in the sweep of history, where the pain of exile and the triumph of courage echo again and again. (**H**) bit.ly/31M1WSZ

Cornelia (Corrie) ten Boom, Holocaust resister, born (1892-1983). During World War II, Corrie ten Boom and her family harbored hundreds of Jews to protect them from arrest by Nazi authorities. Betrayed by a Dutch informant, the entire family was imprisoned. Corrie and her sister were sent to a concentration camp; only Corrie survived. An estimated 800 Jews were saved by the ten Boom family. After the war, she started a worldwide ministry and later told her story in a book entitled *The Hiding Place*.

The "Hiding Place" Curriculum, by the Houston Holocaust Museum. The book, *The Hiding Place*, is the true story of the ten Boom family who were members of the Dutch Resistance during World War II. Their resistance group found shelter for dozens of Jews, including many children. Corrie ten Boom helped children find a safe house or passed them on to a representative from another area. The ten Booms also opened their home to many fugitives and Resistance workers. Holocaust Museum Houston has created and collected resources for educators who are teaching *The Hiding Place*. (**H**) hmh.org/education/hiding-place-curriculum

---

16 Hanuman Jayanti (Hinduism). Hanuman Jayanti commemorates the birth of Hanuman, the Vanara god.

Hanuman Jayanti. This is a religious website that tells the story of the life of Hanuman. Illustrations and links to other festivals and related topics are available on this site. (**M, H**) bit.ly/KntMvy

---

110th anniversary of Harriet Quimby's flight over the English Channel. Harriet Quimby, the first American woman to earn a pilot's license, became the first woman to pilot an aircraft across the English Channel. The flight took 59 minutes to complete. She paved the way for Amelia Earhart, Anne Morrow Lindbergh, and many more. As an accomplished journalist, Quimby was able not only to live her adventures, but to write about them as well. She died in a freak accident at the age of 37.

Women Who Soar: 30 Books About Boundary-Breaking Female Pilots, by A Mighty Girl. From the authors of this annotated list of recommended books: "In this blog post, we've featured our favorite books for all ages about trailblazing female pilots throughout history. Whether they were on the cutting edge of the development of flight, breaking records and testing the limits of what newer and better airplanes could do, or thrilling crowds with their daredevil maneuvers, these airwomen were bold and daring. And, for the mighty girls that read them, these books might just be the inspiration for their dreams of a life in the clouds!" (**E, M**) amightygirl.com/blog?p=20960

160th anniversary of the Compensated Emancipation Act. President Abraham Lincoln signed a bill ending slavery in the District of Columbia, 8 1/2 months before the Emancipation Proclamation. The act brought to a conclusion what anti-slavery advocates called "the national shame" of slavery in the nation's capital. It provided for immediate emancipation, compensation to former owners who were loyal to the Union of up to $300 for each freed slave, among other provisions. Emancipation Day is an official holiday in Washington DC.

Rethinkin' Lincoln on the 150th Birthday of the Emancipation Proclamation, by Bill Bigelow, *Huffington Post*. This article questions the portrayal of President Lincoln as an abolitionist in the movie *Lincoln*. Bigelow also discusses how he and his students approached the study of the Emancipation Proclamation, beginning with Lincoln's inaugural address. (**H, TR**) huff.to/UpgZq8

---

17 Easter (Christianity). Easter is a holiday in which Christians celebrate the resurrection of Jesus Christ.

Celebrate Easter: With Colored Eggs, Flowers, and Prayer (Holidays Around the World), by Deborah Heiligman. This children's book uses *National Geographic* photographs to document the celebration of Easter around the world, including the White House Easter Egg Roll and traditional bonfires in Europe. (**E**) bit.ly/T4xiH4

---

20 10th anniversary of the Racial Justice Act. North Carolina's Racial Justice Act (RJA) allowed death row defendants to bring claims of discrimination in jury selection, charging decisions, or the death penalty. Marcus Robinson, a Black man, was sentenced to death for murdering a White person. A study found that in the county, Black people were removed from juries more than White people, so Judge Gregory Weeks gave Robinson life imprisonment instead. Shortly after the decision, North Carolina weakened the RJA.

A Matter of Life and Death, by Amnesty International. *A Matter of Life and Death* is a collection of lessons, assemblies, and films for students to explore the issues surrounding the use of the death penalty, one of Amnesty International's oldest campaigns. (**H**) bit.ly/1dQdsOg

---

22 Earth Day. Earth Day is an annual event celebrated in 175 countries to raise awareness about environmental issues. According to the Earth Day Network, it is the largest secular civic event in the world.

Don't Take Our Voices Away: A Role Play on the Indigenous Peoples' Global Summit on Climate Change, by Julie Treick O'Neill and Tim Swinehart. This role play on the Indigenous Peoples' Global Summit on Climate Change asks students to develop a list of demands to present to the rest of the world at a mock climate change meeting. (**H**) bit.ly/2l5qxg2

Race, Poverty, and the Environment. This journal links issues of racism and poverty with environmental justice. Some recent resources are available for free download; older resources are available for purchase. (**H, TR**) bit.ly/1r0QFKy

---

24 Armenian Genocide Remembrance Day. This observance is held annually to commemorate the victims of the massacre and deportation of Armenians by the government of the Ottoman Empire between 1915 and 1923. In April 2021, President Biden became the first US President to recognize the slaughter of Armenian people as genocide.

Confronting Genocide: Never Again? by The Choices Program. This site contains supplemental materials to a unit that examines how the US responded to five instances of genocide, including the Armenian genocide. Materials include videos, maps, graphic organizers, surveys, and web links. (**M, H**) bit.ly/136NnUk

---

26 160th anniversary of the Chinese Police Tax law. This law, which levied a tax on all Chinese living in California, was implemented to "protect free White labor against competition with Chinese Coolie labor" and to discourage Chinese immigration to the state. The California Supreme Court declared the law unconstitutional later that year.

Exclusion: Chinese in 19th Century America, a lesson plan by Debbie Wei for Teaching for Change. A comprehensive lesson plan that supports students in learning about the lives and contributions of Chinese immigrants in the US in the 19th century, and analyzing the roots of anti-immigrant sentiment, which led to the passage of the Chinese Exclusion Acts. (**H**) teachingforchange.org/exclusionact

---

27 Yom HaShoa – Holocaust Remembrance Day – begins at sundown on 4/27 (Judaism)

Tropical Secrets: Holocaust Refugees in Cuba, a novel in verse by Margarita Engle. Turned away from the shores of New York, a young Jewish boy seeks refuge in Cuba during WWII. Here in this tropical sanctuary, so far away from Germany, will he be safe from Nazi influence? (**M, H**) bit.ly/2R5lS1h

---

29 30th anniversary of the Los Angeles uprising. Thousands of people in L.A. attacked businesses, cars, and individuals following the acquittal by an all-White jury of four White policemen in the videotaped beating of Black motorist Rodney King. The 5-day uprising left 60 people dead and 2,000 injured, as well as more than $1 billion in property damage. Characterized by the media as a "culture clash" between Blacks and Koreans, participants in the uprising were Black, Latinx, White, and Asian.

"Riots," Racism, and the Police: Students Explore a Century of Police Conduct and Racial Violence, a teaching activity by Ursula Wolfe-Rocca for Zinn Education Project. In this lesson, students explore three documents produced in the wake of three major episodes of racial violence (1919, 1967, and 2014). The goal of the activity is to understand the long trajectory of police violence in Black communities. (**H**) bit.ly/3rLUHpl

Y'all Still Don't Hear Me Though, by Lecia Brooks. This text for grades 6-8 features a 2015 essay by Lecia J. Brooks as she recounts her perspective as a protester who participated in the Los Angeles Race Riots that followed the trial of those who had committed police brutality against Rodney King. Her account details the pervasiveness of police brutality and why demonstrators protest against it. (**M**) bit.ly/3thO8Mm

---

60th anniversary of Linus Pauling's protest of nuclear testing. Linus Pauling, Nobel Prize Laureate in chemistry (and later for Peace), marched with his wife, human rights activist Ava Helen Pauling, and others to protest the US's resumption of atmospheric nuclear testing. The march on the White House took place hours before Pauling was to attend a White House dinner honoring American Nobel Laureates. Pauling had urged President Kennedy to reconsider atmospheric testing because of the enormous damage such testing does to people and the environment.

Nuclear Weapons: What Should Our Policy Be? by The Choices Program. This unit engages students to consider a balanced range of views on the questions that surround the future of nuclear weapons. The material in this 2-day lesson is drawn from a larger curriculum called "The Challenge of Nuclear Weapons." (**H**) bit.ly/2Ex69w5

---

30 **International Jazz Day**. Established in November 2011, International Jazz Day is an official UNESCO designation that celebrates the role Jazz plays in uniting people throughout the world. Each year this international art form is recognized for promoting peace, dialogue among cultures, diversity, and respect for human rights and human dignity; eradicating discrimination; promoting freedom of expression; fostering gender equality; and reinforcing the role of youth in enacting social change.

18 Multicultural Children's Books About Jazz, by Colours of Us. These fun books will inspire your kids (from babies to teenagers) to clap, sing, dance, and play their own Jazz! (**E**) bit.ly/2Vb1Keo

---

70th anniversary of the English translation of *The Diary of Anne Frank*. *The Diary of Anne Frank*, written by a young Jewish victim of the Holocaust, became available in British and American bookshops five years after it was first published in Dutch in 1947. It was translated into French and German in 1950. The moving account of a Jewish family's experience under Nazi occupation has now been translated into 70 languages and has sold more than 30 million copies.

Children's Books About the Holocaust, by the United States Holocaust Memorial Museum. An annotated bibliography compiled to guide parents, educators, and young readers to children's books about the Holocaust and related subjects. (**E, M**) bit.ly/2ImkJJH

The Diary of Anne Frank, Teacher's Guide, by PBS and Facing History and Ourselves. This guide is a detailed curriculum resource that accompanies the PBS Masterpiece Classic series, *The Diary of Anne Frank*. The guide is aimed at middle school and high school teachers. Together the film and guide can serve as a key element within a larger unit on World War II, Holocaust studies, or coming-of-age literature in social studies, history, English, and writing courses. (**H, TR**) bit.ly/3eWwoli

---

130th anniversary of the lynching of Ephraim Grizzard. After two White girls accused Black men of assault in Nashville, TN, Ephraim Grizzard and his brothers were taken to jail. Henry Grizzard was lynched by a White mob and two days later, Ephraim was too. His mutilated body was hung from the Woodland Street Bridge. No one was held accountable for either murder.

An Outrage: A Documentary Film about Lynching in the American South, by the SPLC and the Smithsonian. This film takes viewers to the very communities where heinous acts of violence took place, offering a painful look back at lives lost to lynching and a critical look forward. Stream the film and download the accompanying viewer's guide at the Learning for Justice website. (**H**) bit.ly/3wSawy2

May Resources

1 First day of Asian Pacific American Heritage Month. May is designated as a month to celebrate the history, traditions, and culture of Asian Pacific Americans. It was officially signed into law in 1992.

Asian American Books, by Teaching for Change. An extensive catalog of books compiled by Social Justice Books. (**E, M, H, TR**) bit.ly/2RV6cwq

Different Mirror for Young People: A Young Peoples' History of Multicultural America, by Ronald Takaki and Rebecca Stefoff. Drawing on Takaki's vast array of primary sources, and staying true to his own words whenever possible, *A Different Mirror for Young People* brings ethnic history alive through the words of people, including teenagers, who recorded their experiences in letters, diaries, and poems. (**M, H**) bit.ly/2S3p3pa

---

First Day of Mental Health Awareness Month. Mental Health Awareness Month was initiated in the US in 1949 by the National Association for Mental Health (now known as Mental Health America). The aim is not only to raise awareness about mental health issues, but to reduce the stigma associated with mental health struggles. The organization provides support, educates the public through media campaigns, organizes local events, and offers mental health screenings.

Supporting Students this Mental Health Month, by Learning for Justice. These resources, including an article introducing the Crisis Text Line, recommend practices that can be used at the district, school, or classroom level. (**TR**) bit.ly/33KFieF

International Workers' Day/May Day. International Workers' Day, or May Day, recognizes the social and economic achievements of the International Labor movement. It also commemorates the 1886 Haymarket Massacre in Chicago, in which Chicago police fired on workers during a general strike for the 8-hour day, killing several demonstrators.

Fighting for a Living Wage, by NYSUT. A collection of links and resources related to organizing for the "Fight for $15," a national struggle to increase the minimum wage to $15. In the section titled, "Make the Fight for Living Wage a Teachable Moment," are lesson plans and multimedia resources related to the "Fight for $15." (**H, TR**) bit.ly/2lJEYs9

First Day of National Bike Month. Spearheaded by the League of American Bicyclists (LAB), May has been designated National Bike Month since 1956. The LAB has been instrumental in promoting biking in communities across the country. National Bike Month offers an opportunity to highlight the many benefits of cycling, including fun, fitness, connecting communities, and creating a healthier planet. LAB offers a range of resources to help plan local events with the goal of expanding cycling nationwide.

Tools for Life: A Start-Up Guide for Youth Recycling & Bicycling Programs, by Transportation Alternatives. This website has a guide for helping youth start bicycle recycling programs modeled on the successful NYC Recycle-a-Bicycle program. Includes curricula and resources. (**H**) bit.ly/cC94Dh

---

30th anniversary of the Asian Pacific American Labor Alliance. The Asian Pacific American Labor Alliance (APALA) of the AFL-CIO is the first national organization of Asian American and Pacific Islander (AAPI) workers. APALA works to ensure civil rights and economic justice for Asian American and Pacific Islander workers.

Picture Books with Asian Characters, by No Time for Flash Cards. This annotated elementary book list was created in response to the rise in anti-Asian violence in 2021 as a way to support teachers in ensuring representation as one step in anti-bias education. (**E**) bit.ly/3vMDJdh

---

2 First day of National Children's Book Week. Initiated in 1919, National Children's Book Week is dedicated to celebrating children's literature and encouraging children to read. It is the longest-running national literacy initiative in the US.

The Dark Fantastic: Race and the Imagination from Harry Potter to the Hunger Games, by Ebony Elizabeth Thomas. A provocative exploration of race in popular youth and young adult speculative fiction. Grounded in her experiences as a YA novelist, fanfiction writer, and scholar, Thomas considers four Black girl protagonists from some of the most popular stories of the late 20th and early 21st centuries, analyzing their narratives and audience reactions to them to reveal how these characters mirror the violence against Black and Brown people in our own world. (**H, TR**) bit.ly/2BJY6gQ

Using Picture Books to Explore Identity, Stereotyping, and Discrimination, by Loraine Woodard. In this unit, students explore three picture books to better understand and to promote discussion and action on ideas of identity, stereotyping, and discrimination. (**E, M**) bit.ly/b3u2eC

Eid al-Fitr begins at sunset on 5/2 (Islam). Eid Al-Fitr (Feast of Fast-Breaking) is celebrated at the end of the holy month of Ramadan to mark the end of fasting. It is often celebrated over the course of three days.

Once Upon an Eid: Stories of Hope and Joy by 15 Muslim Voices, edited by S.K. Ali and Aisha Saeed. A collection of short stories that showcase 15 brilliant Muslim voices sharing tales about the most joyful holiday of the year: Eid! The anthology also includes a poem, a graphic novel chapter, and spot illustrations. (**E, M, H**) bit.ly/2TAkYrO

Muslim Booklist, by Teaching for Change. Teaching for Change carefully selects the best multicultural and social justice books for children, young adults, and educators. This list includes many titles about the Muslim holidays and experience. (**E, M, H**) bit.ly/2ShV61l

---

Mabel Hampton, dancer, domestic worker, and lesbian activist, born (1902-1989). Hampton, a pioneering lesbian activist, was a dancer, domestic worker, and a philanthropist for Black and LGBTQ causes. The Harlem Renaissance introduced Hampton to dancers, artists, and a whole community of gay men and lesbians. Cleaning homes for prosperous White families became her longest career and where she met Joan Nestle, the daughter of one of these families, who became a lifelong friend and co-founder of the Lesbian Herstory Archives in New York City.

An Audiovisual Collection on Mabel Hampton, by the Lesbian Herstory Archives. A collection of recordings of interviews and other source material by and from Mabel Hampton, highlighting her work as a champion for lesbian rights, and her career as a domestic worker and dancer. (**H**) bit.ly/3dpTmju

---

3 World Press Freedom Day. World Press Freedom Day is a UNESCO-sponsored event that serves as a reminder to governments throughout the world of their obligation to respect and protect the freedom of the press. This is especially important at this time because of constant threats against the press from those in power. This day is also one of remembrance of journalists who have lost their lives in the pursuit of keeping the public informed.

The Importance of a Free Press, by Facing History and Ourselves. What is the role of the press in a democracy, and how does the First Amendment protect that role in the United States? How can press freedoms come into conflict with other societal needs and priorities? This lesson from the larger unit, *Facing Ferguson: News Literacy in a Digital Age*, invites young people to tackle these questions. (**H**) bit.ly/3eSbgKo

Project Censored's State of the Free Press 2021, edited by Mickey Huff, Andy Lee Roth, and Matt Taibbi. This edition offers a succinct and comprehensive survey of the most important but underreported news stories of 2020. It also offers a comparative analysis of the current state of corporate and independent news media and its effect on democracy. *State of the Free Press 2021* gives readers the critical thinking and media literacy skills required to hold the corporate media to account for distorting or censoring news coverage, with the aim of revitalizing our democracy. (**H**) bit.ly/3sdAecQ

National Teachers' Day. A day set aside to honor teachers for their contributions to learning, child development, and the community.

55 Strong: Inside the West Virginia Teachers' Strike, edited by Elizabeth Catte, Emily Hilliard, and Jessica Salfia. What compelled West Virginia's teachers to strike? How did they organize? What were teachers and allies doing during the strike? And how is the West Virginia labor movement celebrating its victory? *55 Strong: Inside the West Virginia Teachers' Strike* answers these questions and offers unique, on-the-ground insights into this historic strike. The book includes essays by teachers from around the state, organizing documents, images from the picket lines, and material on the history of the Labor movement in West Virginia. (**H, TR**) bit.ly/2RoEoSe

---

5 Cinco de Mayo. Cinco de Mayo commemorates the victory of a small Mexican militia over French forces at the Battle of Puebla on May 5, 1862. Despite this victory, France eventually defeated Mexican forces and occupied the country for three years.

Rethinking Cinco de Mayo, by Sudie Hofmann, Zinn Education Project. In this article, Hofmann critiques a stereotypical Mexican American event meant to celebrate Cinco de Mayo. Readers will find information about the history of Cinco de Mayo and how it is celebrated in the US, art depicting the events of the Battle of Puebla Day, and reactions from Chicana/o students. Links to related materials are provided. (**H, TR**) bit.ly/13VTKtX

Cinco de Mayo Inc. This blog is dedicated to documenting and critically examining the commercialization of Cinco de Mayo. This Mexican holiday has become more popular in the US than in Mexico, in part because of corporate America's desire to make money off the Latinx consumer market. It also perpetuates damaging stereotypes about Latinx people while obscuring the historical significance of this day. (**M, H, TR**) bit.ly/rryYIN

Cinco de Mayo, Yesterday and Today, by Maria Cristina Urrutia and Rebeca Orozco. Cinco de Mayo is one of the most celebrated days in the Mexican calendar, but few people know that it commemorates a decisive victory of the Mexicans against the invading French in 1862. Drawing on historical sources and the photographic record of a contemporary reenactment, this book introduces children to this important, but little understood, event. (**E, M**) bit.ly/2SFfXvSp

---

6 International No Diet Day. No Diet Day is an annual celebration of body acceptance and body shape diversity. This day is also dedicated to promoting a healthy lifestyle and raising awareness of the dangers and futility of extreme dieting.

Reshaping Body Image, by Teaching Tolerance. This lesson is intended to help students examine how people of varying shapes and sizes are typically viewed in our society. How and why do perspectives on beauty and body image change over time? (**H**) bit.ly/dVObJ0

Deconstructing Barbie: Math and Popular Culture, by Swapna Mukhopadhyay. Math activity from the book *Rethinking Mathematics,* which engages students in considering the question: "What would Barbie look like if she were as big as you?" (**M, H**) bit.ly/2IJAKJf

The Body Is Not an Apology, by Sonya Renee Taylor. This book uses a framework of radical self-love to heal the wounds inflicted by violent systems such as patriarchy, White supremacy, and capitalism. She examines how our indoctrinated body shame is connected to systems of oppression and discusses ways to eliminate oppression against all bodies. (**H**) bit.ly/2tDnzHU

140th anniversary of the Chinese Exclusion Act. As Chinese immigrants were recruited to work in the mining and railroad construction industries in the late 1800s, White laborers and politicians felt threatened and imposed xenophobic, racist tactics to control and oppress them. This was the first immigration-related legislation that excluded a specific racial-ethnic group from the US. The Chinese Exclusion Act set the stage for future immigration exclusion acts against virtually every Asian ethnic group until the Hart-Cellar Act of 1965 was passed.

Amend: The Fight for America. In this Netflix series, Will Smith hosts this documentary that examines the evolving, often lethal, fight for equal rights in America through the lens of the US Constitution's 14th Amendment. Episode 4 focuses on immigration with a long segment on the Chinese Exclusion act. (**M, H**) bit.ly/3qKZiHs

Remembering 1882: Fighting for Civil Rights in the Shadow of the Chinese Exclusion Act, by the Chinese Historical Society of America. Multimedia resources, timeline, notable quotes, and images that support teaching and learning about the Chinese Exclusion Act. (**E, M, H**) civilrightssuite.org/1882

---

7 National Barrier Awareness Day. Proclamation 5472 declared National Barrier Awareness Day as an occasion to recognize and fight against the many barriers, both visible and invisible, that people with disabilities face. On this day, we are reminded to work to eliminate the social, legal, economic, and physical barriers that confront individuals with disabilities.

Disability Social History Project. This site contains a wealth of information, including a list of "Famous and Not So Famous" people with disabilities, a timeline, and a history of the word "handicapped" via the Serendipity link. (**E, M, H, TR**) bit.ly/163FXqn

---

8 Mother's Day. Mother's Day is an annual holiday that celebrates mothers, motherhood, and the influence of mothers and mother figures in society. Mother's Day is celebrated in many countries around the world, though some celebrate on a different day.

Asha's Mums, by Rosamund Elwin and Michelle Paulse. When Asha needs a signature for the permission slip for her school trip to the Science Center, she is questioned about which name on the form was her mom's. Asha undergoes the experience of teaching her fellow classmates and her teacher that she and her brother have two moms and they are both number one. (**E**) bit.ly/2KjEynm

Mama's Day, by Strong Families. Each year artists are commissioned to create images that capture the full diversity of family arrangements. These images are offered as free e-cards; the site also offers the opportunity to send an e-card to an incarcerated or detained mama. (**E, M, H**) www.mamasday.org

Free Black Mamas: National Bail Out. This organization works to reunite families, create a national community of leaders who have experienced incarceration, and work with groups across the country to transform harmful systems to keep Black people safe and free. (**TR**) nationalbailout.org

Mother's Day Proclamation – 1870, by Julia Ward Howe. Poem by Julia Ward Howe advocating for women around the world to organize to resolve conflicts peacefully. (**E, M, H**) bit.ly/eT5sy

---

9 10th anniversary of Manal al-Sharif's Václav Havel Prize for Creative Dissent. Manal al-Sharif is an advocate for women's rights and empowerment. She was the first Saudi woman to specialize in Information Security, starting her career in 2002 with Saudi Aramco. In 2011, al-Sharif co-founded the #Women2Drive movement, challenging the ban on women driving in her country. She was arrested and imprisoned for "driving while female." She is also active in other women's causes, especially domestic violence, earning her the Václav Havel Prize for Creative Dissent.

A TED Talk by Manal-al Sharif. In this TED Talk from June 2013, Manal al-Sharif advocates for women's right to drive, male guardianship annulment, and family protection in Saudi Arabia. (**M, H**) ted.com/speakers/manal_al_sharif

---

190th anniversary of the Treaty of Payne's Landing. Signed in secret negotiations with unauthorized representatives, this treaty called for the removal of the Seminole Tribe from Florida, along with the Creeks, to territory that is now Arkansas. It also required the return of all runaway slaves who were being sheltered by the tribe. The removal was to take place within three years, but resistance grew, leading to the Second Seminole War (1835-1842).

The Black Seminoles: History of a Freedom-Seeking People, by Kenneth Porter. A book chronicling the lives of fugitive slaves who aligned themselves with the Seminole Indians in Florida beginning in the 1800s, fought in solidarity with them in the Second Seminole War, and were removed, along with them to Indian Territory, where they struggled to remain free. (**H**) bit.ly/3tFoPEh

---

10 150th anniversary of Victoria Woodhull's becoming the first woman nominated for president. Woodhull was a women's rights activist, newspaper publisher, and the first woman to operate a Wall Street brokerage firm. Her success on Wall Street enabled Woodhull to focus on matters that really mattered to her: women's rights, labor issues, and social reform. Nominated by the Equal Rights Party, Woodhull's presidential campaign platform included universal gender and racial equality, civil service and taxation reform, and opposition to land grants given to railroads and other corporations.

A Woman for President: The Story of Victoria Woodhull, by Kathleen Krull. A revolutionary woman in American history, Victoria Woodhull was many years ahead of her time, breaking boundaries. But her presidential campaign, and the backlash it sparked, left her in political ruin and bankruptcy. Acclaimed biographer Kathleen Krull and beloved illustrator Jane Dyer combine their talents to bring her story to life for young readers. (**E, M**) Teacher's guide: bit.ly/3x1yJC1

---

11 50th anniversary of César Chávez's hunger strike. Chávez fasted for 25 days in protest of an Arizona law banning the right of farm workers to strike, boycott, or organize. The fast and the resulting UFW-sponsored grassroots campaign transformed politics in the heavily Latinx state, leading to the election of Latinx governors and legislative representatives. It was through this campaign that the phrase "¡*Si Se Puede*!" was first used as a rallying cry.

Viva La Causa, film kit by Learning for Justice. A 39-minute documentary film, *Viva La Causa* focuses on one of the seminal events in the march for human rights – the grape strike and boycott led by César Chávez and Dolores Huerta in the 1960s. *Viva la Causa* shows how thousands of people from across the nation joined in a struggle for justice for the most exploited people in our country – the workers who put food on our tables. (**E, M**) bit.ly/3hmif27

---

12 120th anniversary of the Anthracite Coal Strike. Miners in eastern Pennsylvania went on strike for higher wages, shorter workdays, and the recognition of their union. The strike went on for many months and was ended only when President Theodore Roosevelt got involved. Neither side got everything they wanted, but both felt they got enough to end the strike and resume business. Roosevelt considered it the defining moment of his presidency.

Growing Up in Coal Country, by Susan Campbell Bartoletti. This book offers firsthand accounts and compelling facts about the lives of coal miners and their families in northeastern Pennsylvania at the dawn of the 20th century. Bartoletti has also written a children's literature fictional account of the same time period and people, *A Coal Miner's Bride*. (**E, M**) bit.ly/3mUJOjL

---

13 20th anniversary of amendment to Animal Welfare Act limiting the definition of "animal." The Animal Welfare Act (AWA) was amended to redefine "animal" by excluding birds specifically bred for research, rats, and mice, all of which constitute the vast majority of animals used in scientific research. By changing this term, the US Department of Agriculture (USDA) does not have the authority to regulate animals excluded by the new definition. The US is the only country in the developed world that excludes these animals from its animal protection statutes.

Knowing Animals, a podcast by UNSW Australia. *Knowing Animals* is a weekly podcast about all things related to animals and ethics; animals and the law; animals and politics; and animal advocacy. It features interviews with Animal Studies scholars and animal advocates. (**M, H**) knowinganimals.libsyn.com

---

14 World Fair Trade Day. The World Fair Trade Organization (WFTO) draws on support from a membership of 350 Fair Trade organizations in 80 countries. Goals include creating opportunities for economically disadvantaged producers, payment of a fair price, gender equity, and improved working conditions.

Win-Win Solutions: An Introduction to Fair Trade and Cooperative Economics, by Equal Exchange. Composed of four units, this curriculum raises students' awareness of core issues surrounding food production and trade. (**E, M**) bit.ly/2m0N8xt

For a Better World, website by Fair World Project. Campaign information, resources, and publications related to understanding and teaching fair trade. (**TR**) bit.ly/1Slrigj

15 International Conscientious Objectors Day. A day to celebrate those who resist war on moral grounds, especially by refusing to participate in military activities.

Essays on Nonviolence, by the Center on Conscience and War. Essays and statements by historical figures on nonviolence and conscientious objection. (**M, H**) centeronconscience.org/essays-on-nonviolence

80th anniversary of the Women's Army Auxiliary Corp (WAC). As WWII loomed, Representative Edith Nourse Rogers of Massachusetts introduced a bill for the creation of the Women's Army Auxiliary Corps. After seeing the treatment of women in WWI, Rogers wanted to ensure that American women who served in support of the Army had all the rights and benefits afforded to soldiers. Congress approved the creation of WAAC (later WAC) on May 14, 1942, and President Franklin D. Roosevelt signed the bill into law the following day.

The Women's Army Corps: Female Soldiers in WWII, by National Women's History Museum. A multimedia slideshow that includes video clips, photographs, and other primary source documents about the Woman's Auxiliary Army Corps. (**M, H**) bit.ly/3srS4sK

17 International Day Against Homophobia, Biphobia, and Transphobia (IDAHOBIT). IDAHOBIT is a day set aside to draw the attention of policymakers, opinion leaders, the public, and the media to the violence and discrimination experienced by LGBTQI people. Originally called International Day Against Homophobia (IDAHO), Transphobia was added in 2009 and Biphobia in 2015.

International Day Against Homophobia, Biphobia, and Transphobia (IDAHOBIT) Website. Resources about LGBTQI injustices around the world and ways to contribute to campaigns fighting for LGBTQI justice. (**M, H, TR**) bit.ly/1i0e5IG

Hope In a Box. A nonprofit that designed a primer in LGBTQ literature for young adults and now donates this set of 50 books to middle and high schools free of charge. They provide curriculum guides for selected texts and help purchase copies for the full classroom for teachers looking to include an LGBTQ book in a lesson plan. (**M, H, TR**) hopeinabox.org

Queer America Podcast, by Learning for Justice. Without LGBTQ history, there is no American history. From Learning Justice and hosts Leila Rupp and John D'Emilio, *Queer America* takes listeners on a journey that spans from Harlem to the Frontier West, revealing stories of LGBTQ life we should have learned in school. (**E, M, H**) learningforjustice.org/podcasts/queer-america

18 170th anniversary of the first state compulsory education law. Massachusetts was the first state to enact a compulsory education law. They had already passed a similar law in 1647 when it was still a British colony. Under the law, every city and town had to offer primary education, and parents who refused to send their children to school were fined or even stripped of their parental rights. Other states gradually followed suit, with Mississippi being the last to establish compulsory education in 1917.

The Unschooling Movement: Letting Children Lead Their Learning, an audio interview by On Point, WBUR Radio. Three guests talk about the "unschooling movement" on this 45-minute show for WBUR: Maleka Diggs, founder of Eclectic Learning Network, a secular Black and Brown-centered home education network; Peter Gray, psychology professor at Boston College; and Michael Apple, professor of curriculum and instruction at the University of Wisconsin-Madison. (**H**) wbur.fm/32qg4BY

20 160th anniversary of the Homestead Act. The Homestead Act of 1862 accelerated the White settlement of the Western Territory by granting adult heads of families 160 acres of surveyed public land for a minimal filing fee and five years of continuous residence on that land. Passed after Secession and the absence of the Southern legislators who opposed it, the Act encouraged thousands of squatters who took over land that was inhabited by Native tribes and Mexicans.

The Homestead Acts: A Primary Source Set, by Hillary Brady for the Digital Public Library of America. Primary source images, maps, and documents, additional resources, and accompanying teaching guide on the Homestead Acts. (**H**) bit.ly/2QCQLJX

180th anniversary of the Seneca Treaty of Buffalo Creek. US efforts to remove the Seneca from their lands resulted in the Treaty of Buffalo Creek in 1838, which called for the sale of four reservations: Buffalo, Tonawanda, Cattaraugus, and Allegany. The Seneca were to be removed to Kansas. They protested this outrageous deal, and in 1842, a new agreement was struck, leaving the Seneca with Cattaraugus and Allegany – comprising about one-third of their previous land.

Andrew Jackson and the "Children of the Forest," by Bill Bigelow, Zinn Education Project. This lesson supports students in developing critical literacy skills by responding to Andrew Jackson's speech on "Indian Removal." (**H**) bit.ly/2ShQWGx

120th anniversary of end of US occupation of Cuba. After US and Cuban troops defeated Spain in 1898, US forces occupied Cuba until 1902, when a new Cuban government took full control. As a condition of independence, the US insisted on maintaining the right to intervene in Cuba's foreign and domestic affairs in accordance with the Platt Amendment, which also allowed the US to maintain a naval base on the island. The Platt Amendment was repealed in 1934.

Spanish-American War, teaching materials from the Stanford History Education Group. Although the sinking of the *USS Maine* provided an immediate trigger for the Spanish-American War, long-term US military and economic interests provide a more nuanced context for the US invasion of Cuba. In this lesson, students watch a documentary video, read a telegram describing Spanish treatment of Cubans, and examine an American campaign speech to explore the long-term reasons for the US invasion of Cuba in 1898. (**H**) stanford.io/2QfQBsn

20th anniversary of East Timor's independence from Indonesia. In 1975, Indonesia invaded the Democratic Republic of East Timor, taking over the small nation and annexing it in 1978. More than 100,000 East Timorese – most of them civilians – died in the first few years of the occupation. In 1999, a vast majority of East Timorese voted for autonomy in a national referendum. Indonesian forces went on a rampage that ended only when UN peacekeeping forces intervened. East Timor's independence was finally recognized in 2002

21 90th anniversary of Amelia Earhart's transatlantic solo flight. Pioneering aviator Amelia Earhart set off from Harbor Grace, Newfoundland, Canada on May 20, 1932. She arrived in Londonderry, Northern Ireland, 15 hours later on May 21, becoming the first woman pilot to cross the Atlantic Ocean solo.

Amelia to Zora: Twenty-Six Women Who Changed the World, by Cynthia Chin-Lee and Megan Halsey. Detailed collages and illustrations draw from various events of both hardship and triumph in the lives of 26 amazing women. (**E, M**) bit.ly/2EAyiCo

---

22 150th anniversary of the Amnesty Act of 1872. President Ulysses Grant signed the Amnesty Act of 1872 into law, allowing Confederate leaders and officials who fought against the Union to hold office. After Reconstruction ended and federal troops left the South, the people who had fought to suppress the civil rights of Black people could control their state governments and further deny Black people's rights.

Monumental: Oscar Dunn and His Radical Fight in Reconstruction Louisiana, by Brian Mitchell, Barrington Edwards, and Nick Weldon. The incredible story of Oscar James Dunn, a New Orleanian born into slavery who became America's first Black lieutenant governor and acting governor. A graphic history informed by newly discovered primary sources, *Monumental* resurrects in vivid detail Louisiana and New Orleans after the Civil War, and presents an iconic American life that never should have been forgotten. Contextual essays and a map and timeline add layers of depth to the narrative. (**H**) bit.ly/3fJsKvB

20th anniversary of the conviction of Bobby Cherry. Bobby Cherry, a member of the Ku Klux Klan, along with three other Klansmen, bombed the 16th Street Baptist Church in Birmingham, AL in 1963. Four young Black girls, Addie Mae Collins, Denise McNair, Carole Robertson, and Cynthia Wesley, were killed in the bombing. Cherry lived free for nearly 40 years before being tried and convicted of four counts of murder. He was sentenced to life in prison but died two years after his conviction.

16th Street Baptist Church Bombing, by Zinn Education Project. Background information and a useful curated list of multimedia resources, categorized by grade level, for teaching about the 16th Street Baptist Church Bombing. (**E, M, H**) bit.ly/3mYxK0N

---

23 William Ellsworth ("Dummy") Hoy, deaf major league baseball player, born (1862-1961). Hoy was a centerfielder for several different teams in Major League Baseball from 1888 to 1903. He is noted for being the most accomplished deaf player in major league history and is credited by some with creating the hand signals umpires use for calling balls, strikes, safe, and out. That claim is disputed, but it's not important. He managed to play a very difficult sport at the professional level despite being aurally and vocally challenged.

The William Hoy Story: How a Deaf Baseball Player Changed the Game, by Nancy Churnin. All William Ellsworth Hoy wanted to do was play baseball. After losing out on a spot on the local deaf team, William practiced even harder, eventually earning a position on a professional team. But his struggle was far from over. In addition to the prejudice Hoy faced, he could not hear the umpires' calls. One day he asked the umpire to use hand signals: strike, ball, out. That day he not only got on base but also changed the way the game was played forever. This account may not be entirely accurate, but it makes an interesting story. (**E, M**) nancychurnin.com/readme

---

25 African Liberation Day. African Liberation Day, established in 1958 at the first Pan-African conference held on African soil, celebrates the hard-fought freedoms of African countries from European colonizers.

Africa Access. Organization whose aim is to help schools, public libraries, and parents improve the quality of their children's collections on Africa. This site includes an online database of reviews of children's books about Africa, bibliographies for research topics related to Africa, and awards for the best children's books on Africa published in the US. (**E, M, H, TR**) bit.ly/K1g9m

I Didn't Know There Were Cities in Africa! by Learning for Justice. Article with "do's and don'ts" of teaching about modern Africa. (**E**) bit.ly/9pooY

How Big Is Africa? Poster, by African Studies Outreach Program, Boston University. This website features a poster of the map of Africa with other countries superimposed to compare size. Links to other K-12 resources, as well as children's and young adult books, are also provided. (**E, M, H, TR**) bit.ly/1Qd8Uk4

---

26 National Sorry Day (Australia). First commemorated in 1998, National Sorry Day in Australia honors the memories of Aboriginal people who were victims of all forms of genocide (including cultural genocide) at the hands of the Australian government.

Recommended Indigenous Australian Children's Books, by Readings: Australia's Own Since 1969. An annotated list of children's books, topic cards, symbol flashcards, and more, featuring the Indigenous Peoples of Australia. (**E, M**) bit.ly/3fWEB75

---

27 130th anniversary of White mob destroying Memphis office of Ida B. Wells' newspaper. Black journalist Ida B. Wells used her newspapers, *The Free Speech* and *Headlight*, to document lynching in the South. While Wells was visiting Philadelphia, a White mob destroyed the newspaper's office in Memphis, TN and threatened to harm her if she returned. She ended up moving her operations to Chicago, where she continued fighting for racial justice and working to end the racial terrorism of lynching.

Before Rosa Parks: Ida B. Wells, by Learning for Justice. The title "Before Rosa Parks" loosely links a number of lessons that discuss African American women who were active in the fight for civil rights before the 1950s. (**M, H**) bit.ly/2J75lBk

---

28 130th anniversary of the founding of the Sierra Club. The Sierra Club is the oldest and largest grassroots environmental organization in the United States. It was founded in San Francisco, CA by conservationist and preservationist John Muir, who became its first president. The club's original mission was to protect the Sierra Nevada Mountains, but it is now a leading voice in a wide range of environmental issues, especially climate change.

No Planet B: A Teen Vogue Guide to the Climate Crisis, edited by Lucy Diavolo. An urgent call for climate justice from *Teen Vogue*, one of this generation's leading voices, using an intersectional lens – with critical feminist, Indigenous, antiracist and internationalist perspectives. As the political classes watch our world burn, a new movement of young people is rising to meet the challenge of climate catastrophe. This book is a guide, a toolkit, a warning, and a cause for hope. (**M, H**) bit.ly/3mnvAHQ

---

29 80th anniversary of the National Japanese American Student Relocation Council. Eleanor Roosevelt played a key role in the formation of the NJASRC, working with university presidents, her Quaker friend Clarence Pickett, and various government officials to help Japanese American students leave internment camps and continue their education. It was a bureaucratic and logistical nightmare to get all the necessary clearances and funding, but ultimately, 3,613 students were placed in 680 universities across the nation.

Gaijin: American Prisoner of War, by Matt Faulkner. With a White mother and a Japanese father, Koji Miyamoto quickly realizes that his home in San Francisco is no longer a welcoming one after Pearl Harbor is attacked. And once he's sent to an internment camp, he learns that being half White at the camp is just as difficult as being half Japanese on the streets of an American city during WWII. Koji's story is based on true events from the author's family. (**E, M, H**) bit.ly/3dMxPAA

30th anniversary of the EPA report "Reducing Risk for All Communities." The EPA's Environmental Equity Workgroup published its report, "Reducing Risks in All Communities," which found that racial minorities and low-income populations are disproportionately exposed to hazardous toxins and environmental pollutants, increasing public health risks within these communities. The report also made recommendations for remedying the problems, as well as recommending the establishment of an office designated to address these inequities.

One Earth: People of Color Protecting Our Planet, by Anuradha Rao. *One Earth* profiles Black, Indigenous and People of Color who live and work as environmental defenders. Through their individual stories, the book shows that the intersection of environment and ethnicity is an asset to achieving environmental goals. The 20 short biographies introduce readers to diverse activists of all ages and ethnicities from all around the world. (**M, H**) bit.ly/2PVZ4jP

What is Environmental Justice? by Learning for Justice. In this lesson plan for young children, students explore the concept of environmental racism and learn about various environmental hazards that disproportionately affect communities of Color. (**E**) bit.ly/3lkpDuH

Laverne Cox, transgender actor, born (1972). Laverne Cox is a transgender actress. She has been nominated for an Emmy award, produced a documentary, and is an ardent equal rights activist. She encourages people to move past the gender binary, believing that this will allow people to live more authentically.

Toolkit for "Being There for Nonbinary Youth," by Learning for Justice. This toolkit synthesizes the key tips and takeaways from a related article entitled, "Being There for Nonbinary Youth" and offers online resources for supporting transgender students. (**TR**) bit.ly/3sqlXbz

---

10th anniversary of Dolores Huerta's Presidential Medal of Freedom. Dolores Huerta is a prominent labor activist who worked closely with César Chávez and co-founded the National Farm Workers Association, which later evolved into the United Farm Workers. She believes in nonviolence as a way to enact change. She is also an advocate for immigrant and Latinx rights. In 2012, President Obama awarded Huerta the Presidential Medal of Freedom for her activism and social justice work.

Introduction to Activism: A Closer Look at Dolores Huerta, a lesson by Eden McCauslin for The National Women's History Museum. Using videoclips and speeches, this lesson plan takes a closer look at one of the key activists in the Women's, Workers' and Immigrants' Rights movements in the 20th century. (**M, H**) bit.ly/2SlWgsN

---

30 **Memorial Day**. Originally designated as a day to honor those who died in the Civil War, Memorial Day (formerly called Decoration Day) is now celebrated as a tribute to all those who died while serving in the US Armed Forces.

A Day for Rememberin': Inspired by the True Events of the First Memorial Day, by Leah Henderson. Inspired by true events and told through the eyes of a young boy, this is the deeply moving story about what is regarded as the first Memorial Day on May 1, 1865. Eli dresses up in his best clothes, Mama gathers the mayflowers, Papa straightens his hat, and together they join the crowds filling the streets of Charleston, SC, with bouquets, crosses, and wreaths. Abolitionists, missionaries, teachers, military officers, and a sea of faces Black, Brown, and White, they march as one and sing for all those who gave their lives fighting for freedom during the Civil War. (**E**) bit.ly/3a6LC3R

May 30, 1937: Memorial Day Massacre, by Howard Fast. Essay, article, and actual footage of a strike that took place in Chicago on Memorial Day in 1937 and the brutal police response to it. (**H, TR**) bit.ly/2jUKLWX

80th anniversary of the arrest of Fred Korematsu. When Fred Korematsu, an American citizen, refused to evacuate during the internment of Japanese Americans, he was arrested and convicted. The Northern California ACLU represented Korematsu in challenging the constitutionality of Japanese American incarceration, but the Ninth Circuit Court and the US Supreme Court ruled against him. Law professor Peter Irons helped reopen the case and, in 1983, a federal judge reversed Korematsu's conviction. Six states now celebrate Fred Korematsu Day on his birthday.

Fred Korematsu Speaks Up, by Laura Atkins and Stan Yogi. The first in a new series of middle grade books about civil rights and s/heroes, this book covers how Fred Korematsu first evaded and then fought the incarceration of Japanese Americans during World War II all the way to the Supreme Court. (**E, M**) bit.ly/30Ly0Wx

June Resources

1 First day of Caribbean American Heritage Month. Caribbean American Heritage Month is intended as a period to celebrate the history, traditions, and culture of Caribbean Americans and to honor their contributions to American society.

Island Treasures: Growing Up in Cuba, by Alma Flor Ada. These true autobiographical tales from renowned Latina author and educator Alma Flor Ada are filled with family love and traditions, secrets and deep friendships, and a beautiful, emotive picture of the island of Cuba, where Alma Flor grew up. (**E**) bit.ly/2JF664T

Haiti: My Country, illustrated by Rogé and written by Haitian teenagers. Stunning portraits of Haitian children, accompanied by poems written by Haitian teenagers before the earthquake of 2010. (**E, M, H**) bit.ly/2Sgl0ln

Silver People: Voices From the Panama Canal, by Margarita Engle. Multiple voices in free verse share little-known stories of the thousands of workers from the Caribbean who suffered and lost their lives while building the Panama Canal. (**M**) bit.ly/1Bz0sVN; Teacher's Guide: bit.ly/2G0IqKf

---

First day of Lesbian, Gay, Bisexual, and Transgender Pride Month. Lesbian, Gay, Bisexual, and Transgender Pride Month commemorates the 1969 Stonewall riots, where gay rights activists clashed with NYC police over discrimination and police brutality. It also aims to raise awareness about issues surrounding the civil rights of LGBTQ Americans.

Sylvia and Marsha Start a Revolution!: The Story of the Trans Women of Color Who Made LGBTQ+ History, by Joy Ellison. This book introduces children to the story of Sylvia Rivera and Marsha P. Johnson, two transgender Women of Color who helped kickstart the Stonewall Riots and dedicated their lives to fighting for LGBTQ+ equality. It introduces issues surrounding gender identity and diversity, accompanied by a reading guide and teaching materials to further the conversation. (**E**) bit.ly/38A7dkj

Two Spirits, film directed by Lydia Nibley. This film interweaves Fred Martinez's life and murder with an examination of the two-spirit tradition among Native Americans, telling a nuanced story of what it means to be poor, transgender, and Navajo. (**M, H, TR**) bit.ly/1qA6uVK

Gay, Lesbian, and Straight Education Network (GLSEN) Curriculum. This resource helps to ensure that LGBTQ students see themselves reflected in lessons and creates opportunities for all students to gain a more complex and authentic understanding of the world around them. (**E, M, H**) bit.ly/2RZG9nF

---

3 30th anniversary of the Earth Summit. The United Nations Conference on Environment and Development (UNCED), also known as the "Earth Summit," was a major UN conference in which delegates from 179 countries discussed issues pertaining to environmental protection and socioeconomic development. When it was proposed that the Earth Summit consider the effects of the military on environmental degradation, the US delegation objected, and the proposal was defeated.

Meet the Children of Rio, from Reframing Rio. These lessons were designed to introduce young people to the UN Rio Earth Summits and the concept of sustainable development. The lessons focus on the films in the *Zero Ten Twenty* series which followed 11 children in 10 different countries over 20 years. How have their lives changed over the 20 years since the original Earth Summit? What is it like growing up in the 21st century? How have their lives been affected by environmental, economic, and social changes? Explore these issues in the eight lesson plans. (**E, M, H**) bit.ly/32tH1Ew

---

4 Shavuot begins at sunset on 6/4 (Judaism). Shavuot, the Festival of Weeks, is the second of three major festivals that have both agricultural and historical significance. It celebrates the time when the first fruits are harvested and brought to the temple and commemorates the giving of the Torah at Mount Sinai.

A Mountain of Blintzes, by Barbara Diamond Goldin and Anik McGrory. This children's book tells the story of a family saving up to make cheese blintzes, a traditional food eaten during Shavuot. (**E**) bit.ly/2RX0IB3

UN Day of Innocent Children Victims of Aggression. Appalled by the large number of innocent Palestinian and Lebanese children who have been victims of Israel's acts of aggression, in 1982 the United Nations General Assembly designated June 4 of each year as the International Day of Innocent Children Victims of Aggression. It reminds people that there are many children throughout the world who suffer from different forms of abuse and that there is an urgent need to protect the rights of children.

A Little Piece of Ground, by Elizabeth Laird with Sonia Nimr. This novel is about a young boy named Karim, who is living through the Israeli occupation of Palestine. (**E**) bit.ly/2JC3zZf

---

110th anniversary of first Minimum Wage law in the US. The state of Massachusetts enacted the first law in the US requiring a minimum wage, but it only covered women and children. There also were no enforcement provisions, so it had little real effect. It wasn't until the 1938 passage of the Fair Labor Standards Act that a Federal minimum wage was established. However, severe disparities remain among workers' rights and wages based on race and immigration status.

The Minimum Wage and the Value of a Billion, a lesson plan by Rob Lerman for the Morningside Center for Teaching Social Responsibility. While the minimum wage has been losing value, the income of the wealthiest Americans has risen steeply in the past decade. This lesson invites students to grapple with that reality. (**M, H**) bit.ly/3mXv83u

---

50th anniversary of Angela Davis's acquittal in Jonathan Jackson case. Angela Davis is a prominent civil rights and social justice activist. In 1970, she was accused of supplying weapons to Jonathan Jackson, who burst into a courtroom in an attempt to free his brother George Jackson. A shootout ensued, resulting in the deaths of four people, including Jonathan Jackson. Davis was charged as an accessory, but there was scant evidence to support the charge. The case drew international attention and Davis was acquitted of all charges.

Lessons in Liberation: An Abolitionist Toolkit for Educators, by the Education for Liberation Network and Critical Resistance Editorial Collective. The movement for abolition is expanding. Born from Black and Women of Color feminism, disability justice, and environmental movements, the call to end our reliance on imprisonment, policing, and surveillance and to imagine a safer future has a new terrain of struggle. This toolkit for educators, parents, and youth, shines a light on innovative abolitionist projects, particularly in the K–12 teaching and learning contexts. (**TR**) bit.ly/2ROijgp

5 Christy Brown, painter and poet, born (1932-1981). Known mainly for his "left foot," Irish author, poet, and artist Christy Brown was so much more. Born with cerebral palsy, Christy was able to control only the muscles in his left foot. He learned to write and paint using three toes. He produced hundreds of paintings, four novels, and four books of poetry. He related his life story in his autobiography, *My Left Foot*, which was made into an Oscar-winning film in 1989.

My Left Foot, a film by Jim Sheridan. Christy Brown was born with cerebral palsy to a large, poor Irish family. His mother recognized the intelligence and humanity in the boy everyone else regarded as a "vegetable." Eventually, Christy matured into a cantankerous artist who used his dexterous left foot to write and paint. Daniel Day Lewis won an Oscar for his portrayal of Brown in this film. (**M, H**) Streamable on HBOMax or Amazon: amzn.to/3x38Txr

---

7 130th anniversary of the arrest of Homer Plessy. In 1892, Plessy deliberately got himself arrested for refusing to sit in the "Colored" train car, in violation of an 1890 law requiring separate accommodations for Whites and Blacks. He was convicted of breaking the law and took his case all the way to the US Supreme Court. In 1896, in *Plessy v. Ferguson*, the Court ruled that requiring separate accommodations, as long as they are equal in quality, is not unconstitutional.

Plessy v. Ferguson: The Organizing History of the Case, an article by Keith Medley for Zinn Education Project. An excerpt from an article by Keith W. Medley (author of *We as Freemen: Plessy v. Ferguson*) about the organizing by the *Comité des Citoyens* that led to *Plessy v. Ferguson*. It is a powerful story of organizing, fundraising, the use of the media, legal strategies, and more. Additional related teaching resources follow the article. (**H**) zinnedproject.org/materials/plessy-v-ferguson

---

8 10th anniversary of Razan Ghazzawi's Human Rights Defenders at Risk award. After repeated threats, Razan Ghazzawi was arrested by Syrian authorities for her human rights activism. She is an outspoken critic of the Syrian regime and advocates for LGBTQIA+ and Palestinian rights. She is also a staunch defender of freedom of expression and a free media throughout the Arab world. She was the recipient of the 2012 Human Rights Defenders at Risk award by the Dublin-based Front Line Defenders Foundation.

Except for Palestine: The Limits of Progressive Politics, by Marc Lamont Hill and Mitchell Plitnick. *Except for Palestine* deftly argues that progressives and liberals who oppose regressive policies on immigration, racial justice, gender equality, LGBTQ rights, and other issues must extend these core principles to the oppression of Palestinians. In doing so, the authors take seriously the political concerns and wellbeing of both Israelis and Palestinians, demonstrating the extent to which US policy has made peace harder to attain. They also unravel the conflation of advocacy for Palestinian rights with anti-Semitism and hatred of Israel. (**H, TR**) thenewpress.com/books/except-for-palestine

The Teach Palestine Project, by the Middle East Children's Alliance. The Teach Palestine Project website is a resource by and for K-12 teachers and teacher educators focused on bringing Palestine into our classrooms and schools. (**TR**) teachpalestine.org

Determined to Stay: Palestinian Youth Fight for Their Village, by Jody Sokolower. As Silwani youth and community members share their lives with us, their village becomes an easily accessible way to understand Palestinian history and current reality. Written with young people in mind, the richly illustrated text stresses connections between the lives of youth in the US and in Palestine: criminalization of youth, forced relocation, the impact of colonialism on Indigenous communities, efforts to bury history, and inspiring examples of resistance and resilience. (**H**) bit.ly/3410jSD

---

10 200th anniversary of Martin's Act. Richard Martin, an Irish politician known as "Humanity Dick," helped pass the world's first major piece of animal protection legislation, "The Ill Treatment of Horses and Cattle Bill," or Martin's Act; other countries followed suit. In the first known conviction for animal cruelty under this law, Martin himself prosecuted a man for beating a donkey. He made the trial memorable by bringing the donkey into the courtroom.

Teaching Resources from the Animal Welfare Institute. Recommended book titles categorized by age group and grade level, along with linked lesson plans and teaching guides to accompany each title. (**E, M, H, TR**) awionline.org/content/teaching-resources

---

150th anniversary of the 8-hour workday victory celebration. A movement for the 8-hour workday began among working people after the Civil War, helped by the formation of the first national federation of unions, the National Labor Union. A 3-month strike of 100,000 workers in New York won the 8-hour day, and at a victory celebration in June 1872, 150,000 workers paraded through the city.

A History of America in Ten Strikes, by Erik Loomis. Powerful and accessible, this book challenges contemporary assumptions around labor, unions, and American workers. Labor historian Erik Loomis recounts 10 critical workers' strikes in American labor history that everyone needs to know about. He also provides an appendix with an annotated list of the 150 most important moments in American labor history. (**H, TR**) bit.ly/2PB4VWQ

---

11 20th anniversary of the Bari and Cherney decision. In 1990 on the eve of Redwood Summer, a nonviolent protest of logging in California, a car bomb seriously injured Earth First! activists Judi Bari and Darryl Cherney in Oakland, CA. Oakland police and the FBI accused Bari and Cherney of planting the bomb themselves. The case was full of obvious misrepresentations and planted evidence. In a June 2002 civil lawsuit, a jury found for the plaintiffs, Bari and Cherney, who were awarded $4.4 million.

The Feminization of Earth First! By Judi Bari. Firsthand account by Judi Bari, a feminist, union organizer, and environmental activist, about her experience organizing with men for environmental change, and the role of toxic masculinity, misogyny, and violence in social action work. This essay is part of a tremendous collection of first-person writing by activists, available at a site called *History Is a Weapon*. (**H**) bit.ly/2FRb8wq

---

20th anniversary of CCN's victory over Shell Oil Corp. Shell Oil built a chemical plant in the 1950s in the predominantly Black town of Diamond, LA. After residents got sick and two were killed in explosions, Margie Richard founded Concerned Citizens of Norco (CCN). The organization drew attention to the environmental injustice, and in 2002, won their fight with Shell, which was ordered to pay for the relocation of the town's residents.

How One Woman Fought One of the World's Biggest Oil Companies and Won, a story recorded for *Living on Earth* by Reid Frazier and Jared Goyette. A 2015 audio profile and interview with Margie Richard, the former middle school teacher who founded Concerned Citizens of Norco in 2002, suing Shell Oil for issues related to environmental racism. (**M, H**) bit.ly/3n1gRCS

12 World Day Against Child Labor. The World Day Against Child Labor is intended to raise awareness and promote activism to prevent the use of child labor.

Iqbal, by Francesco D'Adamo. This is a powerful story based on the real life and death of a Pakistani child sold into slavery. (**E, M, H**) bit.ly/2S2GyWi

Teaching with Documents: Photographs of Lewis Hine: Documentation of Child Labor. This site contains reproducible copies of photos documenting the role of child labor in the industrial development of the United States. (**M, H**) 1.usa.gov/3qo8vl

---

40th anniversary of the Anti-Nuclear Proliferation Demonstration in Central Park. Nearly one million people demonstrated in New York City's Central Park against nuclear weapons and for an end to the cold war arms race. It was the largest anti-nuclear protest and the largest political demonstration in American history. Although nuclear disarmament was the main focus of the rally, many expressed their enthusiasm for the intersectionality of the demonstration, illuminating the fact that the issue of nuclear weapons is linked to other social justice issues.

African Americans Against the Bomb: Nuclear Weapons, Colonialism, and the Black Freedom Movement, by Vincent Intondi. Some of the earliest and strongest protests against nuclear weapons came from activists in the Black Freedom movement. Intondi's research reveals that decades ago, Black activists recognized the convergence of domestic and foreign policy issues. (**H**) bit.ly/3mXcKHK

---

15 60th anniversary of SDS Port Huron Statement. Growing frustration with the Cold War, economic inequality, and other socioeconomic issues motivated college students in Michigan to come together to form the Students for a Democratic Society (SDS). On June 15, 1962, they finalized "The Port Huron Statement," which outlined their concerns and hopes, and would go on to become the ideological basis of the New Left.

The Port Huron Statement, from *Resistance and Revolution: The Anti-Vietnam War Movement at the University of Michigan*. This page captures an exhibit of primary source documents, interviews, and other multimedia teaching resources related to the Port Huron Statement written by the Students for a Democratic Society in the early 1960s. (**H**) bit.ly/32nhQ6z

---

40th anniversary of *Plyler v. Doe*. In *Plyler v. Doe*, which grew out of a dispute in Texas, the Court, citing the 14th Amendment, determined that states cannot withhold public education from children simply because they are undocumented. Over the past 40 years, some states and local school districts have tried, unsuccessfully, to find a way around this ruling. As anti-immigrant sentiment grows, it can be assumed they will continue to search for ways to deny children an education.

Lesson Plan on Plyer v. Doe: Can States Deny Public Benefits to Illegal Immigrants? By the Constitutional Rights Foundation. This lesson focuses on the 1982 Supreme Court decision in *Plyler v. Doe* on whether a state may deny public education to the children of illegal immigrants. It gives the background on the case and the arguments for both sides. In the activity, students take part in a mock hearing before the Supreme Court on this case. [Note that unfortunately this resource uses the phrase "illegal immigrants" instead of "undocumented people." Consider noting this in discussion with students.] (**H**) bit.ly/3eaTDpG

Una Jornada Hacia La Esperanza/A Journey Toward Hope, Spanish Edition, by Victor Hinojosa and Coert Voorhees. Four unaccompanied migrant children come together along the arduous journey north through Mexico to the United States border in this ode to the power of hope and connection even in the face of uncertainty and fear. (**E, M**) sixfootpress.com/a-journey-toward-hope

---

Anthony Coelho, Congressman and disability rights advocate, born (1942). Coelho, who has epilepsy, is a former US Congressman from California and the primary author and sponsor of the Americans with Disabilities Act (ADA). Coelho was elected to the House six times but resigned during his sixth term over alleged campaign finance improprieties. The passage of the ADA was the most significant achievement of his tenure in office. He served as the Democratic Whip, the first Latinx to hold a high-level leadership position in Congress.

Disability Visibility: First-Person Stories from the 21st Century, edited by Alice Wong. From original pieces by up-and-coming authors such as Keah Brown and Haben Girma, to blog posts, manifestos, eulogies, testimonies before Congress, and beyond, this anthology gives a glimpse of the vast richness and complexity of the disabled experience, highlighting the passions, talents, and everyday lives of this community. It challenges readers to question their own assumptions and understandings of disabilities and people with disabilities. (**M, H**) Discussion guide also included here: disabilityvisibilityproject.com/book

---

16 International Day of the African Child. The International Day of the African Child was established by the Organization of African Unity in 1991 with the aim of raising awareness of the situation of children in Africa and the need for continuing improvement in education. June 16 was chosen in honor of the children of Soweto, South Africa who, on that day in 1976, marched to demand a better education. Many of those children were shot and killed by South African police.

Freedom in Our Lifetime: South Africa's Struggle, by The Choices Program, Brown University. A full curriculum that explores the dilemma faced by Black South Africans in the early 1960s of how best to battle racial discrimination imposed by the apartheid system. Lessons include Poetry and Politics; The Soweto Uprising Through Primary Sources; Steve Biko and Black Consciousness; and more. (**H**) bit.ly/2IF1iyr

---

100th anniversary of the Cable Act. After women gained the right to vote in 1920, Congress passed the Cable Act, which was intended to redress the discriminatory Expatriation Act of 1907, which conferred on women the citizenship of their husbands. The Cable Act restored citizenship to US-born women who had lost their citizenship by marrying non-citizen men. The new law, however, did not apply to women who married "aliens ineligible for citizenship." Its main victims were Asian American women.

When Saying "I Do" Meant Giving Up Your US Citizenship, by Meg Hacker for the National Archives. Short, accessible background reading on the Cable Act of 1922, with primary source documents interwoven throughout. (**H**) bit.ly/2PwFoDr

---

17 70th anniversary of the signing of Decree 900 in Guatemala. Decree 900 redistributed large plots of unused land held in private hands to local peasants. The law was unpopular with US businesses in Guatemala. In addition to the US's obsession with Communism, the law helped prompt intervention by the US government. Two years later, the CIA organized a coup that overthrew the democratically elected Guatemalan government.

Teaching Central America, by Teaching for Change. More than four million Central Americans reside in the United States today, yet the lack of resources in most schools on Central American heritage make the rich history and literature of the region invisible. Teaching for Change launched a campaign to encourage and support teaching about Central America, with collected lessons, book lists, biographies of noted historical figures, and readings for free use by classroom teachers. (**E, M, H, TR**) teachingcentralamerica.org

---

50th anniversary of the Watergate burglary. Five burglars, carrying wiretapping and photo equipment, were caught breaking into the offices of the Democratic National Committee in the Watergate apartment complex in Washington, DC. An investigation revealed that the burglars were linked to President Richard Nixon's re-election campaign. Although he initially denied involvement, when it became clear that the House of Representatives was likely to impeach him, Nixon resigned.

Lesson Plan: Watergate and the Limits of Presidential Power, by PBS NewsHour Extra. A rich lesson plan and related resources to support students in exploring the events of the Watergate scandal and its lasting impact on the American presidency. (**M, H**) to.pbs.org/3vwKDSZ

---

18 Autistic Pride Day. Not to be confused with Autism Awareness Day (April 2), Autistic Pride Day recognizes the innate potential of all people, including autistic people. The celebratory day was initiated by Aspies for Freedom and is now a global event that seeks to empower autistic people worldwide. The rainbow infinity symbol represents Autistic Pride Day and signifies "diversity with infinite variations and infinite possibilities."

I'm Here, by Peter Reynolds and Southwest Autism Research and Resource Center (SARRC). This short film, based on an original story and art by Peter H. Reynolds, and produced by FableVision, movingly conveys the loneliness that children on the autism spectrum often experience, and the life-changing impact each of us can have when we reach out and embrace them. (**E**) bit.ly/2jUTt8m

My Brother Charlie, by Holly Robinson Peete and Ryan Elizabeth Peete. In this story, told from a sister's point of view, we meet a family whose oldest son – who is autistic – teaches them important lessons about togetherness, hope, tolerance, and love. (**E**) bit.ly/2kI0mNa

Temple Grandin. This movie was broadcast on HBO as a miniseries. It chronicles the life of Temple Grandin, a woman with autism, who revolutionized livestock handling in the US and has written several books about her life with autism. (**M, H**) itsh.bo/bmNqNc

---

210th anniversary of the start of War of 1812. The US declared war on Britain in part to expand its territory into Canada, which was still part of the British empire, and into territories held by Native Americans, who were supported by the British. When Britain and the US signed a peace treaty in 1814, the principal losers in the war were Native Americans who lost both land and the possibility of a semi-independent sanctuary promised by the British.

Multiple Perspectives of the War of 1812, by PBS Learning Media. This lesson plan, to be used in conjunction with the program *The War of 1812*, gives students background information about the diverse perspectives of those groups involved in the war: Americans, British, Canadian Colonists, and First Nations people. (**M, H**) bit.ly/3gZi7p9

200th anniversary of the arrest of Denmark Vesey. Vesey, a former slave in South Carolina who bought his freedom, was accused of planning a major slave rebellion involving as many as 9,000 people. He was betrayed by a fellow conspirator and was arrested before he was able to carry out the plan. He was executed along with 35 of his collaborators. Vesey became a hero for many abolitionists who, despite his failure, praised his leadership and ingenuity in striking a blow for freedom.

The Story of Denmark Vesey, by Thomas Wentworth Higginson for *The Atlantic*. A compelling article about the powerful impact of Denmark Vesey's attempted slave rebellion, from the June 1861 issue of *The Atlantic*. (**H**) bit.ly/3vlclwi

---

19 Juneteenth. The oldest known celebration of the end of slavery, Juneteenth commemorates June 19, 1865, when Union General Gordon Granger and 2,000 federal troops arrived in Galveston, TX to take control of the state and enforce the emancipation of its enslaved people, more than two years after the Emancipation Proclamation went into effect.

All Different Now: Juneteenth, the First Day of Freedom, by Angela Johnson and E.B. Lewis. Through the eyes of one little girl, this is the story of the first Juneteenth, the day freedom finally came to the last of the slaves in the South. (**E**) bit.ly/2RWOokf; Curriculum guide here: bit.ly/1mZlDK6

Juneteenth for Mazie, by Floyd Cooper. Mazie is ready to celebrate liberty. She is ready to celebrate freedom. She is ready to celebrate a great day in American history – the day her ancestors were no longer enslaved. Mazie remembers the struggles and the triumph as she prepares to celebrate Juneteenth. (E) bit.ly/2Sltd7Q

Juneteenth Jamboree, by Carole Boston Weatherford. Cassandra wonders what makes June 19th so important. It isn't until Cassandra and her family arrive downtown that she discovers what the commotion is all about. It's Juneteenth, and the town is holding its annual Juneteenth Jamboree. (E) Teacher's guide by Lee and Low here: bit.ly/2tBICqK

Been Here So Long: Selections from the WPA American Slave Narratives, by the New Deal Network. Included are 17 of the approximately 2,300 American Slave Narratives collected by the Federal Writers Project, with lesson plans. (**H**) bit.ly/1Uiqrjw

---

Father's Day. Father's Day is an annual holiday that honors fathers and father figures and celebrates their contributions to the lives of their children and to society.

Daddy, Papa, and Me, by Lesléa Newman. Rhythmic text and illustrations with universal appeal show a toddler spending the day with his daddies. (**E**) bit.ly/2qlJkHq

In Daddy's Arms I Am Tall: African Americans Celebrating Fathers, by 12 African American poets, illustrated by Javaka Steptoe, Lee & Low Books, 2013. The 12 poems in this book deliver an important message to all readers about the powerful bonds between fathers, children, and grandchildren. Exuberance, grace, honor, pain, and humor all have their place in these intergenerational works. The poems reflect the contributions of both new and established African American writers whose outlooks on fatherhood vary widely. (**E, M**) Teacher's Guide: bit.ly/2meuhNi

Missing Daddy, by Mariame Kaba. In this picture book for readers ages 4-8, a little girl who misses her father because he's away in prison shares how his absence affects different parts of her life. She is most excited on the days when she gets to visit her beloved father. With gorgeous illustrations, this book depicts a little girl's love for her father from whom she is separated because of incarceration. (**E**) Resources and discussion questions here: missingdaddy.net

40th anniversary of the murder of Vincent Chin. As Japanese automakers began to challenge the US auto industry's hold on US markets, rising unemployment stirred anti-Japanese bigotry, especially among US autoworkers. Vincent Chin, a 27-year-old Chinese American, was murdered in Detroit in an unprovoked attack by two White autoworkers who thought he was Japanese. The killers were found guilty of manslaughter and received a modest fine, but no jail time. The (White) judge said, "These aren't the kind of men you send to jail."

From a Whisper to a Rallying Cry: The Killing of Vincent Chin and the Trial That Galvanized the Asian American Movement, by Paula Yoo. This book examines the outrage from the Asian American community after Chin's murderers received only a $3,000 fine and three years of probation. A suspenseful portrait of a pivotal moment in civil rights history, and of a man who became a symbol against hatred and racism. (**H**) bit.ly/3c0UQ34

A Day for Vincent Chin and Me, by Jacqueline Turner Banks. A chapter book for young readers about a Japanese American child's efforts to slow down the traffic on a residential street in Kentucky, while his mother organizes the Asian American community to draw attention to the death of Vincent Chin, whom his murderers blamed for Detroit's declining car sales and soaring unemployment. (**E**) bit.ly/30JtdoS

20 World Refugee Day. For many years, several African countries celebrated June 20 as Refugee Day. In 2000, as an expression of solidarity with Africa, which hosts the most refugees, the UN declared June 20 World Refugee Day.

Books to Help Kids Understand What It's Like to Be a Refugee, by Olugbemisola Rhuday-Perkovich. From the author of this annotated book list: "Stories can facilitate dialogue about refugees and promote healthy communication, help to foster empathy and understanding, and even inspire young readers to take action to ensure safe and welcoming environments in their own communities. Here are a few titles that can help." (**E, M**) bit.ly/2k3Djgv

Other Words for Home, by Jasmine Warga. A gorgeously written, hopeful middle-grade novel in verse about a young girl who must leave Syria to move to the United States. (**M, H**) bit.ly/2DlV6Yu

21 Summer Solstice (Northern Hemisphere). The Summer Solstice is when the sun reaches its highest position in the sky. It is the longest day and shortest night of the year.

Under Alaska's Midnight Sun, by Deb Vanasse. When the midnight sun is shining, people and animals stay active even at night. This sweet poetic narrative showcases the many pleasures of this unique time as a little girl dances, fishes, plays games, watches moose and foxes, and communes with family and nature. (**E**) bit.ly/3bWZV9q

22 250th anniversary of the Somerset ruling. James Somerset was an enslaved person taken to England by the Boston customs official who claimed him as property. After two years, he escaped but was recaptured and forced onto a ship bound for Jamaica to be sold as a slave. Lord Chief Justice Mansfield ordered the ship's captain to produce Somerset in court. Mansfield ruled that no man in England could be sold as a slave, and Somerset won his freedom. Britain abolished the Atlantic slave trade in 1807, though slavery was permitted until 1833.

The Tools of the Abolitionists, by Mike Kaye for the BBC. The campaign to abolish the slave trade in Britain launched the use of many advocacy tools that we now take for granted, including investigative research, parliamentary lobbying, media work, consumer boycotts, judicial challenges, the single-issue campaign, branding, and merchandising. This gallery explores some of the tools used by the abolitionists to gain public support for the anti-slavery movement in the 1780s and how they are still used today. (**H**) bbc.in/3t5Hd7P

23 50th anniversary of Title IX. Title IX of the Education Amendments of 1972 prohibits federally funded educational institutions from discriminating against students or employees based on gender. Under Title IX, any school that receives any federal money from the elementary to university level must provide fair and equal treatment of the sexes in all areas, including athletics. Title IX is credited with decreasing girls' high school dropout rates and increasing the number of women who enroll in and complete college.

Title IX at 40, by Carrie Kilman for Teaching for Justice. An essay exploring the ways in which Title IX was never just about sports, and how it radically changed everything about education for girls and women. (**M, H**) bit.ly/3sWhi2p

Mamie on the Mound: A Woman in Baseball's Negro Leagues, by Lean Henderson. Mamie "Peanut" Johnson had one dream: to play professional baseball. She was a talented player, but she wasn't welcome in the segregated All-American Girls Pro Baseball League because of the color of her skin. However, a greater opportunity came her way in 1953 when Johnson signed to play for the Indianapolis Clowns, a Negro Leagues team, becoming the first female pitcher to play on a men's professional team. During the three years she pitched for the Clowns, her record was an impressive 33-8. But more important, she broke ground for other female athletes and for women everywhere. (**E, M**) bit.ly/3eCiva1

24 40th anniversary of ILGWU strike in New York's Chinatown. The International Ladies' Garment Workers' Union (ILGWU) organized the largest strike in the history of New York's Chinatown. About 20,000 Chinatown garment workers, mostly Chinese immigrant women, rallied for better wages, working conditions, and benefits. This strike and another rally in July resulted in increased benefits, including bilingual union staff and resources, English classes, immigration paralegal services, health benefits, and the establishment of a childcare center in Chinatown.

Memories of the 1982 ILGWU Strike in New York's Chinatown, a firsthand account by Katie Quan. An essay by a labor organizer who participated in the largest strike in the history of New York's Chinatown, with accompanying images and related links for further reading. (**H**) bit.ly/3eDl3Vw

25 60th anniversary of *Engel v. Vitale*. The State Board of Regents in New York, concerned about what they saw as a moral decline in public schools, composed a prayer for students to recite every morning, though they could opt out if they wanted. In *Engel v. Vitale* the Supreme Court determined that this practice, even with an opt-out clause, violates the Establishment Clause of the First Amendment. It was the first case to make such a determination.

Engel v. Vitale: Recordings of the Oral Arguments, by Oyez. The New York State Board of Regents authorized a prayer for recitation at the start of each school day. A group of organizations joined forces to challenge the prayer, claiming that it violated the Establishment Clause of the First Amendment. The New York Court of Appeals rejected their arguments. The case and the oral arguments presented here are ripe with opportunities to teach and learn about children's rights related to flag salutes and other recitations required in public schools. Hear recordings of each side's oral arguments here. (**H**) oyez.org/cases/1961/468

50th anniversary of openly gay William Johnson's ordination as a Christian minister. Johnson was ordained in the Community United Church of Christ in California. He faced an uphill battle after surprising himself by coming out in 1970 at an assembly of seminary students and faculty, church leaders from throughout the Bay Area, and LGBT community members. When he first applied for ordination, he was turned down, despite support from his local church. Later, a vote was put before the Ecclesiastical Council, and he was approved by a 62-34 vote.

The God Box, by Alex Sanchez. Paul, a religious teen living in a small conservative town, finds his world turned upside down when he meets Manuel, a young man who says he's both Christian and gay – two things that Paul didn't think could coexist in one person. Doesn't the Bible forbid homosexuality? As Paul struggles with Manuel's interpretation of the Bible, thoughts that Paul has long tried to bury begin to surface, and he finds himself re-examining his whole life. (**H**) bit.ly/2SMcjAp

---

40th anniversary of *Island Trees Board of Education v. Pico*. A New York school board tried to remove books from the school library, claiming the books were "anti-American, anti-Christian, anti-Semitic, and just plain filthy." Among them were *The Best Short Stories by Negro Writers* and *Slaughterhouse Five*. In *Island Trees Board of Education v. Pico*, the Court ruled that, under the First Amendment, school boards cannot remove books from school libraries simply because they dislike the ideas contained in the books.

Resources for Banned Books Week, by Lisa Fink for NCTE. The National Council for Teachers of English, through its Intellectual Freedom Center, offers advice, helpful documents, and other support to teachers and schools faced with challenges to texts (e.g., literary works, films and videos, drama productions) or teaching methods used in their classrooms and schools. (**TR**) bit.ly/3aN0PHC

190th anniversary of the Battle of Velasco. In the Battle of Velasco, a prelude to the Texas Revolution, Henry Smith and John Austin led a group of Texans to Brazoria to secure a cannon for use against the Mexican forces at Anahuac. They encountered Domingo de Ugartechea, commander of the Mexican fort at Velasco, who tried to prevent the passage of the vessel carrying the cannon. The Mexicans ran out of ammunition and were forced to surrender.

Texas Revolution: A Lesson Plan, by the Stanford History Education Group. Why did Texans revolt against the Mexican government? In this lesson, students read the Texas Declaration of Independence, military commanders' letters, and an abolitionist pamphlet to explore causes of the Texas Revolution. (**H**) stanford.io/2RblRbV

---

26 International Day in Support of Victims of Torture. The United Nations General Assembly passed a resolution in 1997 to proclaim June 26 the United Nations International Day in Support of Victims of Torture. Torture is a crime under international law, yet thousands of people are tortured every year throughout the world.

Constitution, War Crimes, and Guantanamo Justice, by Alan Shapiro, Morningside Center for Teaching Social Responsibility. Release of a Justice Department memo raises the issue of how the US treats "terrorist suspects." Two student readings are followed by discussion questions and other student activities. (**H**) bit.ly/3cidbpb

---

National HIV Testing Day. National HIV Testing Day is an annual campaign encouraging people to "Take the test, Take control."

Elbow Is Not a Sexy Word: Approaches to Sex Education, by Jody Sokolower. From Chapter 3 of *Rethinking Sexism, Gender, and Sexuality*, by Rethinking Schools. (**TR**) bit.ly/1P5IlwH

---

27 70th anniversary of the McCarran-Walter Act. Before World War II, American immigration policy was designed specifically to exclude all Asians and Peoples of Color, restrict Southern and Eastern European immigration, and encourage the arrival of Western Europeans. The McCarran-Walter Act eliminated exclusion laws against Asian countries but maintained preference for Western Europeans. It also shifted the focus of immigration law to denying people based on their ideological views, a response to the growing fear of Communism.

This Land is Our Land: A History of American Immigration, by Linda Barrett Osborne. This book explores the way government policy and popular responses to immigrant groups evolved throughout US history, particularly between 1800 and 1965. The book concludes with a summary of events up to contemporary times, as immigration again becomes a hot-button issue. Includes an author's note, bibliography, and index. [Note: Teachers may want to discuss with students the use of the phrase "this land is our land," from the perspective of Indigenous peoples.] (**M, H**) bit.ly/3dXKDW7

Paul Laurence Dunbar, poet and author, born (1872-1906). Paul Laurence Dunbar was the first African American poet to garner national critical acclaim. Many of his poems and essays address issues of racial equality. In his poetry, he wrote in both dialectic and traditional styles. Dunbar's literary body, including novels, short stories, and poetry, is regarded as an impressive representation of Black life in turn-of-the-century America. His standard-English poems are now prized as some of his greatest achievements in verse.

Jump Back, Paul: The Life and Poems of Paul Laurence Dunbar, by Sally Derby. From his childhood in poverty and his early promise as a poet to his immense fame and his untimely death, Dunbar's story is one of triumph and tragedy. But his legacy remains in his much-beloved poetry – told in both Standard English and in dialect – which continues to delight and inspire readers today. More than two dozen of Dunbar's poems are woven throughout this volume, illuminating the phases of his life and serving as examples of dialect, imagery, and tone. (**E, M**) bit.ly/3mlhyAN

---

29 Henry Gerber, gay rights activist, born (1892-1972). Gerber was born in Bavaria and immigrated to Chicago as a young man. He served in the US Army in Germany during World War I, where he saw the persecution of gay men and lesbians. In response, he, along with several friends, formed an organization that became The Society for Human Rights, a nonprofit corporation in Chicago. The organization published a newsletter, *Friendship and Freedom*, which was distributed to its small membership.

Travels In a Gay Nation: Portraits of LGBTQ Americans, by Philip Gambone. In addition to interviews with David Sedaris, George Takei, Barney Frank, and Tammy Baldwin, *Travels in a Gay Nation* brings us lesser-known voices – a retired Naval officer, a transgender scholar and "drag king," a Princeton philosopher, two opera sopranos who happen to be lovers, an Indie Rock musician, the founder of a gay frat house, and a pair of Vermont garden designers. In this age when contemporary gay America is still coming under attack, Gambone captures the humanity of each individual. (**H**) uwpress.wisc.edu/books/4771.htm

July Resources

1 David Ross Brower, environmentalist, born (1912-2000). Brower was a prominent environmentalist and the founder of many environmental organizations, including Friends of the Earth and the Earth Island Institute. He was also the first Executive Director of the Sierra Club, transforming it from a regional to a national organization. Described as a principled and uncompromising advocate of wilderness and ecological values, he is considered the most influential environmental activist of the 20th century.

How to Change Everything: The Young Human's Guide to Protecting the Planet and Each Other, by Naomi Klein, adapted for young readers by Rebecca Stefoff. Full of empowering stories of young leaders all over the world, this information-packed book from award-winning journalist and one of the foremost voices for climate justice, Naomi Klein, offers young readers a comprehensive look at the state of the climate today and how we got here, while also providing the tools they need to join the fight to protect and reshape the planet they will inherit. (**H**) bit.ly/2S19nnJ

60th anniversary of Rwanda's and Burundi's independence from Belgium. The countries now known as Rwanda and Burundi were once a single territory Ruanda-Urundi, which was colonized by Germany. After World War I, Belgium acquired the territory. Belgium's divide-and-conquer policy pitted the largest tribes – the Tutsi and Hutu – against each other, enabling Belgium to maintain control. That tribal animosity remains today. An Independence movement began in the 1950s, culminating in the split of the territory into Rwanda and Burundi as two independent nations in 1962.

Forsaken Cries: The Story of Rwanda, by The Video Project, *Facing History and Ourselves*. A 35-minute documentary that explores the roots of the conflict in Rwanda that led to the genocide of nearly one million Tutsi people by Hutu military extremists beginning in April 1994. *Forsaken Cries* incorporates historical footage from the nation's colonial period with recent survivor interviews. Among the issues the video explores are international genocide laws, the failure of the international community to intervene in the genocide, the refugee crisis, and the War Crimes Tribunal. (**H**) bit.ly/3u10Tvb

---

10th anniversary of the publication of *The Wrong Complexion for Protection*. Subtitled: *How the Government Response to Disaster Endangers African American Communities*, this text was written by Dr. Robert D. Bullard, known as the Father of Environmental Justice. Bullard says one's ZIP code is the most potent predictor of health and wellbeing. The top priority of the Environmental Justice movement is the eradication of environmental, health, economic, and racial disparities.

Earth Democracy: Justice, Sustainability, and Peace, by Vandana Shiva. World-renowned environmental activist and physicist Vandana Shiva calls for a radical shift in the values that govern democracies, condemning the role that unrestricted capitalism has played in the destruction of environments and livelihoods. (**H**) bit.ly/3vr7zCT

120th anniversary of the Land Allotment Acts. The 1830 General Removal Act provided for reservation land belonging in common to each tribe. The Choctaw and Chickasaw Land Allotment Act and the Cherokee Land Allotment Act allowed the government to break up reservation land into small allotments to be parceled out to individuals and force the sale of "surplus land" in their territories to non-Indians. The "surplus land" happened to be the richest in mineral resources, depriving the Natives of their wealth.

Ancestor Approved: Intertribal Stories for Kids, edited by Cynthia Leitich Smith. This collection of intersecting stories by both new and veteran Native writers, bursts with hope, joy, resilience, the strength of community, and Native pride. (**E, M**) bit.ly/3vlobfk

---

4 US Independence Day. On July 4, 1776, the 13 American colonies formally declared independence from Britain, though the resolution to form an independent nation was passed by the Continental Congress two days earlier.

Frederick Douglass Fights for Freedom, by Bill Bigelow. This lesson introduces students to the numerous and varied ways African Americans resisted enslavement, using the autobiographical narrative of *The Life of Frederick Douglass*, published in 1845. It includes a video of Danny Glover reading Douglass's speech questioning what Independence Day means to African Americans. (**M, H, TR**) bit.ly/twlr1s

The Meaning of July Fourth for the Negro, by Frederick Douglass. Full text of a speech delivered by Douglass in Rochester, NY, on July 5, 1852. (**M, H**) bit.ly/1xt0vT3

60th anniversary of Algerian independence, granting women's right to vote and stand for election. Algerian women gained the right to vote and stand for election when Algeria gained independence. Eligibility requirements for voting and running for office are the same for men and women. Women have been both appointed and elected to local and legislative positions. In theory, there are no restrictions on the participation of Algerian women in politics, but women who attempt to gain positions of higher power within political parties often face resistance from male members.

Key Facts About Women's Suffrage Around the World, by Katherine Schaeffer for Pew Research. Perfect for use in mathematics and/or social studies classes, a close look at the history of women's suffrage around the world. Data and analyses focus on when women in various countries won the right to vote in national elections. (**H**) pewrsr.ch/3u5K4zg

---

6 130th anniversary of the Homestead Strike. In a bitter battle between the Amalgamated Association of Iron and Steel Workers and the Carnegie Steel Company, workers were first locked out and then went on strike. Carnegie brought in the Pinkertons to infiltrate the union and a battle ensued, with seven Pinkertons and nine union members dead. Pennsylvania's governor called in the National Guard, shocking the town. More than 100 strikers were arrested; the strike continued until November with no concessions and the union destroyed.

The Homestead Strike, a Teaching Activity by Bill Bigelow and Norm Diamond for the Zinn Education Project. This role play activity on the notorious 1892 Homestead Strike explores the possibility of solidarity among workers of very different backgrounds and at different levels in the workplace hierarchy. This activity is one of the 16 labor history lessons available for free download from *The Power in Our Hands*. (**H**) bit.ly/2OjiXRD

---

7 10th anniversary of Cambridge Declaration on Consciousness. A prominent group of international scientists declared in Cambridge, UK, that evidence shows nonhuman animals, including all mammals, birds, and many other creatures, are conscious beings that are aware of and experience what happens to them. They argued that the capacity to have positive and negative experiences is what makes a being capable of being harmed, which warrants moral and ethical consideration.

The Nonhuman Rights Project. This organization is working toward legal rights for nonhuman animals. The website includes a blog, a breakdown of state-by-state legal action on behalf of nonhuman animals, and current news stories featuring animals. (**M, H, TR**) bit.ly/eEsNCS

---

9 Eid al-Adha begins at sunset 7/19 (Islam). Eid al-Adha ("Sacrifice Feast") is a Muslim holiday commemorating the willingness of Ibrahim (Abraham) to sacrifice his son to God. Satisfied with Ibrahim's devotion, God accepted a sacrificial animal in place of the son. The Muslim tradition of charity and care for the poor has roots in this tradition, as the sacrificed animal (holiday meal) is shared equally among the family, their friends and relatives, and the poor.

The Proudest Blue: A Story of Hijab and Family, by Ibtihaj Muhammad. Faizah admires older sister Asiya's new, strikingly beautiful blue first-day hijab, finding inner strength and pride when facing bullies at school who make fun of it. (**E**) bit.ly/3d0n2RL

---

11 130th anniversary of Coeur d'Alene miners' strike. Miners in Coeur d'Alene, ID, went on strike to protest reduced wages. Mine owners called in agents from the Pinkerton National Detective Agency to infiltrate the union. Union officers were arrested. The Idaho Governor instituted martial law, and the National Guard was called in to suppress strikers. The strike inspired workers to start the Western Federation of Miners Union in 1893.

Fire in the Hole! By Mary Cronk Farrell. Based on the true story of a silver miners' strike in Coeur d'Alene, ID, this book of historical fiction shows the desperate conditions of miners' lives and how the striking miners were detained illegally in a late-19th century version of Guantanamo. (**H**) zinnedproject.org/materials/fire-in-the-hole

---

15 160th anniversary of the Battle of Apache Pass. In the Apache's continued resistance to Anglo settlements, Cochise and Mangas Coloradas, his father-in-law, led a group of 500 Apache warriors in an ambush of the California Column as it rode east through Apache Pass in the Chiricahua Mountains. Using heavy artillery, the US soldiers routed the Apache from their fortified positions overlooking the area. Sixty-six Apache were killed and only five Americans died. The army subsequently built Fort Bowie to prevent future attacks.

Apache Children and Elders Talk Together, by the Library of Intergenerational Learning: Native Americans. Many of us have heard of Geronimo, who fought for the freedom of the Apache. Some of his grandchildren and great-grandchildren relate their family history and the Apache culture as it has evolved through American history. (**E, M**) bit.ly/3e0tqez

---

16 Ida B. Wells, educator, journalist, and activist, born (1862-1931). Wells was born as an enslaved person in Mississippi. She is best known for her work as a journalist, women's rights advocate, suffragist, and anti-lynching crusader. She often clashed with White suffragists for ignoring the plight of Black people, especially victims of White violence. In 1896, she co-founded the National Association of Colored Women (NACW). Wells was present in Niagara Falls when the NAACP was founded, but her name was excluded from the list of charter members.

Ida B. Wells: Let the Truth Be Told, by Walter Dean Myers. In this picture book, Myers highlights Wells' courage and persistence by using her own words and writings to chronicle how she refused to accept discrimination and raised her voice for justice. (**E, M**) bit.ly/3teCtNR

---

23 70th anniversary of the Egyptian Revolution. Feeling he had abandoned them during the disastrous 1948 Arab-Israeli war, a group of Egyptian army officers, calling themselves "The Free Officers," overthrew King Farouk with the goals of abolishing the monarchy, establishing a republic, and ending British colonialism in Egypt and Sudan. Despite its many shortcomings, the Egyptian revolution inspired other Arab and African states to overthrow existing monarchies and declare independence from colonial powers.

Egyptian Streets: The Podcast, by Noran Morsi. Featuring Egyptians around the world who fuel creative social change and their journeys that brought them there, from the intersection of Egyptian identity and creative social change, are stories from street to sound. (**M, H**) egyptianstreets.com/category/the-podcast

---

24 50th anniversary of Tuskegee syphilis experiment exposé. Beginning in 1932, the United States Public Health Service worked with the Tuskegee Institute to study untreated syphilis in Macon County, AL. 600 Black men, most of them impoverished, participated in the study, even after a cure for the disease was found. 128 of these test subjects died because their syphilis went untreated. The *Washington Star* newspaper exposed the unethical treatment of these men, resulting in a public outcry and the end of the experiment in 1972.

Medical Apartheid: Teaching the Tuskegee Syphilis Study, by Gretchen Kraig-Turner for Rethinking Schools. Essay and lesson plan from a high school science teacher about medical apartheid and the Tuskegee Syphilis study. (**H, TR**) rethinkingschools.org/articles/medical-apartheid

---

28 90th anniversary of attack on Bonus Army. World War I veterans who did not receive the wartime bonuses they were promised formed the Bonus Expeditionary Force, or "Bonus Army," and marched on Washington DC. Black and White veterans camped together in "Hoovervilles," named after President Herbert Hoover. Hoover called on troops led by Generals Douglas MacArthur, George Patton, and Dwight D. Eisenhower, who attacked the veterans with tear gas, tanks, and bayonets.

The Bonus Army, by Mickey Z. for the Zinn Education Project. This short article about the history of the 1932 Bonus Expeditionary Force (BEF), or Bonus Army, includes video clips, books for children and teens, and other multimedia resources related to teaching about the WWI veterans who fought for the wartime bonuses they were promised. (**H, TR**) zinnedproject.org/materials/bonus-army

List of resources by theme

Key

E = Elementary School
M = Middle School
H = High School
TR = Teacher Resources

To see an online version of this list with live links, visit:
www.edliberation.org/planbookresources

Contents

Abolition and Slavery

All Different Now: Juneteenth, the First Day of Freedom, by Angela Johnson and E.B. Lewis. Through the eyes of one little girl, this is the story of the first Juneteenth, the day freedom finally came to the last of the slaves in the South. (**E**) bit.ly/2RWOokf; Curriculum guide here: bit.ly/1mZlDK6

Annotated Bibliography for Young Readers of Harriet Beecher Stowe Biographies, by the Harriet Beecher Stowe Center. A list of books for young readers interested in learning more about Harriet Beecher Stowe and her social justice work. (**E, M, H, TR**) bit.ly/3ecm32y

Been Here So Long: Selections from the WPA American Slave Narratives, by the New Deal Network. Included are 17 of the approximately 2,300 American Slave Narratives collected by the Federal Writers Project, with lesson plans. (**H**) bit.ly/1Uiqrjw

Born on the Water, by Nikole Hannah-Jones and Renée Watson, the 1619 Project. The 1619 Project's lyrical picture book chronicles the consequences of slavery and the history of Black resistance in the United States. A young student receives a family tree assignment in school, but she can trace back only three generations. Grandma gathers the whole family, and the student learns that 400 years ago, in 1619, their ancestors were stolen and brought to America by White slave traders. But before that, they had a home, a land, and a language. She learns how the people said to be born on the water survived. (**E, M**) bit.ly/2RyPhRJ

Brick by Brick, by Charles R. Smith, Jr. This story opens with America becoming a new country and our first president, George Washington, needing a home. It then describes how enslaved Africans were put to work to build the White House. Through text and illustrations, *Brick by Brick* tells the story of enslaved people working under the blistering sun for hours a day under grueling conditions. (**E**) bit.ly/2I9NTSD

Created Equal: How Benjamin Banneker Challenged Jefferson on Race and Freedom, by Facing History and Ourselves. A reading on Banneker's challenge to Jefferson's pro-slavery stance, with selections from both Banneker's letter and Jefferson's response. (**H**) bit.ly/2PxSsbv

Dear Benjamin Banneker, by Andrea Davis Pinkney and Brian Pinkney. Benjamin Banneker was born free when most Black people in the United States were still enslaved. It troubled him that not all Black people were free. An accomplished astronomer and mathematician, he decided to take a stand against slavery by writing to then-Secretary of State Thomas Jefferson. This is the story of their extraordinary correspondence. (**E**) bit.ly/3sKExgQ

Frederick Douglass Fights for Freedom, by Bill Bigelow. This lesson introduces students to the numerous and varied ways African Americans resisted enslavement, using the autobiographical narrative of *The Life of Frederick Douglass*, published in 1845. It includes a video of Danny Glover reading Douglass's speech questioning what Independence Day means to African Americans. (**M, H, TR**) bit.ly/twIr1s

How the Word Is Passed: A Reckoning with the History of Slavery Across America, by Clint Smith. Beginning in his own hometown of New Orleans, Clint Smith leads the reader through an unforgettable tour of monuments and landmarks – those that are honest about the past and those that are not – that offer an intergenerational story of how slavery has been central in shaping our nation's collective history and ourselves. (**H**) bit.ly/3sS7448

I Lay My Stitches Down: Poems of American Slavery, by Cynthia Grady. This rich and intricate collection of poems chronicles the various experiences of enslaved people in America. Drawn together through imagery from quilting and fiber arts, each poem is spoken from a different perspective and supplemented by a historical note. (**E, M**) bit.ly/3fDkpt7

Iqbal, by Francesco D'Adamo. This is a powerful story based on the real life and death of a Pakistani child sold into slavery. (**E, M, H**) bit.ly/2S2GyWi

Juneteenth for Mazie, by Floyd Cooper. Mazie is ready to celebrate liberty. She is ready to celebrate freedom. She is ready to celebrate a great day in American history – the day her ancestors were no longer enslaved. Mazie remembers the struggles and the triumph as she prepares to celebrate Juneteenth. (**E**) bit.ly/2Sltd7Q

Juneteenth Jamboree, by Carole Boston Weatherford. Cassandra wonders what makes June 19th so important. It isn't until Cassandra and her family arrive downtown that she discovers what the commotion is all about. It's Juneteenth, and the town is holding its annual Juneteenth Jamboree. (**E**) Teacher's guide by Lee and Low here: bit.ly/2tBICqK

Monumental: Oscar Dunn and His Radical Fight in Reconstruction Louisiana, by Brian Mitchell, Barrington Edwards, and Nick Weldon. The incredible story of Oscar James Dunn, a New Orleanian born into slavery who became

America's first Black lieutenant governor and acting governor. A graphic history informed by newly discovered primary sources, *Monumental* resurrects in vivid detail Louisiana and New Orleans after the Civil War, and presents an iconic American life that never should have been forgotten. Contextual essays and a map and timeline add layers of depth to the narrative. (**H**) bit.ly/3fJsKvB

Nat Turner, by Kyle Baker. This graphic novel depicts the evils of slavery in this moving and historically accurate story of Nat Turner's slave rebellion. Told nearly wordlessly, every image resonates with the reader as the brutal story unfolds. (**M, H**) bit.ly/3vj6wpu; teaching guides at abramsbooks.com/resources

Nat Turner: A Troublesome Property, by director/writer Charles Burnett, California Newsreel. This film chronicles the violent confrontation of Nat Turner's Rebellion and shows how the story has been continuously re-told since 1831. (**H**) bit.ly/d6B1Be

No More! Stories and Songs of Slave Resistance, by Doreen Rappaport. Using true accounts, author Doreen Rappaport puts readers in the shoes of 11 extraordinary individuals and documents the many forms of slave resistance: subversion, uprisings, escape, poetry, religion, and song. (**E, M**) bit.ly/2ufG7xj

Poetry of Defiance: How the Enslaved Resisted, a teaching activity by Adam Sanchez for Rethinking Schools. Through a mixer activity, students are introduced to the various ways that enslaved people resisted the brutal exploitation of slavery. The lesson culminates in a collective class poem highlighting the defiance of the enslaved. (**M, H**) bit.ly/2O5TEPu

Rethinkin' Lincoln on the 150th Birthday of the Emancipation Proclamation, by Bill Bigelow, *Huffington Post*. This article questions the portrayal of President Lincoln as an abolitionist in the movie *Lincoln*. Bigelow also discusses how he and his students approached the study of the Emancipation Proclamation, beginning with Lincoln's inaugural address. (**H, TR**) huff.to/UpgZq8

Slavery by Another Name, directed by Sam Pollard. Based on the Pulitzer Prize-winning book, Douglas A. Blackmon's *Slavery by Another Name*, this 90-minute documentary challenges the view that slavery ended with the 13th Amendment in 1865. The PBS site includes video clips and links to other useful resources. (**M, H, TR**) to.pbs.org/zZnn6p

Teaching A People's History of Abolition and the Civil War, by Adam Sanchez, Rethinking Schools. A collection of 10 classroom-tested lessons on one of the most transformative periods in US history. These lessons encourage students to take a critical look at the popular narrative that focuses on Abraham Lincoln as the Great Emancipator and ignores the resistance of abolitionists and enslaved people. (**TR**) bit.ly/2RrqHSG

Teaching Hard History: A Framework for Teaching American Slavery, by Learning for Justice. Most students leave high school without an adequate understanding of the role slavery played in the development of the United States or how its legacies still influence us today. To try to remedy this, Teaching Tolerance developed a comprehensive guide for teaching and learning this critical topic at the middle and high school levels. Includes primary sources, podcasts, webinars, and more. (**M, H**) bit.ly/2FUocgs

The Abolitionists, by PBS American Experience. Bringing to life the intertwined stories of Frederick Douglass, William Lloyd Garrison, Angelina Grimké, Harriet Beecher Stowe, and John Brown, *The Abolitionists* takes place during some of the most violent and contentious decades in American history, shining a light on the debates of the era. (**M, H**) to.pbs.org/1fgdrWn

The Meaning of July Fourth for the Negro, by Frederick Douglass. Full text of a speech delivered by Douglass in Rochester, NY, on July 5, 1852. (**M, H**) bit.ly/1xt0vT3

The Story of Denmark Vesey, by Thomas Wentworth Higginson for *The Atlantic*. A compelling article about the powerful impact of Denmark Vesey's attempted slave rebellion, from the June 1861 issue of *The Atlantic*. (**H**) bit.ly/3vlclwi

The Women Who Gave Us Christmas, by William Loren Katz. Article about how women organized Christmas bazaars to finance the abolition cause and used the fundraisers as an opportunity to spread anti-slavery messages. (**M, H, TR**) bit.ly/1QvQJe8

Wake: The Hidden History of Women-Led Slave Revolts, by Rebecca Hall. Part graphic novel, part memoir, this book tells the story of Dr. Rebecca Hall, a historian, granddaughter of slaves, and a woman haunted by the legacy of slavery. The accepted history of slave revolts had always told her that enslaved women took a back seat. But Dr. Hall decided to look deeper, and her journey takes her through old court records, slave ship captain's logs, crumbling correspondence, and even the forensic evidence from the bones of enslaved women from the "Negro burying ground" uncovered in Manhattan. She found women warriors everywhere. (**M, H**) bit.ly/3s2TAB7

What Is Modern Slavery? Investigating Human Trafficking, by Holly Epstein Ojalvo. In this lesson, students learn about human trafficking, also known as modern slavery. Using coverage of human trafficking by Nicholas D. Kristof, a *New York Times* columnist, they explore the causes of trafficking and the consequences for victims and traffickers, the role of globalization, and ways to respond effectively. (**M, H**) nyti.ms/XG0Z3n

Write the Truth, by Bob Peterson, Rethinking Schools. Peterson describes an inquiry project in which his 5th graders investigated which US presidents owned slaves, and then wrote letters to textbook publishers to demand that this information be included. (**E, M**) bit.ly/svqysP

African American History, Issues, and Rights

16th Street Baptist Church Bombing, by Zinn Education Project. Background information and a useful curated list of multimedia resources, categorized by grade level, for teaching about the 16th Street Baptist Church Bombing. (**E, M, H**) bit.ly/3mYxK0N

A Black Women's History of the United States, by Daina Ramey Berry and Kali Nicole Gross. This book reaches far beyond a single narrative to showcase the complexity of Black women's lives throughout history. Berry and Gross prioritize many voices: enslaved women, freedwomen, religious leaders, artists, queer women, activists, and women who lived outside the law. (**H, TR**) bit.ly/3exil5r

A Day for Rememberin': Inspired by the True Events of the First Memorial Day, by Leah Henderson. Inspired by true events and told through the eyes of a young boy, this is the deeply moving story about what is regarded as the first Memorial Day on May 1, 1865. Eli dresses up in his best clothes, Mama gathers the mayflowers, Papa straightens his hat, and together they join the crowds filling the streets of Charleston, SC, with bouquets, crosses, and wreaths. Abolitionists, missionaries, teachers, military officers, and a sea of faces Black, Brown, and White, they march as one and sing for all those who gave their lives fighting for freedom during the Civil War. (**E**) bit.ly/3a6LC3R

A Litany for Survival: The Life and Work of Audre Lorde, a film by Ada Gay Griffin and Michelle Parkerson. This documentary explores the life of an activist whose work was entrenched in the Civil Rights movement, the Feminist/Womanist movement, and the Lesbian and Gay Rights movement. (**H, TR**) to.pbs.org/3ezIeBN

A Teacher's Guide to The Souls of Black Folk, by Penguin USA. Several units of lesson plans ranging from DuBois's disagreements with Booker T. Washington to Jim Crow, to Emancipation and its aftermath. (**H**) bit.ly/2mh3ajn

All Different Now: Juneteenth, the First Day of Freedom, by Angela Johnson and E.B. Lewis. See *Abolition and Slavery* section. (**E**) bit.ly/2RWOokf; Curriculum guide here: bit.ly/1mZlDK6

Amend: The Fight for America. In this student-friendly Netflix series, Will Smith hosts an examination of the evolving, often lethal, fight for equal rights in America through the lens of the US Constitution's 14th Amendment. (**M, H**) bit.ly/3qKZiHs

An Interview with Ralph Ellison, by Alfred Chester and Vilma Howard for the *Paris Review*. A rich and beautiful interview with Ralph Ellison about his work, his life, and his views on "the American Negro writer." (**H**) bit.ly/2P1liRw

An Outrage: A Documentary Film about Lynching in the American South, by the SPLC and the Smithsonian. This film takes viewers to the very communities where heinous acts of violence took place, offering a painful look back at lives lost to lynching and a critical look forward. Stream the film and download the accompanying viewer's guide at the Learning for Justice website. (**H**) bit.ly/3wSawy2

Barack Obama: Son of Promise, Child of Hope, by Nikki Grimes. Even as a boy, Barack knew he wasn't quite like anybody else, but through his journeys he found the ability to listen to Hope and become what he was meant to be: a bridge to bring people together. This is the moving story of our 44th President, told by Nikki Grimes and illustrated by Bryan Collier, both winners of the Coretta Scott King Award. (**E**) bit.ly/3laT3LD; printable educator's guide: bit.ly/2ufyRkV

Been Here So Long: Selections from the WPA American Slave Narratives, by the New Deal Network. See *Abolition and Slavery* section. (**H**) bit.ly/1Uiqrjw

Before Rosa Parks: Ida B. Wells, by Learning for Justice. The title "Before Rosa Parks" loosely links a number of lessons that discuss African American women who were active in the fight for civil rights before the 1950s. (**M, H**) bit.ly/2J75lBk

Black Indians: A Hidden Heritage, by William Loren Katz. This startling and readable work of people's history chronicles the attempts to keep Black people and Indians divided in the Americas and the two groups' efforts to unite. This expanded and updated edition includes additional research and documentary and photographic evidence illustrating the Native American and African American alliance that for four centuries challenged European conquest and slavery. (**M, H**) zinnedproject.org/materials/black-indians

Black Lives Matter at School Website, by a national coalition of organizers. A comprehensive website for #BLMatSchool that includes the demands, the principles, and a ton of lesson plans, posters, and classroom resources to support your planning for this annual week of action affirming the lives of Black students and Black people in general. (**TR**) blacklivesmatteratschool.com

Black Lives Matter at School: An Uprising for Educational Justice, by Denisha Jones and Jesse Hagopian. This book succinctly generalizes lessons from successful challenges to institutional racism that have been won through the Black Lives Matter at School movement. (**TR**) bit.ly/3qJs773

Black Pioneers of Science and Invention, by Louis Haber. A readable, perceptive account of the lives of 14 gifted innovators who have played important roles in scientific and industrial progress. The achievements of Benjamin Banneker, Granville T. Woods, George Washington Carver, and others have made jobs easier, saved countless lives, and in many cases, altered the course of history. (**E, M**) bit.ly/2PORrf2

Black Women in Science: A Black History Book for Kids, by Kimberly Brown Pellum. Fifteen powerful stories of fearless female scientists who advanced their STEM fields and fought to build a legacy. (**E, M**) bit.ly/3rJKg55

Born on the Water, by Nikole Hannah-Jones and Renée Watson, the 1619 Project. See *Abolition and Slavery* section. (**E, M**) bit.ly/2RyPhRJ

Brick by Brick, by Charles R. Smith, Jr. See *Abolition and Slavery* section. (**E**) bit.ly/2l9NTSD

Chisolm '72: Unbought and Unbossed, a POV documentary. This site includes lesson plans and resources for using *Chisholm '72*. Also provides access to a lending library where teachers can borrow the video for free. The film is available with Amazon Prime and is streaming for under $4 from a variety of sites such as YouTube. (**M, H, TR**) bit.ly/2RW7q8z

Created Equal: How Benjamin Banneker Challenged Jefferson on Race and Freedom, by Facing History and Ourselves. See *Abolition and Slavery* section. (**H**) bit.ly/2PxSsbv

Dear Benjamin Banneker, by Andrea Davis Pinkney and Brian Pinkney. See *Abolition and Slavery* section. (**E**) bit.ly/3sKExgQ

Don't Call Us Dead: Poems, by Danez Smith. These poems by nonbinary poet Danez Smith come from a place of too many funerals and too few miracles. Touching on topics from police brutality toward African Americans to the realities of an HIV diagnosis, this is a heartrending collection. (**H**) bit.ly/2ARmRHa

Feed Your Mind: A Story of August Wilson, by Jen Bryant. As a child, August Wilson, the two-time Pulitzer Prize-winning playwright, read soup can labels and cereal boxes. When his mother took him to the library, his whole world opened up. After facing intense prejudice at school from both students and some teachers, August dropped out. However, he continued reading and educating himself independently. *Feed Your Mind* is told in two acts, revealing how Wilson grew up to be one of the most influential American playwrights. The book includes an author's note, a timeline of August Wilson's life, a list of Wilson's plays, and a bibliography. (**M, H**) bit.ly/3dWMlG8

Frederick Douglass Fights for Freedom, by Bill Bigelow. See *Abolition and Slavery* section. (**M, H, TR**) bit.ly/twlr1s

Freedom Libraries: The Untold Story of Libraries for African Americans in the South, by Mike Selby. Although illegal, racial segregation was strictly enforced in a number of American states, and public libraries were not immune. Numerous libraries were desegregated on paper only: there would be no cards given to African Americans, no books for them read, and no furniture for them to use. It was these exact conditions that helped create Freedom Libraries. More than 80 of these parallel libraries appeared in the Deep South, staffed by civil rights voter registration workers. (**H**) bit.ly/3se9QPV

Getting Away with Murder: The True Story of the Emmett Till Case, by Chris Crowe. Although the two White men who murdered Emmett Till were tried and acquitted by an all-White jury, they later bragged publicly about the crime. It was a galvanizing moment for Black leaders and ordinary citizens, including activists such as Rosa Parks. In clear, vivid detail accessible to high school students, Chris Crowe investigates the before-and-aftermath of the crime, as well as the dramatic court trial, and places it in the context of the nascent Civil Rights movement. (**H**) zinnedproject.org/materials/getting-away-with-murder

How the Word Is Passed: A Reckoning with the History of Slavery Across America, by Clint Smith. See *Abolition and Slavery* section. (**H**) bit.ly/3sS7448

"I am Somebody," by Jesse Jackson. Full audio of Jesse Jackson's 1971 speech entitled, "I am Somebody," in which he affirms the dignity of Black people. (**E, M, H**) Original speech here: bit.ly/39Ftbmu; Version of the speech that he delivered on an episode of Sesame Street for young children here: bit.ly/3udW1lU

I Lay My Stitches Down: Poems of American Slavery, by Cynthia Grady. See *Abolition and Slavery* section. (**E, M**) bit.ly/3fDkpt7

Ida B. The Queen: The Extraordinary Life and Legacy of Ida B. Wells, by Michelle Duster. The awe-inspiring story of a pioneering woman who was often overlooked and underestimated – a woman who refused to exit a train car meant for White passengers; a woman who brought to light the horrors of lynching in America; a woman who co-founded the NAACP. Written by Wells' great-granddaughter Michelle Duster, this "warm remembrance of a civil rights icon" (*Kirkus Reviews*) is a unique visual celebration of Wells' life, and of the Black experience. (**M, H**) bit.ly/3wUMl1O

Ida B. Wells: Let the Truth Be Told, by Walter Dean Myers. In this picture book, Myers highlights Wells' courage and persistence by using her own words and writings to chronicle how she refused to accept discrimination and raised her voice for justice. (**E, M**) bit.ly/3teCtNR

In Daddy's Arms I Am Tall: African Americans Celebrating Fathers, by 12 African American poets, illustrated by Javaka Steptoe, Lee & Low Books, 2013. The 12 poems in this book deliver an important message to all readers about the powerful bonds between fathers, children, and grandchildren. Exuberance, grace, honor, pain, and humor all have their place in these intergenerational works. The poems reflect the contributions of both new and established African American writers whose outlooks on fatherhood vary widely. (**E, M**) Teacher's Guide: bit.ly/2meuhNi

Jump Back, Paul: The Life and Poems of Paul Laurence Dunbar, by Sally Derby. From his childhood in poverty and his early promise as a poet to his immense fame and his untimely death, Dunbar's story is one of triumph and tragedy. But his legacy remains in his much-beloved poetry – told in both Standard English and in dialect – which continues to delight and inspire readers today. More than two dozen of Dunbar's poems are woven throughout this volume, illuminating the phases of his life and serving as examples of dialect, imagery, and tone. (**E, M**) bit.ly/3mlhyAN

Juneteenth for Mazie, by Floyd Cooper. See *Abolition and Slavery* section. (**E**) bit.ly/2Sltd7Q

Juneteenth Jamboree, by Carole Boston Weatherford. See *Abolition and Slavery* section. (**E**) Teacher's guide by Lee and Low here: bit.ly/2tBICqK

Let It Shine: Stories of Black Women Freedom Fighters, by Andrea Davis Pinkney. Beautifully illustrated by Stephen Alcorn, Pinkney's short biographies emphasize one common theme: These 10 African American women spoke out fearlessly in the fight for racial justice. (**E, M**) bit.ly/3dYjmBQ

Liberation Curriculum, by the Martin Luther King, Jr. Research and Education Institute. Lesson plans, primary resources, and articles based on the Martin Luther King, Jr. Archives at Stanford University. (**H**) stanford.io/1DNVv1M

Lifting as We Climb: Black Women's Battle for the Ballot Box, by Evette Dionne. An eye-opening book that tells the important, overlooked story of Black women as a force in the Suffrage movement when fellow suffragists did not accept them as equal partners in the struggle. (**M, H**) bit.ly/2PY7Yx9

Little Leaders: Bold Women in Black History, by Vashti Harrison. This 96-page book features 40 biographies, accompanied by charming illustrations, of African American women who helped shape history. It was an instant *New York Times* bestseller when it debuted in December 2017. (**E**) bit.ly/2p5UijE

Love to Langston, by Tony Medina. This biography in poems was published in 2002 in honor of American poet and author Langston Hughes (1902–1967) on the anniversary of his 100th birthday. Each poem explores a significant event or theme in the life of Hughes. Young readers learn about his lonely childhood, the racism he faced, his decision to become a writer, his years of travel, his love of New York's Harlem neighborhood, and his success as a poet. (**E, M**) Teacher's guide here: bit.ly/3ti1nMO

Lynching in America, by The Equal Justice Initiative. Two units that total 13 lesson plans exploring lynching and racial terror historically and its ongoing legacy today. (**H, TR**) bit.ly/2JsovSt

Lynching in America: Confronting the Legacy of Racial Terror, by Equal Justice Initiative. EJI's report is based on investigation of thousands of racial terror lynchings. In addition to this comprehensive report, EJI opened the Memorial for Peace and Justice in Montgomery, AL, a 6-acre site using sculpture, art, and design to contextualize the history of racial terror. (**H, TR**) Report: bit.ly/3eDnvNu; Memorial: bit.ly/3eBGrvS

Mamie on the Mound: A Woman in Baseball's Negro Leagues, by Lean Henderson. Mamie "Peanut" Johnson had one dream: to play professional baseball. She was a talented player, but she wasn't welcome in the segregated All-American Girls Pro Baseball League because of the color of her skin. However, a greater opportunity came her way in 1953 when Johnson signed to play for the Indianapolis Clowns, a Negro Leagues team, becoming the first female pitcher to play on a men's professional team. During the three years she pitched for the Clowns, her record was an impressive 33-8. But more important, she broke ground for other female athletes and for women everywhere. (**E, M**) bit.ly/3eCiva1

Medical Apartheid: Teaching the Tuskegee Syphilis Study, by Gretchen Kraig-Turner for Rethinking Schools. Essay and lesson plan from a high school science teacher about medical apartheid and the Tuskegee Syphilis study. (**H, TR**) rethinkingschools.org/articles/medical-apartheid

Monumental: Oscar Dunn and His Radical Fight in Reconstruction Louisiana, by Brian Mitchell, Barrington Edwards, and Nick Weldon. See *Abolition and Slavery* section. (**H**) bit.ly/3fJsKvB

Muhammad Ali, a film by Ken Burns, Sarah Burns, and David McMahon for PBS. In total, an 8-hour documentary series on the life of Muhammad Ali. (**H**) to.pbs.org/3ymU3Tn

Of Thee I Sing: A Letter to My Daughters, by Barack Obama. In this tender, beautiful letter to his daughters, President Obama writes a moving tribute to 13 groundbreaking Americans and the ideals that have shaped our nation. (**E, M**) bit.ly/2EqAcq0

Nat Turner, by Kyle Baker. See *Abolition and Slavery* section. (**M, H**) bit.ly/3vj6wpu; teaching guides at abramsbooks.com/resources

Nat Turner: A Troublesome Property, by director/writer Charles Burnett, California Newsreel. See *Abolition and Slavery* section. (**H**) bit.ly/d6B1Be

No More! Stories and Songs of Slave Resistance, by Doreen Rappaport. See *Abolition and Slavery* section. (**E, M**) bit.ly/2ufG7xj

Plessy v. Ferguson: The Organizing History of the Case, an article by Keith Medley for Zinn Education Project. An excerpt from an article by Keith W. Medley (author of *We as Freemen: Plessy v. Ferguson*) about the organizing by the *Comité des Citoyens* that led to *Plessy v. Ferguson*. It is a powerful story of organizing, fundraising, the use of the media, legal strategies, and more. Additional related teaching resources follow the article. (**H**) zinnedproject.org/materials/plessy-v-ferguson

Poetry of Defiance: How the Enslaved Resisted, a teaching activity by Adam Sanchez for Rethinking Schools. See *Abolition and Slavery* section. (**M, H**) bit.ly/2O5TEPu

Putting the Movement Back into Civil Rights Teaching, by Deborah Menkart, Alana Murray, and Jenice L. View. The book includes interactive and interdisciplinary lessons, readings, writings, photographs, graphics, and interviews, with sections on education, labor, citizenship, and culture, and reflections on teaching about the Civil Rights movement. (**E, M, H**) bit.ly/1iv4HhU

Rethinkin' Lincoln on the 150th Birthday of the Emancipation Proclamation, by Bill Bigelow, *Huffington Post*. See *Abolition and Slavery* section. (**H, TR**) huff.to/UpgZq8

Seven Principles, by Sweet Honey in the Rock. This is a song that teaches the seven principles of Kwanzaa. (**E, M, H**) bit.ly/vNc77L

She Was the First!: The Trailblazing Life of Shirley Chisholm, by Katheryn Russell-Brown. This book highlights the accomplishments of Shirley Chisholm, a woman of many firsts, who was a political trailblazer, a candidate of the people, and catalyst of change who opened the door for women in the political arena. (**E**) bit.ly/3laM7yj

Slavery by Another Name, directed by Sam Pollard. See *Abolition and Slavery* section. (**M, H, TR**) to.pbs.org/zZnn6p

Teaching A People's History of Abolition and the Civil War, by Adam Sanchez, Rethinking Schools. See *Abolition and Slavery* section. (**TR**) bit.ly/2RrqHSG

Teaching for Black Lives, by Rethinking Schools. From the editors' introduction: "*Teaching for Black Lives* grows directly out of the Movement for Black Lives. We recognize that anti-Black racism constructs Black people, and Blackness generally, as not counting as human life. The chapters here push back directly against this construct by providing educators with critical perspectives on the role of schools in perpetuating anti-Blackness, and by offering educators concrete examples of what it looks like to humanize Black people in curriculum, teaching, and policy." (**TR**) teachingforblacklives.org

Teaching Hard History: A Framework for Teaching American Slavery, by Learning for Justice. See *Abolition and Slavery* section. (**M, H**) bit.ly/2FUocgs

Tell All the Children Our Story, by Tonya Bolden. From the first recorded birth of a Black child in Jamestown all the way up to the present day, this is African American history from the perspective of the children who lived through it. A scrapbook of letters, photos, artwork, testimonials, and more, this is the history that didn't make it into the original history books – the agonies and the sweet victories of African American children. (**M**) Discussion guide included here: bit.ly/2US1hKv

The Abolitionists, by PBS American Experience. See *Abolition and Slavery* section. (**M, H**) to.pbs.org/1fgdrWn

The Black Radical Tradition: A Compilation of Essential Texts. A free PDF of 500+ pages of the most essential critical texts about Black Power, African American history, and civil rights. (**H, TR**) bit.ly/1O0CvTj

The Black Seminoles: History of a Freedom-Seeking People, by Kenneth Porter. A book chronicling the lives of fugitive slaves who aligned themselves with the Seminole Indians in Florida beginning in the 1800s, fought in solidarity with them in the Second Seminole War, and were removed along with them to Indian Territory, where they struggled to remain free. (**H**) bit.ly/3tFoPEh

The Colored Conventions Movement: Black Organizing in the Nineteenth Century, edited by P. Gabrielle Foreman, Jim Casey, and Sarah Lynn Patterson. This volume of essays is the first to focus on the Colored Conventions movement, the 19th century's longest campaign for Black civil rights. Well before the founding of the NAACP and other 20th century pillars of the Civil Rights movement, tens of thousands of Black leaders organized state and national conventions across North America. (**H**) bit.ly/3tikshU

The Dark Fantastic: Race and the Imagination from Harry Potter to the Hunger Games, by Ebony Elizabeth Thomas. A provocative exploration of race in popular youth and young adult speculative fiction. Grounded in her experiences as a YA novelist, fanfiction writer, and scholar, Thomas considers four Black girl protagonists from some of the most popular stories of the late 20th and early 21st centuries, analyzing their narratives and audience reactions to them to reveal how these characters mirror the violence against Black and Brown people in our own world. (**H, TR**) bit.ly/2BJY6gQ

The Greatest: Muhammad Ali, by Walter Dean Myers. This book follows the extraordinary career and accomplishments of Muhammad Ali, focusing on Ali's impact on race relations inside and outside the sports world. (**M, H**) bit.ly/38xQfmR

The HistoryMakers: The Nation's Largest African American Video Oral History Collection. An easy-to-use online database of video oral history interviews with thousands of African Americans from a broad range of backgrounds and experiences. The HistoryMakers Digital Archive provides high-quality video content and fully searchable transcripts. Interviews are separated into 15 categories – Art, Civics, Education, STEM, etc. – and the corpus is searchable by subject and keyword. (**E, M, H, TR**) bit.ly/2HZSrsg

The Homestead Acts: A Primary Source Set, by Hillary Brady for the Digital Public Library of America. Primary source images, maps, and documents, additional resources, and accompanying teaching guide on the Homestead Acts. (**H**) bit.ly/2QCQLJX

The Legacy Museum and Curriculum. Opened in 2018, the Legacy Museum memorializes the enslavement of African Americans, the evolution of racial terror lynching, legalized racial segregation, and racial hierarchy in America. This museum explores the history of racial inequality and its relationship to a range of contemporary issues from mass incarceration to police violence. The second link is to the museum's curriculum on the "Legacy of Lynching." (**H, TR**) bit.ly/3rP2l2t; bit.ly/3lgrQrd

The Meaning of July Fourth for the Negro, by Frederick Douglass. See *Abolition and Slavery* section. (**M, H**) bit.ly/1xt0vT3

The Sound of Kwanzaa, by Dimitrea Tokunbo. Hear the words, sing the songs, dance to the beat, and shout "Harambee!" as you jump into this joyful celebration of the sounds of Kwanzaa! The sound is Umoja – bringing us together. The sound is Kuumba – the songs of our ancestors. The sound is Kwanzaa! Lively verse and colorful illustrations guide you through the seven principles of this festive holiday. (**E**) bit.ly/2AMDX9l

The Story of Denmark Vesey, by Thomas Wentworth Higginson for *The Atlantic*. See *Abolition and Slavery* section. (**H**) bit.ly/3vlclwi

The Story of Kwanzaa, by Donna Washington. Light the candles on the *kinara* (candelabrum)! Fly the *bendera* (flag or banner) and tell stories from Africa! The festival of Kwanzaa was originated by Dr. Maulana Karenga to honor the customs and history of African Americans. (**E**) This site includes an author essay: bit.ly/2DjGv0a

The Undefeated, by Kwame Alexander. Originally performed for ESPN's *The Undefeated*, this poem (in the form of a picture book illustrated by Kadir Nelson) is a love letter to Black life in the United States. (**E**) bit.ly/2PNXDEB

The Women Who Caught the Babies: A Story of African American Midwives, by Eloise Greenfield. This book for children highlights important aspects of the training and work of African American midwives and the ways in which they have helped, and continue to help, so many families by "catching" their babies at birth. (**E, M**) bit.ly/3wMGICZ

Thirteen Ways of Looking at a Black Boy, by Tony Medina and 13 artists. This book offers a counternarrative of Black boyhood by depicting 13 views of everyday life: young boys dressed in their Sunday best, running to catch a bus, and growing up to be teachers, all while emphasizing intergenerational, community love. (**E, M**) bit.ly/3tdfLWc

What Do You Do with a Voice Like That?: The Story of Extraordinary Congresswoman Barbara Jordan, by Chris Barton. Even as a child growing up in the 5th Ward of Houston, Texas, Barbara Jordan stood out for her big, bold, booming, crisp, clear, confident voice. It was a voice that made people sit up, stand up, and take notice. So, what do you do with a voice like that? This is a remarkable picture book biography about a woman whose struggles and mission continue to inspire today. (**E, M**) bit.ly/3gd1qpt

What We Believe: A Black Lives Matter Principles Activity Book, by Laleña Garcia and Caryn Davidson. Created by two teacher activists, the book presents the 13 guiding principles of BLM Week of Action in down-to-earth, child-friendly language, with each principle accompanied by writing prompts, space for children or adults to create their own reflections, and a coloring page. Supporting materials guide adults in sharing the principles with children and encourage kids to dream big and take action within their communities. (**E**) bit.ly/3vnbiCg

What's My Name, Fool?: Sports and Resistance in the United States, by Dave Zirin. This book examines US history with a focus on racism, sexism, and homophobia in sports, along with the profound connection between sports and patriotic nationalism. Chapter 3 focuses on Muhammad Ali, his critical consciousness and activist spirit. (**H, TR**) bit.ly/3ciCvNG

When They Call You a Terrorist (Newly Adapted Young Adult Edition): A Story of Black Lives Matter and the Power to Change the World, by Patrisse Cullors and Asha Bandele. From one of the co-founders of the Black Lives Matter movement comes a poetic memoir and reflection on humanity that reminds us that protest in the interest of the most vulnerable comes from love; that love is the push to search for justice for those victimized by the powerful. With journal entries, photos, and notes that show the formation of an activist from a very young age, this meaningful, empowering account of survival, strength, and resilience seeks to change the culture that declares innocent Black life expendable. (**M, H**) bit.ly/2Q6vOHr

African and African Diaspora History, Issues, and Rights

Africa Access. Organization whose aim is to help schools, public libraries, and parents improve the quality of their children's collections on Africa. This site includes an online database of reviews of children's books about Africa, bibliographies for research topics related to Africa, and awards for the best children's books on Africa published in the US. (**E, M, H, TR**) bit.ly/K1g9m

Freedom in Our Lifetime: South Africa's Struggle, by the CHOICES Program, Brown University. A full curriculum that explores the dilemma faced by Black South Africans in the early 1960s of how best to battle the racial discrimination imposed by the Apartheid system. Lessons include Poetry and Politics; The Soweto Uprising Through Primary Sources; Steve Biko and Black Consciousness; and more. (**H**) bit.ly/2IF1iyr

Freedom Soup, by Tami Charles. Every year, Haitians all over the world ring in the new year by eating a special soup, a tradition dating back to the Haitian Revolution. This year, Ti Gran is teaching Belle how to make the soup – Freedom Soup – just like she was taught when she was a little girl. Together, they dance and clap as they prepare the holiday feast, and Ti Gran tells Belle about the history of the soup, the history of Belle's family, and the history of Haiti, where Belle's family is from. (**E**) bit.ly/3mCzUTI

Haiti: My Country, illustrated by Rogé and written by Haitian teenagers. Stunning portraits of Haitian children, accompanied by poems written by Haitian teenagers before the earthquake of 2010. (**E, M, H**) bit.ly/2Sgl0ln

How Big Is Africa? Poster, by African Studies Outreach Program, Boston University. This website features a poster of the map of Africa with other countries superimposed to compare size. Links to other K-12 resources, as well as children's and young adult books, are also provided. (**E, M, H, TR**) bit.ly/1Qd8Uk4

I Didn't Know There Were Cities in Africa! by Learning for Justice. Article with "do's and don'ts" of teaching about modern Africa. (**E**) bit.ly/9pooY

Island Treasures: Growing Up in Cuba, by Alma Flor Ada. These true autobiographical tales from renowned Latina author and educator Alma Flor Ada are filled with family love and traditions, secrets and deep friendships, and a beautiful, emotive picture of the island of Cuba, where Alma Flor grew up. (**E**) bit.ly/2JF664T

Lesson of the Day: "A Continent Remade," by *NYTimes* Learning Network. In this lesson, students will learn about the Year of Africa in 1960, when 17 African countries declared their independence. (**H**) nyti.ms/3u1jJCj

Mama Africa!: How Miriam Makeba Spread Hope with Her Song, by Kathryn Erskine. Set defiantly in the present tense, this biography offers readers an intimate view of Makeba's fight for equality. Kathryn Erskine's call-and-response-style text and Charly Palmer's bold illustrations come together in a raw, riveting duet of protest song and praise poem. A testament to how a single voice helped to shake up the world – and can continue to do so. (**E, M**) kathrynerskine.com/book/title/mama_africa

Movers and Movements: Fighting for Social Justice in South Africa, by Brenda Randolph, published in *Putting the Movement Back into Civil Rights Teaching: A Resource Guide for Classrooms and Communities*. Teaching lesson that highlights both unsung activists and well-known people such as Miriam Makeba, associated with the Anti-Apartheid movement in South Africa. (**M, H**) bit.ly/1ziLORr

Routes of Passage: Rethinking the African Diaspora, by Ruth Simms Hamilton. A conceptual, substantive, and empirical orientation to the study of African people worldwide. The book addresses issues of geographical mobility and geosocial displacement; changing cultural, political, and economic relationships between Africa and its diaspora; inter-diaspora relations; political and economic agency and social mobilization, including cultural production and psychocultural transformation; existence in hostile and oppressive political and territorial space; and confronting interconnected relations of social inequality, especially class, gender, nationality, and race. (**H**) bit.ly/3deMc1u

Silver People: Voices From the Panama Canal, by Margarita Engle. Multiple voices in free verse share little-known stories of the thousands of workers from the Caribbean who suffered and lost their lives while building the Panama Canal. (**M**) bit.ly/1Bz0sVN; Teacher's Guide: bit.ly/2G0IqKf

Teaching About Haiti, by Teaching for Change. This page provides resources, lessons, and a link to an extensive booklist with insights into Haiti's strong history of resistance and serves as a critical tool in helping students gain an understanding of current issues. (**M, H**) bit.ly/5ONMaQ

The Legacy of Nelson Mandela, a lesson plan by AFT Human Rights. In this lesson, students explore the life and career of Nelson Mandela. With videos and other multimedia resources, students consider what it means to be a leader in difficult times. (**M, H**) bit.ly/3s5gVSH

Asian/Asian Pacific Islander/Asian American History, Issues, and Rights

A Bowl Full of Peace: A True Story, by Caren Stelson. In this moving nonfiction picture book, award-winning author Caren Stelson tells the story of Sachiko Yasui's experiences during and survival of the atomic bombing of Nagasaki and brings her message of peace to a young audience. (**E, M**) carenstelson.com/books/

A Day for Vincent Chin and Me, by Jacqueline Turner Banks. A chapter book for young readers about a Japanese American child's efforts to slow down the traffic on a residential street in Kentucky, while his mother organizes the Asian American community to draw attention to the death of Vincent Chin, whom his murderers blamed for Detroit's declining car sales and soaring unemployment. (**E**) bit.ly/30JtdoS

A Different Mirror for Young People: A History of Multicultural America (For Young People Series), by Ronald Takaki and Rebecca Stefoff. Drawing on Takaki's vast array of primary sources, and staying true to his own words whenever possible, *A Different Mirror for Young People* brings ethnic history alive through the words of people, including teenagers, who recorded their experiences in letters, diaries, and poems. (**M, H**) bit.ly/2S3p3pa

A Map into the World, by Kao Kalia Yang. As the seasons change, so too does a young Hmong girl's world. She moves into a new home with her family and encounters both birth and death. As this curious girl explores life inside her house and beyond, she collects bits of the natural world. But who are her treasures for? (**E, M**) lernerbooks.com/shop/show/17915; link to author video: bit.ly/324DeO2

After Atlanta: Teaching About Asian American Identity and History, by Elizabeth Kleinrock for Learning for Justice. One elementary classroom teacher shares the conversation she started with students the day after the attacks in Atlanta and recommends resources anyone can use to teach about Asian American history and identity. (**TR**) bit.ly/3dzuG77

Ahimsa, by Supriya Kelkar. In 1942, after Mahatma Gandhi asked Indians to give one family member to the Freedom movement, 10-year-old Anjali is devastated to think of her father risking his life for the freedom struggle. But it turns out he isn't the one joining. Anjali's mother is. And with this change comes many more adjustments designed to improve their country and use "ahimsa" – non-violent resistance – to stand up to the British government. (**M, H**) Teacher's guide from Lee & Low Books here: leeandlow.com/books/ahimsa

Amend: The Fight for America. In this Netflix series, Will Smith hosts this documentary that examines the evolving, often lethal, fight for equal rights in America through the lens of the US Constitution's 14th Amendment. Episode 4 focuses on immigration with a long segment on the Chinese Exclusion act. (**M, H**) bit.ly/3qKZiHs

Arundhati Roy: A Digital Collection of Interviews and Conversations, assembled by Alternative Radio: Audio Energy for Democracy. An amazing audio collection of interviews and other conversations with Roy, all linked for easy access. The first program linked is a conversation between Arundhati Roy and Howard Zinn recorded in 2002. Other topics include "Confronting Empire," "A Writer's Place in Politics," "Surviving the Future," and many more. (**H**) alternativeradio.org/speaker/arundhati-roy

Asian American Books, by Teaching for Change. An extensive catalog of books compiled by Social Justice Books. (**E, M, H, TR**) bit.ly/2RV6cwq

Asian American Racial Justice Toolkit. From the organizers: "This toolkit represents the work and thinking of 15 grassroots organizations with Asian American bases living in the most precarious margins of power: low-income tenants, youth, undocumented immigrants, low-wage workers, refugees, women and girls, and queer and trans people. It reflects their experiences with criminalization, deportation, homophobia, xenophobia and Islamo-racism, war, gender violence, poverty, and worker exploitation. All of the modules are designed to begin with people's lived experiences, and to build structural awareness of why those experiences are happening, and how they are tied to the oppression of others." **(TR)** asianamtoolkit.org

Asian/Asian American Children's Books, Lee & Low Books. A collection of titles from Lee and Low publishers that highlight the diversity of Asian and Asian American identities. (**E, TR**) leeandlow.com/cultures/asian-asian-american-interest

Bringing in the New Year! By Grace Lin. This exuberant story follows a Chinese American family as they prepare for the Lunar New Year. Each member of the family lends a hand as they sweep out the dust of the old year, hang decorations, and make dumplings. (**E**) bit.ly/2SkTYJp

Coolies, by Yin. Shek marvels at the new world as he and his brother, Little Wong, arrive in California. Along with hundreds of other workers, the brothers are going to build a great railroad across the West. Inspired by actual events, this story reveals the harsh truth about life for the Chinese railroad workers in 1865, while celebrating their perseverance and bravery. (**E, M**) bit.ly/2Rc5En1; lesson plans to accompany the book at yinauthorvisits.com

Exclusion: Chinese in 19th Century America, a lesson plan by Debbie Wei for Teaching for Change. A comprehensive lesson plan that supports students in learning about the lives and contributions of Chinese immigrants in the US in the 19th century, and analyzing the roots of anti-immigrant sentiment, which led to the passage of the Chinese Exclusion Acts. (**H**) teachingforchange.org/exclusionact

Eyes that Kiss in the Corners, by Joanna Ho. A young Asian girl notices that her eyes look different from those of her peers. They have big, round eyes and long lashes. She realizes that her eyes are like her mother's, her grandmother's, and her little sister's. Drawing from the strength of these powerful women in her life, she recognizes her own beauty and discovers a path to self-love and empowerment. This powerful, poetic picture book will resonate with readers of all ages. (**E**) bit.ly/3fJq68X

Fish for Jimmy: Inspired by One Family's Experience in a Japanese American Internment Camp, by Katie Yamasaki. With the family forced to leave their home and go to an internment camp, Jimmy loses his appetite. Older brother Taro takes matters into his own hands and, night after night, sneaks out of the camp and catches fresh fish for Jimmy to help make him strong again. This affecting tale of courage and love is an adaptation of the author's true family story and includes a letter to readers with more information about the historical background and inspiration. (**E, M**) bit.ly/3mgFwTB

Fred Korematsu Speaks Up, by Laura Atkins and Stan Yogi. The first in a new series of middle-grade books about civil rights and s/heroes, this book covers how Fred Korematsu first evaded and then fought the incarceration of Japanese Americans during World War II all the way to the Supreme Court. (**E, M**) bit.ly/30Ly0Wx

From a Whisper to a Rallying Cry: The Killing of Vincent Chin and the Trial That Galvanized the Asian American Movement, by Paula Yoo. This book examines the outrage from the Asian American community after Chin's murderers received only a $3,000 fine and three years of probation. A suspenseful portrait of a pivotal moment in civil rights history, and of a man who became a symbol against hatred and racism. (**H**) bit.ly/3c0UQ34

Gaijin: American Prisoner of War, by Matt Faulkner. With a White mother and a Japanese father, Koji Miyamoto quickly realizes that his home in San Francisco is no longer a welcoming one after Pearl Harbor is attacked. And once he's sent to an internment camp, he learns that being half White at the camp is just as difficult as being half Japanese on the streets of an American city during WWII. Koji's story is based on true events from the author's family. (**E, M, H**) bit.ly/3dMxPAA

Going Home, Coming Home, by Truong Tran. This summer, Ami Chi is taking a trip to Vietnam, where the streets are crowded with zipping scooters and fruit is shaped like dragons and stars. To her parents, Vietnam is still home – a home they haven't seen since they left during the war. But all this talk of going back home leaves Ami Chi confused. How can you go back home to a place you've never been? (**E**) bit.ly/3g8fiS3

Haiku and Hiroshima: Teaching About the Atomic Bomb, by Wayne Au. Lesson for high school students on the bombing of Hiroshima, using haiku and the film *Barefoot Gen*. (**H**) bit.ly/2SdYmL4

Humanizing Asian Americans in the Classroom Through Children's Literature, by Monisha Bajaj, Learning for Justice. Too often, Asian American stories are absent from classroom libraries. In this article, one educator explains why this gap is so harmful and recommends ways to fix it. (**TR**) bit.ly/31Oas43

In the Shadow of My Country: A Japanese American Artist Remembers, by Densho. One Japanese American family's memories of living behind barbed wire during World War II are captured in this bilingual multimedia website. The acclaimed artist Roger Shimomura, who was held at Minidoka, Idaho as a 3-year-old, found inspiration in his grandmother's journals. A virtual exhibition, *In the Shadow of My Country* displays the artist's sharply ironic paintings tempered by the grandmother's patient, hopeful words. Complementing the central images are photos of daily life in the detention camps, an interview with the artist, and quotations of Japanese Americans incarcerated as children. (**E, M, H**) Teacher's guide to the exhibit included here: densho.org/in-the-shadow-of-my-country

Landed, by Milly Lee. *Landed* tells the story of Sun, a young Chinese man who emigrates to America during the age of the Chinese Exclusion Act. Lee based the story on that of her father-in-law and provides useful historical background information. (**E**) bit.ly/2qne0rv

Memories of the 1982 ILGWU Strike in New York's Chinatown, a firsthand account by Katie Quan. An essay by a labor organizer who participated in the largest strike in the history of New York's Chinatown, with accompanying images and related links for further reading. (**H**) bit.ly/3eDI3Vw

My Footprints, by Bao Phi. Every child feels different in some way, but Thuy feels "double different." She is Vietnamese American and she has two moms. Thuy walks home one winter afternoon, angry and lonely after a bully's taunts. Then a bird catches her attention and sets Thuy on an imaginary exploration. What if she could fly away like a bird? What if she could sprint like a deer, or roar like a bear? Mimicking the footprints of each creature in the snow, she makes her way home to the arms of her moms. (**E**) bit.ly/3wJBsjm

Never Give Up!: Minoru Yasui and the Fight for Justice, a documentary film by Holly Yasui and Will Doolittle. This award-winning documentary explores the life of Minoru (Min) Yasui, born in Hood River, Oregon in 1916 of immigrant parents. He was the first Japanese American attorney in Oregon. During World War II, he initiated a legal test case by deliberately violating military orders that led to the incarceration of more than 110,000 persons of Japanese ancestry in concentration camps. He spent nine months in solitary confinement awaiting his appeal to the US Supreme Court, which ruled against him. The film depicts his family's wartime experiences in the temporary detention centers and the Tule Lake and Minidoka concentration camps. (**M, H**) minoruyasuifilm.org

Picture Books with Asian Characters, by No Time for Flash Cards. This annotated elementary book list was created in response to the rise in anti-Asian violence in 2021 as a way to support teachers in ensuring representation as one step in anti-bias education. (**E**) bit.ly/3vMDJdh

Remembering 1882: Fighting for Civil Rights in the Shadow of the Chinese Exclusion Act, by the Chinese Historical Society of America. Multimedia resources, timeline, notable quotes, and images that support teaching and learning about the Chinese Exclusion Act. (**E, M, H**) civilrightssuite.org/1882

Righting a Wrong: Japanese Americans and World War II, by the National

Museum of American History. Based on an exhibition that was on view at the National Museum of American History, this website offers artifacts and primary resources on Japanese immigration, executive order 9066, and life in internment camps and beyond. (**E, M, H**) s.si.edu/3r9LW7v

The Little Book of Hindu Deities: From the Goddess of Wealth to the Sacred Cow, by Sanjay Patel. Pixar animator and Academy Award-nominated director Sanjay Patel brings to life Hinduism's most important gods and goddesses (and one sacred stone) in fun, full-color illustrations, each accompanied by a short, lively profile. (**E**) bit.ly/2D23VXI

They Called Us Enemy, by George Takai. In this autobiographical graphic novel, actor, author, and activist George Takei recounts his childhood imprisoned in American concentration camps during World War II. (**M, H**) bit.ly/3eEIaSf

Us vs. Them – The Chinese Exclusion Act of 1882, by The National Museum of American History. This lesson plan is a case study that establishes what "exclusion" in immigration law looked like, particularly in the late 19th and early 20th centuries. Students will explore the selective and racist nature of quotas and their impact on the US population. Reading arguments made in Congress and reflected in political cartoons, students analyze the attitudes and beliefs about "others" undergirding restrictive immigration policies. (**M, H**) s.si.edu/3eYohog

Vietnamese Americans: Lessons in American History, by Learning for Justice. This curriculum guide sheds light on the complexities of the Vietnamese American experience. (**M, H**) bit.ly/9Q1L0r

We Are Not a Stereotype: Breaking Down Asian Pacific Islander Bias, a video series by The Smithsonian Asian Pacific American Center. This series explores and challenges the complexity surrounding the term Asian Pacific American, breaking it down into topics that span multiple timelines, geographies, and identities. (**H**) bit.ly/3r2sObD

We Are Not Free, a book of Young Adult Fiction by Traci Chee. For 14-year-old budding artist Minoru Ito, her two brothers, her friends, and the other members of the Japanese American community in southern California, the three months since Pearl Harbor was attacked have become a waking nightmare: attacked, spat on, and abused with no way to retaliate – and now things are about to get worse, their lives forever changed by the mass incarcerations in the relocation camps. (**M, H**) tracichee.com/we-are-not-free

We Too Sing America: South Asian, Arab, Muslim, and Sikh Immigrants Shape Our Multiracial Future, by Deepa Iyer. Renowned activist Deepa Iyer asks whether hate crimes should be considered domestic terrorism and explores the role of the state in perpetuating racism through detentions, national registration programs, police profiling, and constant surveillance. Reframing the discussion of race in America, she addresses the complexity and diversity of the South Asian community and provides ideas from the front lines of post-9/11 America. (**H**) bit.ly/1KtM1pM

Write to Me: Letters from Japanese American Children to the Librarian They Left Behind, by Cynthia Grady. Through the three years of their internment, the children correspond with Miss Breed, sharing their stories, providing feedback on books, and creating a record of their experiences. Using excerpts from children's letters held at the Japanese American National Museum, author Cynthia Grady presents a difficult subject with honesty and hope. (**E, M**) bit.ly/3d8XLY9

Civil Rights, Black Power, Student and 1960s Movements

African Americans Against the Bomb: Nuclear Weapons, Colonialism, and the Black Freedom Movement, by Vincent Intondi. Some of the earliest and strongest protests against nuclear weapons came from activists in the Black Freedom movement. Intondi's research reveals that decades ago, Black activists recognized the convergence of domestic and foreign policy issues. (**H**) bit.ly/3mXcKHK

Civil Rights Martyrs, by the Civil Rights Memorial. Chronology briefly describing the lives of martyrs of the Civil Rights movement – activists who were targeted for death because of their civil rights work, random victims of vigilantes determined to halt the movement, and individuals who, in the sacrifice of their own lives, brought new awareness to the struggle. (**M, H, TR**) bit.ly/1oWUxuX

Congress of Racial Equality (CORE), by Digital SNCC Gateway. Background information with hyperlinked additional information throughout, and multimedia primary sources related to the Student Nonviolent Coordinating Committee (SNCC) and CORE, and their work together in the South. (**M, H**) bit.ly/3dvMph7

Getting Away with Murder: The True Story of the Emmett Till Case, by Chris Crowe. See *African American History, Issues, and Rights* section. (**H**) zinnedproject.org/materials/getting-away-with-murder

Liberation Curriculum, by the Martin Luther King, Jr. Research and Education Institute. See *African American History, Issues, and Rights* section. (**H**) stanford.io/1DNVv1M

Mahalia, a film produced by Robin Roberts. A Lifetime Channel biopic featuring the life and accomplishments of Mahalia Jackson, starring Danielle Brooks. (**M, H**) bit.ly/3rL2OTr

Mighty Justice: The Untold Story of Civil Rights Trailblazer Dovey Johnson Roundtree, by Katie McCabe, adapted for young readers by Jabari Asim. A young reader's adaptation of the memoir of activist and trailblazer Dovey Johnson Roundtree. She was one of the first Black women to break the racial and gender barriers in the US Army; a fierce attorney in the segregated courtrooms of Washington, DC; and a minister in the AME church, where women had never before been ordained as clergy. In 1955, Roundtree won a landmark bus desegregation case that eventually helped end "separate but equal" and dismantle Jim Crow laws across the South. (**E, M**) bit.ly/32dGdDG

Open Wide the Freedom Gates: A Memoir, by Dorothy Height. In her memoir, Dr. Height, at the age of 91, reflects on a life of service and leadership. We witness her childhood encounters with racism and the thrill of New York college life during the Harlem Renaissance. We see her protest the lynching of Black people. We sit with her onstage as Martin Luther King, Jr. delivers his "I Have a Dream" speech. And we watch as she leads the National Council of Negro Women for 41 years during which her diplomatic counsel was sought by presidents from Eisenhower to Clinton. (**H**) https://n.pr/3diUnd0

Putting the Movement Back into Civil Rights Teaching, by Deborah Menkart, Alana Murray, and Jenice L. View. See *African American History, Issues, and Rights* section. (**E, M, H**) bit.ly/1iv4HhU

SNCC Digital Gateway, by the SNCC Legacy Project and the Duke Center for Documentary Studies. The SNCC Digital Gateway documentary website provides profiles, stories, a timeline, map, and much more about the Student Nonviolent Coordinating Committee. This is an invaluable classroom resource on the voting rights struggle and the overall fight for human rights and democracy in the United States. (**M, H, TR**) bit.ly/2FKYfmM

Teaching SNCC: The Organization at the Heart of the Civil Rights Revolution, Teaching Activity by Adam Sanchez. In this series of role plays, students explore the history and evolution of the Student Nonviolent Coordinating Committee, including freedom rides and voter registration. Click "download to read in full" and register for a free account to access full lesson. (**H**) bit.ly/3bJnpC1

The Albany Movement: A Collection of Papers and Resources, from the MLK, Jr. Research and Education Institute, Stanford University. Shining light on the lesser known Albany Movement coalition, this collection of information, resources, and primary source documents includes Dr. King's diary entries from an Albany jail, an "Albany Manifesto," and other key documents. (**H, TR**) kinginstitute.stanford.edu/mlk-topic/albany-movement

The Black Panthers: Vanguard of the Revolution, by Stanley Nelson. The first feature-length documentary to explore the Black Panther Party, its significance to the broader American culture, its cultural and political awakening for Black people, and the painful lessons wrought when a movement is derailed. Guide for educators included. (**H, TR**) pbs.org/1ol7BE6; bit.ly/1ooi5Zk

The Huey P. Newton Reader, edited by David Hilliard and Donald Weise. The first comprehensive collection of writings by the Black Panther Party founder and revolutionary icon of the Black Liberation era, this reader combines now-classic texts with previously unpublished writings from the Black Panther Party archives and Newton's private collection. (**H**) bit.ly/2Q3UzUJ

The Port Huron Statement, from *Resistance and Revolution: The Anti-Vietnam War Movement at the University of Michigan*. This page captures an exhibit of primary source documents, interviews, and other multimedia teaching resources related to the Port Huron Statement written by the Students for a Democratic Society in the early 1960s. (**H**) bit.ly/32nhQ6z

The Speech: The Story Behind Dr. Martin Luther King Jr.'s Dream, by Gary Younge. Younge brings to life the fascinating chronicle of King's "I Have a Dream" speech and other events surrounding the March on Washington. The book is short, engaging, accessible, and contains thoughtful analyses of race and racism in America in the 50 years since the march. (**H, TR**) bit.ly/19JfxW2

Troublemaker for Justice: The Story of Bayard Rustin, the Man Behind the March on Washington, by Jacqueline Houtman, Walter Naegle, and Michael G. Long. A biography for young adult readers about one of the most influential activists of our time, who was an early advocate for both African American and gay rights. (**E, M**) bit.ly/2Q0nSHA

What We Don't Learn About the Black Panther Party — but Should, a teaching activity By Adam Sanchez and Jesse Hagopian for Zinn Education Project. This mixer role play introduces students to the pivotal and largely untold history of the Black Panthers. Students are given a role with a thumbnail sketch of that person's biography along with details that help illuminate aspects of the party. (**H**) bit.ly/3ctdBuX

'What We Want, What We Believe': Teaching with the Black Panthers' Ten Point Program, Teaching Activity, by Wayne Au. This lesson leads students to study the Black Panthers' Ten Point Program to help assess issues in their own communities and to develop Ten Point Programs of their own. (**H**) bit.ly/KbuoS7

Disability History Issues, and Rights

10 Quick Ways to Analyze Children's Books for Ableism, by Chloë Myers and Hank Bersani, Jr. This article from Rethinking Schools gives teachers the tools to become aware of the omission of persons with disabilities in children's literature. This exclusion decreases the likelihood that the histories, experiences, or feelings of people with disabilities will be discussed in our classrooms. (**TR**) bit.ly/2qk6Nb2

All He Knew, by Helen Frost. A novel in verse about a young deaf boy during World War II, the sister who loves him, and the conscientious objector who helps him. Inspired by true events. (**M, H**) bit.ly/39HC4vZ

Being Heumann: An Unrepentant Memoir of a Disability Rights Activist, by Judith Heumann with Kristen Joiner. One of the most influential disability rights activists in US history tells her personal story of fighting for the right to receive an education, have a job, and just be human. (**H**) beacon.org/Being-Heumann-P1691.aspx

Classroom Resources on Disability, by the Nora Project. Free, linked resources for both classrooms and families to support the work of disability awareness and inclusion. (**E, TR**) bit.ly/3uFkLDP

Crip Camp, a film by Nicole Newnham and James LeBrecht. A powerful documentary about a summer camp for children with disabilities in the 1970s, which traces how the independence and experience of the campers helped them create a loose network that contributed to the Disability Rights movement. Website includes lesson plans. (**M, H**) cripcamp.com

Disability History Museum. This site was designed "to promote understanding about the historical experience of people with disabilities by recovering, chronicling, and interpreting their stories." This searchable collection offers documents and images related to disability history in the United States. (**M, H, TR**) bit.ly/JAD9r

Disability Social History Project. This site contains a wealth of information, including a list of "Famous and Not So Famous" people with disabilities, a timeline, and a history of the word "handicapped" via the Serendipity link. (**E, M, H**) bit.ly/163FXqn

History Through Deaf Eyes, by Gallaudet University. The DEAF EYES project at Gallaudet University was established to bring Deaf history to the public and expand our understanding of the Deaf community in the US. It includes an online exhibition, a book, and a documentary film. (**M, H**) bit.ly/U73AW2

I'm Here, by Peter Reynolds and Southwest Autism Research and Resource Center (SARRC). This short film, based on an original story and art by Peter H. Reynolds, and produced by FableVision, movingly conveys the loneliness that children on the autism spectrum often experience, and the life-changing impact each of us can have when we reach out and embrace them. (**E**) bit.ly/2jUTt8m

Mad in America: Bad Science, Bad Medicine, and the Enduring Mistreatment of the Mentally Ill, by Robert Whitaker. A haunting, deeply compassionate book, updated with a new introduction and prologue, bringing in the latest medical treatments and trends, this book raises important questions about our obligations to the mad, the meaning of "insanity," and what we value most about the human mind. (**H, TR**) bit.ly/2PAvcto

Museum of disABILITY History. This site features an extensive virtual exhibition of images that help raise awareness of people with disabilities and their contributions to society. Lesson plans on disability-related topics for all grade levels are also provided. (**E, M, H**) bit.ly/1jDKHWi

My Brother Charlie, by Holly Robinson Peete and Ryan Elizabeth Peete. In this story, told from a sister's point of view, we meet a family whose oldest son – who is autistic – teaches them important lessons about togetherness, hope, tolerance, and love. (**E**) bit.ly/2kl0mNa

My Friend Isabelle, by Eliza Woloson. This is a story about Charlie and Isabelle's friendship. At first, Charlie sees only the differences between him and Isabelle, who has Down Syndrome, but in the end, he recognizes all the similarities they share. Book description is on 6 Elements of Social Justice Ed. Book Blog, which offers a summary of this book and other social justice children's literature titles. (**E**) bit.ly/154hueW

My Left Foot, a film by Jim Sheridan. Christy Brown was born with cerebral palsy to a large, poor Irish family. His mother recognized the intelligence and humanity in the boy everyone else regarded as a "vegetable." Eventually, Christy matured into a cantankerous artist who used his dexterous left foot to write and paint. Daniel Day Lewis won an Oscar for his portrayal of Brown in this film. (**M, H**) Streamable on HBOMax or Amazon: amzn.to/3x38Txr

Observing Deaf History Month, by Alexandra Gomez. This article provides information about milestones in Deaf history, as well as links to fiction and nonfiction books about deaf people. (**M, H, TR**) on.nypl.org/VDs76u

Raising Deaf Kids: A Book List. A compilation of children's books about hearing loss and deafness. (**E, M**) bit.ly/2ds3xCR

Resources from The Abolition and Disability Justice Coalition. Guiding principles, shareables, and other resources related to alternatives to policing based in disability justice. (**H, TR**) abolitionanddisabilityjustice.com

Skin, Tooth, and Bone: The Basis of Movement Is Our People: A Disability Justice Primer, by Sins Invalid. Provides an overview of what disability justice is, and more important, what it can become, through the use of art, quotes, conversation, poetry, and more. Sins Invalid published this guide as a resource for activists and disabled and D/deaf communities to reclaim the term "disability justice" for queer and gender nonconforming disabled People of Color, who originated the movement. **(H, TR)** bit.ly/2Gmsi4U

Temple Grandin. This movie was shown on HBO as a mini-series. It chronicles the life of Temple Grandin, a woman with autism, who revolutionized livestock handling in the USA and has written several books about her life with autism. (**M, H**) itsh.bo/bmNqNc

The Sound of Colors: A Journey of the Imagination, by Jimmy Liao. This story follows the narrator, a woman who has lost her sight, through her journey around the city. She navigates the subway and the city she knows with language and descriptions that tap into her imagination as well as her innermost thoughts and feelings. (**E**) bit.ly/2s4hwaV

The William Hoy Story: How a Deaf Baseball Player Changed the Game, by Nancy Churnin. All William Ellsworth Hoy wanted to do was play baseball. After losing out on a spot on the local deaf team, William practiced even harder, eventually earning a position on a professional team. But his struggle was far from over. In addition to the prejudice Hoy faced, he could not hear the umpires' calls. One day he asked the umpire to use hand signals: strike, ball, out. That day he not only got on base but also changed the way the game was played forever. This account may not be entirely accurate, but it makes an interesting story. (**E, M**) nancychurnin.com/readme

Environmental Justice Issues

A Fierce Green Fire: Love Canal: Children and Toxic Waste, a film by American Masters. The one-hour documentary chronicles one of the largest movements of the 20th century. *A Fierce Green Fire* spans 50 years of grassroots and global activism from the 1960s to 2009 and connects the major causes of environmentalism, from conservation to climate change. First link includes clips from the film; the second link is to teacher resources. (**H**) to.pbs.org/2Omdq9l; bit.ly/2u1FHvk

A People's Curriculum for the Earth: Teaching Climate Change and the Environmental Crisis, edited by Bill Bigelow and Tim Swinehart, *Rethinking Schools*. This book features some of the best articles from *Rethinking Schools* magazine, along with classroom-friendly readings on climate change, energy, water, food, and pollution, as well as on people who are working to improve the environment. (**E, M, H**) bit.ly/1VKElav

A Tale of Two Cities, by The Story of Stuff Project. This film tells the story of citizens from two very different Michigan communities – picturesque, small town Evart, and gritty, industrial Flint – that have found their futures inextricably linked by a threat to the one thing that all life requires: water. This short documentary explores the growing threat of water privatization and what happens when government runs a critical function, like providing clean drinking water, as if it were a business. (**M, H**) bit.ly/2LJg0nr

Analyzing Environmental Justice, by Learning for Justice. This lesson helps students understand how pollution disproportionately affects people who are poor and members of racial and ethnic minorities. It also teaches them how to use a map to locate environmental injustice. (**M, H**) bit.ly/39AiJN6

As Long as Grass Grows: The Indigenous Fight for Environmental Justice, from Colonization to Standing Rock, by Dina Gilio-Whitaker. Through the unique lens of "Indigenized environmental justice," Indigenous researcher and activist Dina Gilio-Whitaker explores the fraught history of treaty violations, struggles for food and water security, and protection of sacred sites, while highlighting the important leadership of Indigenous women in this centuries-long struggle. (**H**) bit.ly/3mlDxgF

As We Have Always Done: Indigenous Freedom Through Radical Resistance, by Leanne Betasamosake Simpson. Across North America, Indigenous acts of resistance have in recent years opposed the removal of federal protections for forests and waterways in Indigenous lands, halted the expansion of tar sands extraction and the pipeline construction at Standing Rock, and demanded justice for murdered and missing Indigenous women. In *As We Have Always Done*, Simpson identifies Indigenous political resurgence as a practice rooted in uniquely Indigenous theorizing, writing, organizing, and thinking. (**H**) akpress.org/aswehavealwaysdone

Buried Sunlight: How Fossil Fuels Have Changed the Earth, by Molly Bang and Penny Chisholm. Using simple language and breathtaking paintings, Bang and Chisholm present a clear, concise explanation of the fossil fuel energy cycle that began with the sun and now runs most of our transportation and energy use in our world. Readers will be mesmerized by this engaging fourth book in the award-winning Sunlight Series by Bang and Chisholm. (**E, M**) bit.ly/3ucdDia

Cast Away: Poems for Our Time, by Naomi Shihab Nye. With poems about food wrappers, lost mittens, plastic straws, refugee children, trashy talk, the environment, connection, community, esponsibility to the planet, politics, mmigration, time, junk mail, trash collectors, garbage trucks, all that we carry and all that we discard, this is a ich, engaging, moving, and sometimes humorous collection for readers ages 12 to adult. (**M, H**) bit.ly/2PwZGwz

Debate Kit: Is Animal Agriculture Harmful to the Environment? by PETA. "Here at PETA, our core belief is that animals are not ours to use. We know that many schools assign debates on topical issues to help their students learn to speak and write persuasively, develop research skills, and recognize multiple sides of a controversial or multifaceted issue. The impact of various industries on the environment is certainly one such topic. This student debate kit lists a variety of resources that can be shared with students to support the argument that animal agriculture is harmful to the environment and that eating vegan is one solution." (**H**) bit.ly/3mKugyR

Don't Take Our Voices Away: A Role Play on the Indigenous Peoples' Global Summit on Climate Change, by Julie Treick O'Neill and Tim Swinehart. This role play on the Indigenous Peoples' Global Summit on Climate Change asks students to develop a list of demands to present to the rest of the world at a mock climate change meeting. (**H**) bit.ly/2l5qxg2

Earth Democracy: Justice, Sustainability, and Peace, by Vandana Shiva. World-renowned environmental activist and physicist Vandana Shiva calls for a radical shift in the values that govern democracies, condemning the role that unrestricted capitalism has played in the destruction of environments and livelihoods. (**H**) bit.ly/3vr7zCT

Editorial Cartoons: Poverty/ Environmental Justice, by Learning for Justice. The fourth lesson in the series "Using Editorial Cartoons to Teach Social Justice," this lesson plan engages students in analyzing editorial cartoons about environmental injustice. The cartoons help students understand the disproportionate share of environmental problems people in poverty face, too often living near environmentally undesirable and dangerous places. (**M, H**) bit.ly/3fYPvvo

Got Coal? Teaching About the Most Dangerous Rock in America, by Bill Bigelow. This teaching activity gives students the opportunity to play and analyze a game created by The American Coal Foundation. Students will also write from different perspectives and watch excerpts from films to expand their knowledge of coal mining and think critically about the industry's motives and goals. (**H, TR**) bit.ly/2n9WMxu

How One Woman Fought One of the World's Biggest Oil Companies and Won, a story recorded for *Living on Earth* by Reid Frazier and Jared Goyette. A 2015 audio profile and interview with Margie Richard, the former middle school teacher who founded Concerned Citizens of Norco in 2002, suing Shell Oil for issues related to environmental racism. (**M, H**) bit.ly/3n1gRCS

How to Change Everything: The Young Human's Guide to Protecting the Planet and Each Other, by Naomi Klein, adapted for young readers by Rebecca Stefoff. Full of empowering stories of young leaders all over the world, this information-packed book from award-winning journalist and one of the foremost voices for climate justice, Naomi Klein, offers young readers a comprehensive look at the state of the climate today and how we got here, while also providing the tools they need to join the fight to protect and reshape the planet they will inherit. (**H**) bit.ly/2S19nnJ

Meet the Children of Rio, from Reframing Rio. These lessons were designed to introduce young people to the UN Rio Earth Summits and the concept of sustainable development. The lessons focus on the films in the *Zero Ten Twenty* series which followed 11 children in 10 different countries over 20 years. How have their lives changed over the 20 years since the original Earth Summit? What is it like growing up in the 21st century? How have their lives been affected by environmental, economic, and social changes? Explore these issues in the eight lesson plans. (**E, M, H**) bit.ly/32tH1Ew

No Planet B: A Teen Vogue Guide to the Climate Crisis, edited by Lucy Diavolo. An urgent call for climate justice from *Teen Vogue*, one of this generation's leading voices, using an intersectional lens – with critical feminist, Indigenous, antiracist and internationalist perspectives. As the political classes watch our world burn, a new movement of young people is rising to meet the challenge of climate catastrophe. This book is a guide, a toolkit, a warning, and a cause for hope. (**M, H**) bit.ly/3mnvAHQ

One Earth: People of Color Protecting Our Planet, by Anuradha Rao. *One Earth* profiles Black, Indigenous and People of Color who live and work as environmental defenders. Through their individual stories, the book shows that the intersection of environment and ethnicity is an asset to achieving environmental goals. The 20 short biographies introduce readers to diverse activists of all ages and ethnicities from all around the world. (**M, H**) bit.ly/2PVZ4jP

Poisoned Water: How the Citizens of Flint, Michigan Fought for Their Lives and Warned the Nation, by Candy Cooper and Marc Aronson. Based on original reporting by a Pulitzer Prize finalist and an industry veteran, this is the first book for young adults about the Flint water crisis. The book shows not just how the crisis unfolded in 2014, but also the history of racism and segregation that led up to it, the beliefs and attitudes that fueled it, and how the people of Flint fought – and are still fighting – for clean water and healthy lives. (**M, H**) bit.ly/3fDy8QT

Race, Poverty, and the Environment. This journal links issues of racism and poverty with environmental justice. Some recent resources are available for free download; older resources are available for purchase. (**H, TR**) bit.ly/1r0QFKy

Standing with Standing Rock: A Role Play on the Dakota Access Pipeline, by Ursula Wolfe-Rocca, Bill Bigelow, and Andrew Duden. This role play helps students recognize the issues at stake in the historic struggle of the Standing Rock Sioux to block construction of the Dakota Access Pipeline. (**E, M, H**) bit.ly/2j9JkW3

Standing with Standing Rock: Voices from the #NoDAPL Movement, edited by Nick Estes and Jaskiran Dhillon. Amid the Standing Rock movement to protect the land and the water that millions depend on for life, the Oceti Sakowin (the Dakota, Nakota, and Lakota people) reunited. Through poetry and prose, essays, photography, interviews, and polemical interventions, the contributors reflect on Indigenous history and politics and on the movement's significance. Their work challenges our understanding of colonial history not simply as "lessons learned" but as essential guideposts for activism. (**H**) bit.ly/3fZbtys

The Feminization of Earth First! By Judi Bari. Firsthand account by Judi Bari, a feminist, union organizer, and environmental activist, about her experience organizing with men for environmental change, and the role of toxic masculinity, misogyny, and violence in social action work. This essay is part of a tremendous collection of first-person writing by activists, available at a site called *History Is a Weapon.* (**H**) bit.ly/2FRb8wq

The Story of Stuff, by Annie Leonard. *A* 20-minute, free downloadable video that explores consumption and exposes the connections between various environmental and social issues, while providing suggestions for action. (**E, M, H**) Website: bit.ly/vXj7EC; Reading Guide: bit.ly/1TQdXO0

The World According to Monsanto. A French documentary that looks at the domination of the agricultural industry by one of the world's most powerful companies. (**H, TR**) bit.ly/37hc1Zi

Tools for Life: A Start-Up Guide for Youth Recycling & Bicycling Programs, by Transportation Alternatives. This website has a guide for helping youth to start bicycle recycling programs based on the successful NYC Recycle-a-Bicycle program. Includes curricula and resources. (**H**) bit.ly/cC94Dh

We Are Water Protectors, by Carole Lindstrom. Inspired by the many Indigenous-led movements across North America, *We Are Water Protectors* issues an urgent rallying cry to safeguard the Earth's water from harm and corruption. A bold and lyrical picture book written by Carole Lindstrom and vibrantly illustrated by Michaela Goade. (**E**) bit.ly/2AeJ2tH

What Is a National Park? A lesson plan from the National Park Service. Students analyze the arrowhead logo as an introduction to the National Park Service. They learn how the design of the National Park Service arrowhead is made up of symbols, and then have a chance to create their own designs specific to their own states. They then learn ways that we can help care for our parks through the seven "Leave No Trace" principles, helping students to understand that the National Parks are our collective responsibility. (**E**) bit.ly/2QpNzkP

What is Environmental Justice? by Learning for Justice. In this lesson plan for young children, students explore the concept of environmental racism and learn about various environmental hazards that disproportionately affect communities of Color. (**E**) bit.ly/3lkpDuH

Genocide

Children's Books About the Holocaust, by the United States Holocaust Memorial Museum. An annotated bibliography compiled to guide parents, educators, and young readers to children's books about the Holocaust and related subjects. (**E, M**) bit.ly/2ImkJJH

Confronting Genocide: Never Again? by The Choices Program. This site contains supplemental materials to a unit that examines how the US responded to five instances of genocide, including the Armenian genocide. Materials include videos, maps, graphic organizers, surveys, and web links. (**M, H**) bit.ly/136NnUk

Forsaken Cries: The Story of Rwanda, by The Video Project, *Facing History and Ourselves*. A 35-minute documentary that explores the roots of the conflict in Rwanda that led to the genocide of nearly one million Tutsi people by Hutu military extremists beginning in April 1994. *Forsaken Cries* incorporates historical footage from the nation's colonial period with recent survivor interviews. Among the issues the video explores are international genocide laws, the failure of the international community to intervene in the genocide, the refugee crisis, and the War Crimes Tribunal. (**H**) bit.ly/3u10Tvb

The Diary of Anne Frank, Teacher's Guide, by PBS and Facing History and Ourselves. This guide is a detailed curriculum resource that accompanies the PBS Masterpiece Classic series, *The Diary of Anne Frank*. The guide is aimed at middle school and high school teachers. Together the film and guide can serve as a key element within a larger unit on World War II, Holocaust studies, or coming-of-age literature in social studies, history, English, and writing courses. (**H, TR**) bit.ly/3eWwoli

U.S. Holocaust Memorial Museum. USHMM provides resources for students and educators. It includes samples of primary documents and suggested lessons and activities for students and teachers. (**E, M, H, TR**) bit.ly/A0dotD

Hate and Oppression

American Islamophobia: Understanding the Roots and Rise of Fear, by Khaled Beydoun. Using his unique lens as a critical race theorist and law professor, Khaled A. Beydoun captures the many ways in which law, policy, and official state rhetoric have fueled the frightening resurgence of Islamophobia in the United States. (**H, TR**) bit.ly/3fRy3Jx

Countering Islamophobia, by Learning for Justice. This lesson helps students explore, confront, and deconstruct stereotypes targeted at Muslims. Students will learn about the impact of Islamophobia and create an anti-Islamophobia campaign to display in school. (**H**) bit.ly/2R8ggDc

Freedom in Our Lifetime: South Africa's Struggle, by the CHOICES Program, Brown University. See *African and African Diaspora History, Issues, and Rights* section. (**H**) bit.ly/2IF1iyr

The Body Is Not an Apology, by Sonya Renee Taylor. This book uses a framework of radical self-love to heal the wounds inflicted by violent systems such as patriarchy, White supremacy, and capitalism. She examines how our indoctrinated body shame is connected to systems of oppression and discusses ways to eliminate oppression against all bodies. (**H**) bit.ly/2tDnzHU

The White Supremacy and Me Workbook, by Layla Saad. A text and a process for those holding White privilege to examine and dismantle their complicity in White supremacy. (**TR**) bit.ly/2Agvf2C

They Called Themselves the KKK: The Birth of an American Terrorist Group, by Susan Campbell Bartoletti. This is the story of how a secret terrorist group took root in America's democracy. Filled with chilling and vivid personal accounts unearthed from oral histories, congressional documents, and diaries, this account from Newbery Honor-winning author Susan Campbell Bartoletti is a book to read and remember. A YALSA Award for Excellence in Nonfiction for Young Adults Finalist. (**M, H**) bit.ly/3rN2DGk

Unlearning "Indian" Stereotypes, by Rethinking Schools. Narrated by Native American children, this DVD teaches about racial stereotypes and provides an introduction to Native American history through the eyes of children. Includes a teacher's guide and other resources. (**E, M, H**) bit.ly/2H64BOK

We Are Not Yet Equal: Understanding Our Racial Divide, by Carol Anderson and Tonya Bolden. Adapted from Anderson's bestselling *White Rage* (2016), this book summons young people to bear witness to the devastatingly expansive strategies White citizens have taken up to preserve the racialized violence that emerged from the founding of the nation. (**M, H**) bit.ly/2w1AiVE

What Do Halloween Costumes Say? by Learning for Justice. This lesson, adaptable across grades, can help students think critically about the ways Halloween costumes are marketed and how certain costumes perpetuate stereotypes. For school Halloween celebrations, the activity can be used to develop guidelines for acceptable costumes. (**E, M, H**) bit.ly/3mQOVBD

White Rage: The Unspoken Truth of Our Racial Divide, by Carol Anderson. In this video, Anderson discusses her book in which she chronicles where Black progress in history has been met by what she calls "White rage." (**H**) bit.ly/36ey6Xj

Health and Nutrition

An Interview with Zackie Achmat: AIDS Activism in South Africa, by amfAR: Making AIDS History. A 2004 interview with Zackie Achmat about his activist work, the state of global politics related to HIV/AIDS, and more. (**H**) bit.ly/2OVcZqa

AVERT: Averting HIV and AIDS. A variety of resources and information, including quizzes, handouts, videos, and lessons for teachers and teens about living with and preventing HIV/AIDS. (**M, H**) bit.ly/uq5WS7

Critical Condition and other films about healthcare. Films about healthcare from P.O.V. and Media that Matters. (**H**) to.pbs.org/sGen3S

Decolonize Your Diet: Plant-Based Mexican-American Recipes for Health and Healing, by Luz Calvo and Catriona Rueda Esquibel. More than a cookbook, this book redefines what is meant by "traditional" Mexican food by reaching back through hundreds of years of history to reclaim heritage crops as a source of protection from modern diseases of development. (**M, H, TR**) bit.ly/3vfaYFE

Deconstructing Barbie: Math and Popular Culture, by Swapna Mukhopadhyay. Math activity from the book *Rethinking Mathematics,* which engages students in considering the question: "What would Barbie look like if she were as big as you?" (**M, H**) bit.ly/2lJAKJf

Elbow Is Not a Sexy Word: Approaches to Sex Education, by Jody Sokolower. From Chapter 3 of *Rethinking Sexism, Gender, and Sexuality*, by Rethinking Schools. (**TR**) http://bit.ly/1P5IlwH

How To Survive a Plague, a documentary film by David France. From ZinnEd Project's Films with a Conscience collection: "The riveting and heartbreaking story of the founding and growth of ACT UP (AIDS Coalition to Unleash Power), a central player in the struggle to pressure drug companies and the US government to aggressively pursue a treatment and cure for AIDS. Through rich and intimate archival material, viewers learn about the people who comprised ACT UP... and see, in real time, how their bold civil disobedience was mobilized at key moments in the struggle. (**H**) zinnedproject.org/materials/films-with-a-conscience/#lgbtq

Mad in America: Bad Science, Bad Medicine, and the Enduring Mistreatment of the Mentally Ill, by Robert Whitaker. See *Disability History, Issues, and Rights* section. (**H, TR**) bit.ly/2PAvcto

Medical Apartheid: Teaching the Tuskegee Syphilis Study, by Gretchen Kraig-Turner for Rethinking Schools. See *African American History, Issues, and Rights* section. (**H, TR**) rethinkingschools.org/articles/medical-apartheid

Multicultural Collection of Early Childhood Education Books About Food and Farming, by Ready to Grow. This list of recommended books, primarily featuring BIPOC characters and written by BIPOC authors, features stories about food and farming locally and internationally. (**E**) pareadysetgrow.org/book-list

Reshaping Body Image, by Teaching Tolerance. This lesson is intended to help students examine how people of varying shapes and sizes are typically viewed in our society. How and why do perspectives on beauty and body image change over time? (**H**) bit.ly/dVObJ0

Rights, Respect, Responsibility: A K-12 Sexuality Curriculum, by Advocates for Youth. This website offers an education resource center, which includes K-12 lesson plans, curricula, national standards, and state legislation about sex education. (**H**) bit.ly/2HnHGjv

Supporting Students this Mental Health Month, by Learning for Justice. These resources, including an article introducing the Crisis Text Line, recommend practices that can be used at the district, school, or classroom level. (**TR**) bit.ly/33KFieF

The Vegan Society. The Vegan Society is an educational charity that promotes and supports the vegan lifestyle. The Society was formed in 1944 by a group of vegetarians who recognized the ethical compromises of eating eggs and dairy products. (**M, H**) bit.ly/SY3Tx

What Is Sex Education? For Educators, by Planned Parenthood. Sex education helps people gain the information, skills, and motivation to make healthy decisions about sex and sexuality. Planned Parenthood provides guidelines, resources, standards, and more for K-12 educators to share with young people. (**H**) bit.ly/2vb0Cao

Human Rights and Democracy

A Few Books about 9/11, a blog post by Pernille Ripp. From a practicing classroom teacher, a collection of recommended books for use with younger students about September 11, 2001. (**E, M**) bit.ly/3wng2bB

A Matter of Life and Death, by Amnesty International. *A Matter of Life and Death* is a collection of lessons, assemblies, and films for students to explore the issues surrounding the use of the death penalty, one of Amnesty International's oldest campaigns. (**H**) bit.ly/1dQdsOg

African Americans Against the Bomb: Nuclear Weapons, Colonialism, and the Black Freedom Movement, by Vincent Intondi. Some of the earliest and strongest protests against nuclear weapons came from activists in the Black Freedom movement. Intondi's research reveals that decades ago, Black activists recognized the convergence of domestic and foreign policy issues. (**H**) bit.ly/3mXcKHK

Amend: The Fight for America. See *African American History, Issues, and Rights* section. (**M, H**) bit.ly/3qKZiHs

An Interview with Nawal El Saadawi: "Do you Feel You Are Liberated? I Feel I Am Not." by Rachel Cooke for *The Guardian*. Video clips from a rich interview with Egyptian revolutionary Nawal El Saadawi with relevance to the issues of today. (**H**) bit.ly/3daNZ7J

***Celebrate People's History: The Poster Book of Resistance and Revolution,* 2nd Edition,** edited by Josh MacPhee. These posters pay tribute to the longstanding human legacy of revolution, creative activism, and grassroots organizing. In this book, contemporary artists imagine and interpret often overlooked events and figures in movements for racial justice, women's rights, queer liberation, labor organizing, and environmental conservation. Includes a poster about the Battle of Blair Mountain. (**E, M, H**) bit.ly/3rXauSo

Engel v. Vitale: Recordings of the Oral Arguments, by Oyez. The New York State Board of Regents authorized a prayer for recitation at the start of each school day. A group of organizations joined forces to challenge the prayer, claiming that it violated the Establishment Clause of the First Amendment. The New York Court of Appeals rejected their arguments. The case and the oral arguments presented here are ripe with opportunities to teach and learn about children's rights related to flag salutes and other recitations required in public schools. Hear recordings of each side's oral arguments here. (**H**) oyez.org/cases/1961/468

Human Rights and Service-Learning: Lesson Plans and Projects, by Kristine Belisle and Elizabeth Sullivan, Amnesty International-USA and Human Rights Education Associates (HREA). This manual contains lessons and service-learning projects. The lesson plans are divided into five human rights topics: Environment; Poverty; Discrimination; Children's Rights to Education and Health; and Law and Justice. (**E, M, H, TR**) bit.ly/2mObd9C

Iqbal, by Francesco D'Adamo. See *Abolition and Slavery* section. (**E, M, H**) bit.ly/2S2GyWi

Key Facts About Women's Suffrage Around the World, by Katherine Schaeffer for Pew Research. Perfect for use in mathematics and/or social studies classes, a close look at the history of women's suffrage around the world. Data and analyses focus on when women in various countries won the right to vote in national elections. (**H**) pewrsr.ch/3u5K4zg

Lesson Plan: Watergate and the Limits of Presidential Power, by PBS NewsHour Extra. A rich lesson plan and related resources to support students in exploring the events of the Watergate scandal and its lasting impact on the American presidency. (**M, H**) to.pbs.org/3vwKDSZ

More Than a Score: The New Uprising Against High-Stakes Testing, edited by Jesse Hagopian. A collection of essays, poems, speeches, interviews, and accounts of personal courage, and trenchant insights from frontline fighters who are defying the corporate education reformers, often at great personal and professional risk, and fueling a national movement to reclaim and transform public education. (**TR**) haymarketbooks.org/books/618-more-than-a-score

One Person, No Vote: How Not All Voters are Treated Equally (Young Adult Edition), by Carol Anderson. Complete with a discussion guide, photographs, and information about getting involved with elections in teens' own communities, this is an essential explanation of the history of voting rights and a call to action for a better future. (**H**) bit.ly/3fRMTjd

Project Censored's State of the Free Press 2021, edited by Mickey Huff, Andy Lee Roth, and Matt Taibbi. This edition offers a succinct and comprehensive survey of the most important but underreported news stories of 2020. It also offers a comparative analysis of the current state of corporate and independent news media and its effect on democracy. *State of the Free Press 2021* gives readers the critical thinking and media literacy skills required to hold the corporate media to account for distorting or censoring news coverage, with the aim of revitalizing our democracy. (**H**) bit.ly/3sdAecQ

Resources for Banned Books Week, by Lisa Fink for NCTE. The National Council for Teachers of English, through its Intellectual Freedom Center, offers advice, helpful documents, and other support to teachers and schools faced with challenges to texts (e.g., literary works, films and videos, drama productions) or teaching methods used in their classrooms and schools. (**TR**) bit.ly/3aN0PHC

Resources for Students and Teachers from the 9/11 Memorial & Museum. Links to virtual school programs and field trips, lesson plans, and other teaching materials about the events of 9/11 and how the attacks continue to affect our lives. (**E, M, H, TR**) 911memorial.org/learn/students-and-teachers

Teach Films with a Conscience, by Zinn Education Project. An annotated list of vetted films to support teaching and learning of social justice and critical political issues. The films are organized by themes, including Black Lives Matter, Colonialism, Criminal Justice, Labor Organizing, and many more. (**TR**) zinnedproject.org/materials/films-with-a-conscience

Teaching at the Intersections: Honor and Teach About Your Students' Multiple Identities, by Monita K. Bell for Learning for Justice. This article provides definitions and examples of intersectionality and videos and lesson plans for teaching intersectionality in school. It also provides links to resources on how to apply an intersectional lens to student data and school policies, as well as a teaching toolkit. (**E, M, H, TR**) bit.ly/2Rv2ZCz

Teaching Elementary Students in Times of Crisis, by Marieke van Woerkom for Morningside Center for Social Responsibility. Written in 2021, this blog post provides some basic guidelines for opening up discussion on difficult issues with your elementary and middle school students. (**E, TR**) bit.ly/3cthnV7

Teaching on Days After: Dialogue & Resources for Educating Toward Justice, initiated by Alyssa Haley Dunn. This Facebook group is a space for progressive educators to share resources and support for teaching on "days after" major historical events. (**TR**) bit.ly/3cv9nTB

Teaching When the World Is On Fire, edited by Lisa Delpit. An energizing volume that speaks to our contentious world and the necessary conversations we all must have about it, *Teaching When the World Is On Fire* is sure to inspire teachers to support their students in navigating the current events, cultural shifts, and social dilemmas that shape our communities and our country. (**TR**) bit.ly/2z1VtYZ

Teaching with Documents: Photographs of Lewis Hine: Documentation of Child Labor. This site contains reproducible copies of photos documenting the role of child labor in the development of the industrial United States. (**M, H**) 1.usa.gov/3qo8vl

"That's Your Right," by Annenberg Classroom. An interactive online card game that helps students learn about their rights under the Bill of Rights, the first 10 amendments to the Constitution. The game offers three levels of play: Easy, Normal, and Difficult. (**E, M**) bit.ly/3t9UQ6S

The Berlin Wall and Beyond: An Online High School Curriculum, by Sarah Tellier. With six units of lesson plans, activities, discussion questions, primary source documents, and analysis worksheets, this website offers the tools that educators need to teach their students about the Berlin Wall, post-World War II Europe, and the Cold War through interactive activities, videos, photos, and other media. (**H**) bit.ly/3wpHBRx

The Dark Side of Chocolate, by Miki Mistrati and U. Roberto Romano. A team of journalists investigate how human trafficking and child labor in the Ivory Coast fuels the worldwide chocolate industry. The crew interview both participants and opponents of these alleged practices and use hidden camera techniques to delve into the gritty world of cocoa plantations. (**H**) bit.ly/2HogD3E

The Importance of a Free Press, by Facing History and Ourselves. What is the role of the press in a democracy, and how does the First Amendment protect that role in the United States? How can press freedoms come into conflict with other societal needs and priorities? This lesson from the larger unit, *Facing Ferguson: News Literacy in a Digital Age*, invites young people to tackle these questions. (**H**) bit.ly/3eSbgKo

The Unschooling Movement: Letting Children Lead Their Learning, an audio interview by On Point, WBUR Radio. Three guests talk about the "unschooling movement" on this 45-minute show for WBUR: Maleka Diggs, founder of Eclectic Learning Network, a secular Black and Brown-centered home education network; Peter Gray, psychology professor at Boston College; and Michael Apple, professor of curriculum and instruction at the University of Wisconsin-Madison. (**H**) wbur.fm/32qg4BY

The Voting Booth, by Brandy Colbert. From the Zinn Ed Project: "*The Voting Booth*, a novel for ages 12+, lives up to its dedication to Fannie Lou Hamer. Two storylines sweep readers along – one about contemporary challenges of voting on election day and the other a budding love story." (**M, H**) brandycolbert.com/book-inner

Toolkit for Schools to Become Human Rights-Friendly, by Amnesty International. Human rights-friendly schools are founded on the principles of equality, dignity, respect, non-discrimination, and participation. They are communities where human rights are learned, taught, practiced, respected, protected, and promoted. The *Human Rights-Friendly Schools* package contains a toolkit, pamphlets for students, schools, teachers, communities, and families, as well as a poster. (**E, M, H, TR**) bit.ly/2AkWpYp

Unconstitutional: The War On Our Civil Liberties, a film by Nonny de la Peña. A 70-minute documentary that investigates the ways in which the civil liberties of US citizens and immigrants have been rolled back since 9/11/2001 and the passage of the Patriot Act. (**H**) zinnedproject.org/materials/unconstitutional

Vanguard: How Black Women Broke Barriers, Won the Vote, and Insisted on Equality for All, by Martha Jones. In *Vanguard*, acclaimed historian Martha Jones offers a new history of African American women's political lives in America. She recounts how they defied both racism and sexism to fight for the ballot, and how they wielded political power to secure the equality and dignity of all persons. From the earliest days of the republic to the passage of the 1965 Voting Rights Act and beyond, Jones excavates the lives and work of Black women--Maria Stewart, Frances Ellen Watkins Harper, Fannie Lou Hamer, and more--who were the vanguard of women's rights, calling on America to realize its best ideals. (**H**) bit.ly/39JVwse

What Is Modern Slavery? Investigating Human Trafficking, by Holly Epstein Ojalvo. See *Abolition and Slavery* section. (**M, H**) nyti.ms/XG0Z3n

When Saying "I Do" Meant Giving Up Your US Citizenship, by Meg Hacker for the National Archives. Short, accessible background reading on the Cable Act of 1922, with primary source documents interwoven throughout. (**H**) bit.ly/2PwFoDr

Women's Suffrage, by Justice for Education. Students will explore, using primary and secondary documents, how over a period of 75 years a movement of American women used nonviolent measures to persuade both federal and state governments to allow women to vote. In 1920, the 19th amendment to the Constitution was passed, securing women's right to vote. (**M, H**) bit.ly/2IOoO9c

Humane Education and Animal Rights

Amos's Sweater, by Janet Lunn. Amos the sheep is old and cold and tired of giving up all his wool. But, despite his noisy objections, Aunt Hattie shears Amos once again and knits his wool into a brightly colored sweater for Uncle Henry. Poor Amos decides that this time he has had enough, and he sets out to reclaim what is rightfully his. (**E**) bit.ly/1nuzw9i

Animal Protection Activities, by the Institute for Humane Education. Activity topics include the connections between animal and human oppression, the inconsistencies in how we make choices about how we treat others, and more. (**E, M, H**) bit.ly/2m0xO49

Becoming a Solutionary, by the Institute for Humane Education. This activity explores skills and processes needed to address problems of concern to students and develop meaningful solutions. In this activity, students practice critical-, creative-, strategic-, and systems-thinking skills in order to brainstorm potential solutions to a problem that concerns them. (**M, H**) bit.ly/3vnvJz6

Debate Kit: Is Animal Agriculture Harmful to the Environment? by PETA. See *Environmental Justice Issues* section. (**H**) bit.ly/3mKugyR

Knowing Animals, a podcast by UNSW Australia. *Knowing Animals* is a weekly podcast about all things related to animals and ethics; animals and the law; animals and politics; and animal advocacy. It features interviews with Animal Studies scholars and animal advocates. (**M, H**) knowinganimals.libsyn.com

Meat.org: The Website the Meat Industry Doesn't Want You to See. A website with films and resources about animals killed for food. Free vegetarian starter kits and DVDs available. Warning: Explicit imagery that some may find hard to watch. (**H, TR**) bit.ly/17fyrKa

Teaching About Farmed Animals in Elementary School, by TeachHeart. A free resource guide containing age-appropriate lessons about the treatment of animals on factory farms, aimed at grades 3-8. (**E, M**) bit.ly/3ddKRb3

Teaching Resources from the Animal Welfare Institute. Recommended book titles categorized by age group and grade level, along with linked lesson plans and teaching guides to accompany each title. (**E, M, H, TR**) awionline.org/content/teaching-resources

Teaching Youth About Veganism, by Whitney Blomquist, The Vegetarian Resource Group. A brief lesson plan, resources and handouts, activities, and related PowerPoint slides to teach kids the basics of vegetarianism and veganism. (**E**) bit.ly/3nPFanw

TeachKind Materials, from PETA. PETA offers FREE classroom kits at both the primary and secondary levels that include comic books, informational leaflets and magazines on Humane Education topics, as well as sticker sheets and other materials. (**E, M, H**) bit.ly/2H49QM4

The Nonhuman Rights Project. This organization is working toward legal rights for nonhuman animals. The website includes a blog, a breakdown of state-by-state legal action on behalf of nonhuman animals, and current news stories featuring animals. (**M, H, TR**) bit.ly/eEsNCS

The Omnivore's Dilemma, Young Readers Edition: The Secrets Behind What You Eat, by Michael Pollan. Based on Pollan's best-selling book of the same title, this version is written for teens, and challenges readers to consider the origin of the foods we eat and the broad ramifications of our eating habits. (**M, H, TR**) bit.ly/2s02Rxk

The Vegan Society. See *Health and Nutrition* section. (**M, H**) bit.ly/SY3Tx

Vegan Is Love: Having Heart and Taking Action, by Ruby Roth. Roth explores the many opportunities we have to make ethical decisions: refusing products tested on or made from animals; avoiding sea parks, circuses, animal races, and zoos; choosing to buy organic food; and more. Roth's message is direct but sensitive, bringing into sharp focus what it means to "put our love into action." (**E**) Book trailer by the author here: bit.ly/2OjIF8w

Immigrant and Refugee History, Issues, and Rights

A Different Mirror for Young People: A History of Multicultural America (For Young People Series), by Ronald Takaki and Rebecca Stefoff. See *Asian/Asian Pacific Islander/Asian American History, Issues, and Rights* section. (**M, H**) bit.ly/2S3p3pa

Amend: The Fight for America. See *Asian/Asian Pacific Islander/Asian American History, Issues, and Rights* section. (**M, H**) bit.ly/3qKZiHs

Books to Help Kids Understand What It's Like to Be a Refugee, by Olugbemisola Rhuday-Perkovich. From the author of this annotated book list: "Stories can facilitate dialogue about refugees and promote healthy communication, help to foster empathy and understanding, and even inspire young readers to take action to ensure safe and welcoming environments in their own communities. Here are a few titles that can help." (**E, M**) bit.ly/2k3Djgv

Caravan to the North: Misael's Long Walk, by Jorge Argueta. This short novel in verse follows Misael and his family as they join the caravan from El Salvador to the Mexico/US border. Misael details the violence he is fleeing and the beauty of his country that he will miss. (**M, H**) bit.ly/3qHrwTr

Dreams from Many Rivers: A Hispanic History of the United States Told in Poems, by Margarita Engle. From Juana Briones and Juan Ponce de León, to 18th century slaves and modern-day 6th graders, the many and varied people depicted in this moving narrative speak to the experiences and contributions of Latinx people throughout the history of the United States, from the earliest known stories up to present day. It's a portrait of a great, enormously varied, and enduring heritage. (**E, M, H**) bit.ly/3dhGw73

Explore Ellis Island: Stories of Yesterday and Today, by Scholastic Teachers. An interactive tour of and virtual field trip to Ellis Island, along with stories from young immigrants, immigration data, book lists, interactive maps of immigrant settlement patterns, and more. (**E, M**) bit.ly/3d8TbJ6

Going Home, Coming Home, by Truong Tran. See *Asian/Asian Pacific Islander, Asian American History, Issues, and Rights* section. (**E**) bit.ly/3g8fiS3

Harvest of Empire: A History of Latinos in America, by Juan Gonzalez. Featuring family portraits of immigrants, as well as accounts of the events and conditions that compelled them to leave their homelands, this book is for anyone wishing to understand the history and legacy of this increasingly influential group. (**H**) bit.ly/3dxD2Mi

Lesson Plan on Plyer v. Doe: Can States Deny Public Benefits to Illegal Immigrants? By the Constitutional Rights Foundation. This lesson focuses on the 1982 Supreme Court decision in *Plyler v. Doe* on whether a state may deny public education to the children of illegal immigrants. It gives the background on the case and the arguments for both sides. In the activity, students take part in a mock hearing before the Supreme Court on this case. [Note that unfortunately this resource uses the phrase "illegal immigrants" instead of "undocumented people." Consider noting this in discussion with students.] (**H**) bit.ly/3eaTDpG

Let the Faithful Come, by Zetta Elliott. This lyrical retelling of the traditional Christmas story serves as a plea for greater compassion and unity in our contemporary world. Peace and goodwill are values celebrated during the holidays, but they should also be applied to the daily struggle of those traveling over land and sea in search of hope and sanctuary. This simple nativity narrative urges readers to recognize the value of every child, and to respect our shared responsibility for all the members of our global community. (**E, M**) bit.ly/2VZUGim

Other Words for Home, by Jasmine Warga. A gorgeously written, hopeful middle-grade novel in verse about a young girl who must leave Syria to move to the United States. (**M, H**) bit.ly/2DlV6Yu

Rethinking Bilingual Education, by Rethinking Schools. A new, edited collection of articles about bringing students' home languages into our classrooms. The stories offer powerful examples of social justice curricula taught by bilingual teachers. The volume also includes ideas and strategies for how to honor students' home languages in schools with no bilingual programming. (**TR**) bit.ly/2njKRdr

The Christmas Gift/El Regalo de Navidad, by Francisco Jiménez. With honesty and grace, Jiménez shares his most poignant Christmas memory in this beautifully illustrated picture book. As Christmas approaches, Panchito can't wait to see what present he gets. But on Christmas Day, he is disappointed when all he gets is a bag of candy, until he sees the gift his father gives his mother. Panchito then realizes that gifts of the heart are the most precious of all. (**E**) bit.ly/2Veahtj

Things Are Good Now, by Djamila Ibrahim. In the pages of this collection of short stories, men, women, and children who have crossed continents in search of a better life find themselves struggling with the chaos of displacement and the religious and cultural clashes they face in their new homes. (**H**) bit.ly/2EH3WzP

This Land Is Our Land: A History of American Immigration, by Linda Barrett Osborne. This book explores the way government policy and popular responses to immigrant groups evolved throughout US history, particularly between 1800 and 1965. The book concludes with a summary of events up to contemporary times, as immigration again becomes a hot-button issue. Includes an author's note, bibliography, and index. [Note: Teachers may want to discuss with students the use of the phrase "this land is our land," from the perspective of Indigenous peoples.] (**M, H**) bit.ly/3dXKDW7

Una Jornada Hacia La Esperanza/A Journey Toward Hope, Spanish Edition, by Victor Hinojosa and Coert Voorhees. Four unaccompanied migrant children come together along the arduous journey north through Mexico to the United States border in this ode to the power of hope and connection even in the face of uncertainty and fear. (**E, M**) sixfootpress.com/a-journey-toward-hope

Us vs. Them – The Chinese Exclusion Act of 1882, by The National Museum of American History. See *Asian/Asian Pacific Islander, Asian American History, Issues, and Rights* section. (**M, H**) s.si.edu/3eYohog

Vietnamese Americans: Lessons in American History, by Learning for Justice. See *Asian/Asian Pacific Islander, Asian American History, Issues, and Rights* section. (**M, H**) bit.ly/9Q1L0r

We Came to America, by Faith Ringgold. A timely and beautiful look at America's rich historical diversity, with an appropriate complication of the "nation of immigrants" narrative that includes recognition of Indigenous peoples and the forced migration of the slave trade. (**E**) bit.ly/2llxdp8

Independence

El Grito: A Lesson Plan, by Patricia Schwarz. In this elementary-middle school lesson plan, students read a book written by students (*El Grito*) to learn the story of Mexico's fight for independence. Vocabulary activities, extension activities, links to build background information, and other resources are included. (**TR**) bit.ly/1cNPPpp

Lesson of the Day: "A Continent Remade," by *NYTimes* Learning Network. See *African and African Diaspora History, Issues and Rights* section. (**H**) nyti.ms/3u1jJCj

Indigenous History, Issues, and Rights

A Coyote Columbus Story, by Thomas King. Thomas King uses a bag of literary tricks to shatter the stereotypes surrounding Columbus's voyages. He invites children to laugh with him at the crazy antics of Coyote, who unwittingly causes Columbus to bring about the downfall of her human friends. He also makes the point that history is influenced by the culture of the storyteller. (**E**) bit.ly/1RyuKQl

A Coyote Solstice Tale, by Thomas King. Trickster Coyote is having his friends over for a festive solstice get-together in the woods when a little girl comes by unexpectedly. She leads the partygoers through the snowy woods to a shopping mall – a place they have never seen before. Winner of the American Indian Library Association Youth Literature Awards, Best Picture Book. (**E**) bit.ly/1TleAtW

A Racial Justice Guide to Thanksgiving for Educators and Families, by Border Crossers. This guide includes a wealth of teaching approaches, lesson plans, study guides, resources for families, a reading list, and more. All vetted resources are categorized and hyperlinked. (**E, M, H, TR**) bit.ly/2o3fJAp

Alcatraz Is Not an Island, by PBS. This PBS website provides lesson plans and resources for teaching about the American Indian Movement. (**M, H**) bit.ly/2dZjx4l

All My Relations: A Podcast, by Matika Wilbur and Adrienne Keene. From the creators: "All My Relations is a podcast hosted by Matika Wilbur (Swinomish and Tulalip) and Adrienne Keene (Cherokee Nation) to explore our relationships – relationships to land, to our creatural relatives, and to one another. Each episode invites guests to delve into a different topic facing Native peoples today as we keep it real, play games, laugh a lot, and even cry sometimes." (**H**) allmyrelationspodcast.com

American Indian Law: When Two Sovereigns Collide, by Reasonably Speaking Podcast. In this episode, American Indian law and policy experts, Matthew Fletcher and Wenona Singel, discuss the nuanced and highly complex field of American Indian Law. They begin by exploring the history of tribal sovereignty and discuss the rights of American Indians as both tribal citizens and US citizens. They explore jurisdiction across border lines, particularly in a criminal context and discuss the history of violence against Native women, and why, until recently, prosecution has been so difficult. Court challenges, both past and present, to the Indian Child Welfare Act are also examined. (**H**) bit.ly/3mDNmqv

An Indigenous People's History of the United States for Young People, by Roxanne Dunbar-Ortiz. Acclaimed historian and activist Roxanne Dunbar-Ortiz offers a history of the United States told from the perspective of Indigenous peoples and reveals how Native Americans actively resisted expansion of the US empire for centuries. (**M, H**) bit.ly/31EZLQA; link to teacher's guide: bit.ly/2UzuFYZ.

Ancestor Approved: Intertribal Stories for Kids, edited by Cynthia Leitich Smith. This collection of intersecting stories by both new and veteran Native writers, bursts with hope, joy, resilience, the strength of community, and Native pride. (**E, M**) bit.ly/3vlobfk

Andrew Jackson and the "Children of the Forest," by Bill Bigelow, Zinn Education Project. This lesson supports students to develop critical literacy skills by responding to Andrew Jackson's speech on "Indian Removal." (**H**) bit.ly/2ShQWGx

Apache Children and Elders Talk Together, by the Library of Intergenerational Learning: Native Americans. Many of us have heard of Geronimo, who fought for the freedom of the Apache. Some of his grandchildren and great-grandchildren relate their family history and the Apache culture as it has evolved through American history. (**E, M**) bit.ly/3e0tqez

As Long as Grass Grows: The Indigenous Fight for Environmental Justice, from Colonization to Standing Rock, by Dina Gilio-Whitaker. See *Environmental Justice Issues* section. (**H**) bit.ly/3mlDxgF

As We Have Always Done: Indigenous Freedom Through Radical Resistance, by Leanne Betasamosake Simpson. See *Environmental Justice Issues* section. (**H**) akpress.org/aswehavealwaysdone

At the Mountain's Base, by Traci Sorell. A family, separated by duty and distance, waits for a loved one to return home in this lyrical picture book celebrating the bonds of a Cherokee family and the bravery of history-making women pilots. (**E, M**) bit.ly/2Xc7hSp

Black Indians: A Hidden Heritage, by William Loren Katz. See *African American History, Issues, and Rights* section. (**M, H**) zinnedproject.org/materials/black-indians

Celebrate My Hopi Corn, by Anita Poleahla. This board book, written in Hopi and English, is the story of how corn is planted, cultivated, harvested, and prepared for use in the Hopi home. The colorful illustrations by Hopi artist Emmett Navakuku depict the changing seasons and daily activities in a Hopi village. (**E**) bit.ly/2n7lqep

Creek Trail of Tears: Historic Sites and Points of Interest, by Explore Southern History. Linked images and informational text about sites and events associated with the Creek Trail of Tears. (**E, M, H**) exploresouthernhistory.com/creektrail

Don't Take Our Voices Away: A Role Play on the Indigenous Peoples' Global Summit on Climate Change, by Julie Treick O'Neill and Tim Swinehart. See *Environmental Justice Issues* section. (**H**) bit.ly/2l5qxg2

Everything You Wanted to Know About Indians but Were Afraid to Ask: Young Readers Edition, by Anton Treuer. From the acclaimed Ojibwe author and professor Anton Treuer comes an essential book of questions and answers for Native and non-Native young readers alike. This expanded edition includes a new section on social activism. (**M, H**) bit.ly/31lIJTu

How We Go Home: Voices from Indigenous North America, edited by Sara Sinclair. A collection of narrators' voices describing the ways in which their lives have been shaped by loss, injustice, and resilience, and by the struggle of how to share space with settler nations whose essential aim is to take all that is Indigenous. (**H**) bit.ly/2PW6SSI

Indigenous Struggle and the Bolivian National Revolution: Land and Liberty! by James Kohl. In a critical revision of conventional works, the author reappraises and reconfigures the tortuous history of insurrection and revolution, counterrevolution and resurrection, and overthrow and aftermath in Bolivia. Underlying the history of Creole conflict between dictatorship and democracy lies another conflict – the unrelenting 500-year struggle of the conquered Indigenous peoples to reclaim usurped lands, resist White supremacist dominion, and seize autonomous political agency. (**H, TR**) bit.ly/3tn1XZT

Interview with Vernon Bellecourt About the American Indian Movement. Bellecourt speaks about the state of nations and the demands being made in the American Indian Movement. **(H, TR)** bit.ly/9qBLCK

Jingle Dancer, by Cynthia Leitich Smith. Jenna, a contemporary Muscogee (Creek) girl in Oklahoma, wants to honor a family tradition by jingle dancing at the next powwow. But where will she find enough jingles for her dress? (**E**) cynthialeitichsmith.com/kidbooks

Life Story: Grace Thorpe, from Women & The American Story. The story of a Native American woman who served her country on the Pacific front during World War II and became an advocate for Native rights and the Anti-Nuclear movement, told through primary source multimedia resources, teaching materials, and suggested activities. (**M, H**) bit.ly/3dWMdXb

Margo Tamez, from the Poetry Foundation Information page, with select poems from and about Margo Tamez. (**M, H**) poetryfoundation.org/poets/margo-tamez

Mary and the Trail of Tears: A Cherokee Removal Survival Story, by Andrea Rogers. Twelve-year-old Mary and her Cherokee family are forced out of their home in Georgia by US soldiers in May 1838. Featuring nonfiction support material, a glossary, and reader response questions, this story explores the tragedy of forced removals following the Indian Removal Act of 1830. (**E, M**) bit.ly/3dEGJjl

Napí, by Antonio Ramirez. Napí is a young Mazateca girl who lives with her family in a little village on the bank of a river in the state of Oaxaca, Mexico. Each afternoon the family sits beneath the shade of a huge ceiba tree and listens to the grandfather's stories. As Napí listens dreamily, the afternoons take on different colors in her imagination. The ceiba tree sends Napí dreams every night, and in her favorite one, she becomes a heron, gliding freely along the river. Spanish language edition available. (**E**) amzn.to/39Ek6KV

Recommended Indigenous Australian Children's Books, by Readings: Australia's Own Since 1969. An annotated list of children's books, topic cards, symbol flashcards, and more, featuring the Indigenous Peoples of Australia. (**E, M**) bit.ly/3fWEB75

Reconsider Columbus Day, presented by Nu Heightz Cinema. This short PSA asks people to reconsider whether the crimes of Columbus should be celebrated. (**E, M, H**) bit.ly/9ILuXF

Seasons of Alaska Board Books, by Joni Spiess, Carla Snow, Yaari Toolie-Walker, and Angela Y. Gonzalez. Four board books about each of the seasons, all set in Alaska, written by Indigenous authors and including information about the Indigenous peoples of Alaska. (**E**) bit.ly/3s7ygdU

She Sang Promise: The Story of Betty Mae Jumper, Seminole Tribe Leader, by Jan Godown Annino. The compelling and inspiring story of Betty Mae Tiger Jumper, one of modern America's first female elected tribal leaders. With its lyrical, poetic text, and rich, vibrant illustrations, this biographical book will charm and amaze young readers. (**E, M**) bit.ly/2QVWKd6

Standing with Standing Rock: A Role Play on the Dakota Access Pipeline, by Ursula Wolfe-Rocca, Bill Bigelow, and Andrew Duden. See *Environmental Justice Issues* section. (**E, M, H**) bit.ly/2j9JkW3

Standing with Standing Rock: Voices from the #NoDAPL Movement, edited by Nick Estes and Jaskiran Dhillon. See *Environmental Justice Issues* section. (**H**) bit.ly/3fZbtys

Talking with Mother Earth/Hablando con Madre Tierra, by Jorge Argueta. Tetl's skin is brown, his eyes are black, and his hair is long. He's different from the other children, whose taunts wound him deeply, leaving him confused and afraid. But Tetl's grandmother knows the ancient teachings of their Aztec ancestors and how they viewed the earth as alive with sacred meaning. Tetl's journey from self-doubt to proud acceptance of his Nahuatl heritage is told in a series of powerful poems, beautifully expressed in both English and Spanish. (**E**) bit.ly/3d7dg2B

Teaching Critically About Lewis and Clark: Challenging Dominant Narratives in K-12 Curriculum, by Alison Schmitke, Leilani Sabzalian, and Jeff Edmundson. The Lewis and Clark Corps of Discovery is often presented as an exciting adventure story of discovery, friendship, and patriotism. However, this same period in US history can be understood quite differently when viewed through an anticolonial lens and the Doctrine of Discovery. This book challenges dominant narratives and packaged curricula about Lewis and Clark to support more responsible social studies instruction. The authors provide a conceptual framework, ready-to-use lesson plans, and teaching resources to address oversimplified versions of the Lewis and Clark expedition. (**TR**) bit.ly/3drvmMR

Tecumseh, by James Laxer. Two hundred years after his death, the Shawnee Chief Tecumseh is still considered one of the greatest leaders of North America's First Peoples. This richly illustrated biography tells the story of his remarkable life, culminating in the War of 1812. The book includes an epilogue, a timeline, a glossary, and maps. (**M**) bit.ly/2R2K4RU

Tecumseh's Speech to the Osages (Winter 1811-12). Tecumseh, a Shawnee leader, sought to persuade all Indian tribes to unify against the growing White incursion into Indian lands. Links lead to primary text and Brian Jones's video re-enactment of the speech. **(E, M, H, TR)** bit.ly/3tEIRht

The Black Seminoles: History of a Freedom-Seeking People, by Kenneth Porter. See *African American History, Issues, and Rights* section. (**H**) bit.ly/3tFoPEh

The Homestead Acts: A Primary Source Set, by Hillary Brady for the Digital Public Library of America. See *African American History, Issues, and Rights* section. (**H**) bit.ly/2QCQLJX

The Night the Moon Fell: A Maya Myth, by Pat Mora. A whoosh from her grandfather's blowgun causes Luna, the moon, to tumble from the sky and fall to pieces in the dark ocean. To save herself, she enlists the help of little fish to glue her back together. At last she rises, beautiful and round again, taking her new friends with her to create the Milky Way. Pat Mora and artist Domi have taken the traditional Mopan Maya (Belize) myth in which the moon is a young weaver and the Milky Way a fish and transformed it into a magical story of friendship and imagination. (**E**) bit.ly/3dt4xqn

The People vs. Columbus, et al., by Bill Bigelow. This role play begins with the premise that a monstrous crime was committed in the years after 1492, when an estimated three million Taínos on the island of Hispaniola lost their lives. It's a free download excerpted from *Rethinking Columbus*. (**E, M, H**) bit.ly/hRdbSf

Tips for Teachers: Developing Instructional Materials About American Indians, compiled by Debbie Reese and Jean Mendoza. A helpful list of guiding information and principles for educators working to develop and choose instructional resources about American Indians. (**TR**) bit.ly/328xT8g

Two Spirits, film directed by Lydia Nibley. This film interweaves Fred Martinez's life and murder with an examination of the two-spirit tradition among Native Americans, telling a nuanced story of what it means to be poor, transgender, and Navajo. (**M, H, TR**) bit.ly/1qA6uVK

Under Alaska's Midnight Sun, by Deb Vanasse. When the midnight sun is shining, people and animals stay active even at night. This sweet poetic narrative showcases the many pleasures of this unique time as a little girl dances, fishes, plays games, watches moose and foxes, and communes with family and nature. (**E**) bit.ly/3bWZV9q

Unlearning "Indian" Stereotypes, by Rethinking Schools. See *Hate and Oppression* section. (**E, M, H**) bit.ly/2H64BOK

We Are Still Here: Native American Truths Everyone Should Know, by Traci Sorell. Twelve Native American kids present historical and contemporary laws, policies, struggles, and victories in Native life, each with a powerful refrain: *We are still here*! Precise, lyrical writing presents topics including forced assimilation, land allotment and Native tribal reorganization, termination, relocation, self-determination, Native civil rights, the Indian Child Welfare Act (ICWA), religious freedom, economic development, Native language revival efforts, cultural persistence, and nationhood. (**E, M**) tracisorell.com/we-are-still-here

We Are Water Protectors, by Carole Lindstrom. See *Environmental Justice Issues* section. (**E**) bit.ly/2AeJ2tH

We Shall Remain. This PBS miniseries and multimedia project establishes Native history as an essential part of American history. Five 90-minute documentaries, spanning 300 years, tell the story of pivotal moments in US history from the Native American perspective. Website includes teacher's guides. (**H**) to.pbs.org/2SvdUu2

What's in a Mascot? by Pamela Gasway, Learning for Justice. A 9th grade English unit helps students analyze the legacy behind Native American mascots. (**H, TR**) bit.ly/3h3R5g8

When the Shadbush Blooms, by Carla Messinger and Susan Katz. Today when a Lenape Indian girl ventures to the stream to fish for shad, she knows that another girl did the same thing generations before. Through the cycle of the seasons, what is important has remained: being with family, knowing when berries are ripe for picking, and listening to stories in a warm home. (**E, M**) Teacher's guide from Lee & Low Books here: bit.ly/3mKxHWh

Labor and Economic Issues

1981 Strike Leaves Legacy for American Workers, by Kathleen Schalch for NPR. An informational article about the effects of the 1981 Air Traffic Controllers strike. Also includes a timeline of events related to the strike and "Voices from 1981," a small collection of firsthand audio recordings. (**H, TR**) n.pr/3wn6Kwf

55 Strong: Inside the West Virginia Teachers' Strike, edited by Elizabeth Catte, Emily Hilliard, and Jessica Salfia. What compelled West Virginia's teachers to strike? How did they organize? What were teachers and allies doing during the strike? And how is the West Virginia labor movement celebrating its victory? *55 Strong: Inside the West Virginia Teachers' Strike* answers these questions and offers unique, on-the-ground insights into this historic strike. The book includes essays by teachers from around the state, organizing documents, images from the picket lines, and material on the history of the Labor movement in West Virginia. (**H, TR**) bit.ly/2RoEoSe

A History of America in Ten Strikes, by Erik Loomis. Powerful and accessible, this book challenges contemporary assumptions around labor, unions, and American workers. Labor historian Erik Loomis recounts 10 critical workers' strikes in American labor history that everyone needs to know about. He also provides an appendix with an annotated list of the 150 most important moments in American labor history. (**H, TR**) bit.ly/2PB4VWQ

Battle of Blair Mountain, by David Rovics. This song is about the biggest battle in the West Virginia Coal Mine War of 1920-1921. The site includes the lyrics, link to the audio, and a link to the book on which the song is based. (**M, H**) bit.ly/3eynOJm

"Bread and Roses," by James Oppenheim. Oppenheim's poem is closely associated with the Strike of 1912. This site has the words of the poem, "Bread and Roses," as well as a song version recorded by Mimi Fariña, which has become an anthem for women's and workers' rights. (**E, M, H**) bit.ly/a4iuHP

Bread and Roses, Too, by Katherine Paterson. With two teenagers as the protagonists of this historical fiction novel, Paterson introduces the reader to the Industrial Workers of the World, major figures such as Big Bill Haywood and Elizabeth Gurley Flynn, worker solidarity, the role of labor songs, and the various tactics used by the company to undermine the strike. (**M, H**) bit.ly/Lhb8PS

Cinco de Mayo Inc. This blog is dedicated to documenting and critically examining the commercialization of Cinco de Mayo. This Mexican holiday has become more popular in the US than in Mexico, in part because of corporate America's desire to make money off the Latinx consumer market. It also perpetuates damaging stereotypes about Latinx people while obscuring the historical significance of this day. (**M, H, TR**) bit.ly/rryYIN

Cultivate.Coop. Cultivate.Coop is an online hub for pooling knowledge and resources on cooperatives. It is a space to collect free information for those interested in cooperatives, and where people can build useful educational tools for the co-op community. (**H, TR**) bit.ly/ekaidO

Ella Jenkins and a Union of Friends Pulling Together, by Ella Jenkins. Legendary children's performer Ella Jenkins and a group of young and older musical friends introduce children to the ideas of unity, cooperation, and labor unions through songs, recitation, and poetry. Recorded in 1999, this CD features harmonica, piano, percussion, banjo, guitar, vocals, and chorus. The recording reminds us how unity and strength are part of family ties as well as adult life and work. (**E**) s.si.edu/3wXuk3d

Fannie Never Flinched: One Woman's Courage in the Struggle for American Labor Rights, by Mary Cronk Farrell. This beautiful book about early 20th century labor organizer Fannie Sellins begins with her murder by sheriff's deputies, in broad daylight, at the age of 47. No one is prosecuted. The author then jumps back 20 years to trace Sellins' life organizing garment and mine workers. Full of photos and primary documents, *Fannie Never Flinched* puts Sellins' story in the context of the struggles of workers and the Labor movement during the "Gilded Age." (**E, M**) bit.ly/328Y6nn

Fighting for a Living Wage, by NYSUT. A collection of links and resources related to organizing for the "Fight for $15," a national struggle to increase the minimum wage to $15. In the section titled, "Make the Fight for Living Wage a Teachable Moment," are lesson plans and multimedia resources related to the "Fight for $15." (**H, TR**) bit.ly/2lJEYs9

Finding Solutions to Hunger, by Kids Can Make a Difference. This educational program for middle and high school students focuses on the root causes of hunger and poverty, the people most affected, solutions, and how students can help. (**M, H**) bit.ly/cYEDNd

Fire in the Hole! By Mary Cronk Farrell. Based on the true story of a silver miners' strike in Coeur d'Alene, ID, this book of historical fiction shows the desperate conditions of miners' lives and how the striking miners were detained illegally in a late-19th century version of Guantanamo. (**H**) zinnedproject.org/materials/fire-in-the-hole

Flower Workers Lesson Plans, International Labor Rights Forum. This lesson plan explores workers' rights in the cut flower industry and how consumerism on Valentine's Day in the US affects workers abroad. (**E, M**) bit.ly/tFAlAq

For a Better World, website by Fair World Project. Campaign information, resources, and publications related to understanding and teaching fair trade. (**TR**) bit.ly/1Slrigj

For the Win, by Cory Doctorow. *For the Win* introduces the reader to the global economy and the history of organizing, with a focus on the Industrial Workers of the World (IWW). The characters in *For the Win* make a living in virtual gaming all over the world. They connect and organize online (forming the Webblies), and after initial skepticism convince the traditional labor unions to join them. (**H**) bit.ly/123xmA6

Growing Up in Coal Country, by Susan Campbell Bartoletti. This book offers firsthand accounts and compelling facts about the lives of coal miners and their families in northeastern Pennsylvania at the dawn of the 20th century. Bartoletti has also written a children's literature fictional account of the same time period and people, *A Coal Miner's Bride*. (**E, M**) bit.ly/3mUJOjL

Harvesting Hope: The Story of César Chávez, by Kathleen Krull. This picture book chronicles Chávez's youth and the struggles he endured on his journey to becoming a leader. The second link is to a teacher's guide. (**E**) bit.ly/2qkxOfj; link to Teacher's Guide: bit.ly/1Qd1FZx

Haymarket: A Novel, by Martin Duberman. This moving work of historical fiction makes working-class life and organizing come alive. The detail and drama of the struggle for an 8-hour workday, as seen through the lives of labor activists Lucy and Albert Parsons, hold the reader's attention. The author deftly weaves together critical themes of race and gender. (**H**) bit.ly/2mgA17U

It's a Mystery – White Workers Against Black Workers, by Bill Bigelow and Norm Diamond. Teachers are provided with a unit plan depicting the history and social factors that contributed to the racial tensions between workers in the 1920s. (**H, TR**) bit.ly/1mFmfZV

Labor Matters, a lesson plan by Learning for Justice. In recent decades, the right to collective bargaining, ensured by the National Labor Relations Act, has been called into question. This lesson, from the Southern Poverty Law Center, draws on prior knowledge and uses primary source documents to help students understand the origins of union goals and tactics in the US. (**M, H**) bit.ly/185DPul

Labor Unions and Working Conditions: United We Stand, a lesson plan by the Library of Congress. Students work with primary source documents from the Library of Congress online collections to study the working conditions of US laborers at the turn of the century and consider the question: "Was there a need for organized labor unions?" (**H**) bit.ly/3rISYRe

Lawrence, 1912: The Singing Strike, a teaching activity by Bill Bigelow and Norm Diamond for Zinn Education Project. Through role play, students in this lesson explore some of the actual dilemmas faced by strikers in Lawrence, MA in 1912. The teaching methodology is designed to match the history itself, as students portray Industrial Workers of the World (I.W.W.) organizers deciding how – and for what cause – to conduct a massive strike. (**H**) bit.ly/3hkL4f1

May 30, 1937: Memorial Day Massacre, by Howard Fast. Essay, article, and actual footage of a strike that took place in Chicago on Memorial Day in 1937 and the brutal police response to it. (**H, TR**) bit.ly/2jUKLWX

Memories of the 1982 ILGWU Strike in New York's Chinatown, a firsthand account by Katie Quan. See *Asian/Asian Pacific Islander/Asian American History, Issue,s and Rights* section. (**H**) bit.ly/3eDl3Vw

Migrant, by Maxine Trottier. Each spring Anna leaves her home in Mexico and travels north with her family where they work on farms. Sometimes she feels like a bird, flying north in the spring and south in the fall. She wonders what it would be like to stay in one place. The Low German-speaking Mennonites from Mexico are a unique group of migrants who moved from Canada to Mexico in the 1920s and became an important part of the farming community. But it has become increasingly difficult for them to earn a livelihood, so they come back to Canada each year as migrant workers. (**E**) bit.ly/32baKlB

Model Curriculum and Resources for Teachers. This curriculum on the life and work of César Chávez, from the California Department of Education, includes biographies, pictures, and other resources to help teachers prepare lessons for this holiday. (**E, M, H**) bit.ly/1mFT0W3

Mutual Aid Toolbox, by Big Door Brigade. We cannot rely on the government to provide what people need, especially when vulnerable people are under attack by government agencies and agents. This toolbox is a list of models and tools for starting mutual aid projects – projects that help materially support people facing eviction, deportation, criminalization, poverty, isolation, and violence. (**M, H, TR**) bit.ly/2kL2cup

Side by Side/Lado a Lado: The Story of Dolores Huerta and César Chávez, by Monica Brown and Joe Cepeda. This picture book pairs the stories of Huerta and Chávez. Each double-page spread features text in both Spanish and English, with Huerta's story on the left and Chávez's on the right. (**E**) bit.ly/2NcFlao

Teachers Unions and Social Justice: Organizing for the Schools and Communities Our Students Deserve, edited by Michael Charney, Jesse Hagopian, and Bob Peterson. An anthology of more than 60 articles documenting the history and the methods of social justice unionism. Together, they describe the growing movement to forge multiracial alliances with communities to defend and transform public education. (**TR**) rethinkingschools.org/books/teacher-unions-and-social-justice/

Teaching Economics As If People Mattered, by United for a Fair Economy. A collection of lesson plans about economics from a social justice perspective. bit.ly/6Aly7u

Teaching with Documents: Photographs of Lewis Hine: Documentation of Child Labor. See *Human Rights and Democracy* section. (**M, H**) 1.usa.gov/3qo8vl

The Bobbin Girl, by Emily Arnold McCully. Rebecca is a "bobbin girl," trying to help her struggling family by working all day in a hot, noisy cotton mill. Working conditions at the mill are abysmal, and there is talk of lowering the workers' wages. Rebecca's friend Judith wants to protest the pay cut, but the organizers at the mill are dismissed. Does Rebecca have the courage to join the protest? The story is followed by a note from the author about the historical context. (**E, M**) zinnedproject.org/materials/bobbin-girl

The Bonus Army, by Mickey Z. for the Zinn Education Project. This short article about the history of the 1932 Bonus Expeditionary Force (BEF), or Bonus Army, includes video clips, books for children and teens, and other multimedia resources related to teaching about the WWI veterans who fought for the wartime bonuses they were promised. (**H, TR**) zinnedproject.org/materials/bonus-army

The Dark Side of Chocolate, by Miki Mistrati and U. Roberto Romano. See *Human Rights and Democracy* section. (**H**) bit.ly/2HogD3E

The Five Basic Steps to Organizing a Union. Student-friendly step-by-step guide to starting a union from the United Electrical, Radio and Machine Workers of America's website. (**M, H, TR**) bit.ly/VVGMxk

The Homestead Strike, a Teaching Activity by Bill Bigelow and Norm Diamond for the Zinn Education Project. This role play activity on the notorious 1892 Homestead Strike explores the possibility of solidarity among workers of very different backgrounds and at different levels in the workplace hierarchy. This activity is one of the 16 labor history lessons available for free download from *The Power in Our Hands.* (**H**) bit.ly/2OjiXRD

The Minimum Wage and the Value of a Billion, a lesson plan by Rob Lerman for the Morningside Center for Teaching Social Responsibility. While the minimum wage has been losing value, the income of the wealthiest Americans has risen steeply in the past decade. This lesson invites students to grapple with that reality. (**M, H**) bit.ly/3mXv83u

The Real Bread and Roses Story Missing from Textbooks, by Robert Forrant. The author challenges the myth that the Bread and Roses Strike was spontaneous and provides a counternarrative of the events. Additional resources for teaching the strike are available from Zinn Education Project at the end of the article. (**H, TR**) bit.ly/3wJYKpv

The Story of Change, by Annie Leonard. A follow-up video to *The Story of Stuff*, *The Story of Change* asks if shopping can save the world, urging viewers to put down their credit cards and start exercising their civic muscles to build a more sustainable, just, and fulfilling world. (**M, H**) bit.ly/Vo6GIQ

The US Labor Movement Mixer, by Rethinking Schools. A "mixer" activity designed to engage students in playing the part of a worker during a particular period in US labor history. Includes role sheets with descriptions, clear instructions for the teacher, and pages of additional books and resources for teaching about US labor history. (**E, M, H**) bit.ly/2BBthKU

Viva La Causa, film kit by Learning for Justice. A 39-minute documentary film, *Viva La Causa* focuses on one of the seminal events in the march for human rights – the grape strike and boycott led by César Chávez and Dolores Huerta in the 1960s. *Viva la Causa* shows how thousands of people from across the nation joined in a struggle for justice for the most exploited people in our country – the workers who put food on our tables. (**E, M**) bit.ly/3hmif27

What Rights Do We Have? by Bill Bigelow and Norm Diamond. A teaching activity that provides teachers with five units centered around labor movements, history, and rights. (**M, H, TR**) bit.ly/1kaTKy8

Win-Win Solutions: An Introduction to Fair Trade and Cooperative Economics, by Equal Exchange. Composed of four units, this curriculum raises students' awareness of core issues surrounding food production and trade. (**E, M**) bit.ly/2m0N8xt

Latinx/Latin American History, Issues, and Rights

500 Years of Chicana Women's History, by Elizabeth Martinez. This bilingual text, along with hundreds of photos and other images, ranges from female-centered stories of pre-Columbian Mexico to profiles of contemporary social justice activists, labor leaders, youth organizers, artists, and environmentalists, among others. (**H**) bit.ly/3ba7sEh

An Educator's Guide to the Mexican Revolution, by University of New Mexico's Latin American & Iberian Institute (LAII). This curriculum guide is inspired by, although it stands apart from, an exhibit of photos of the Mexican Revolution – many never published before. This guide provides K-12 educators resources for exploring the Mexican Revolution and offers suggestions for how to incorporate the topic into their classrooms. (**M, H**) bit.ly/3blodHe

Caravan to the North: Misael's Long Walk, by Jorge Argueta. See *Immigrant and Refugee History, Issues, and Rights* section. (**M, H**) bit.ly/3qHrwTr

Cinco de Mayo Inc. See *Labor and Economic Issues* section. (**M, H, TR**) bit.ly/rryYIN

Cinco de Mayo, Yesterday and Today, by Maria Cristina Urrutia and Rebeca Orozco. Cinco de Mayo is one of the most celebrated days in the Mexican calendar, but few people know that it commemorates a decisive victory of the Mexicans against the invading French in 1862. Drawing on historical sources and the photographic record of a contemporary reenactment, this book introduces children to this important, but little understood, event. (**E, M**) bit.ly/2SFfXvSp

Decolonize Your Diet: Plant-Based Mexican-American Recipes for Health and Healing, by Luz Calvo and Catriona Rueda Esquibel. See *Health and Nutrition* section. (**M, H, TR**) bit.ly/3vfaYFE

Dreams from Many Rivers: A Hispanic History of the United States Told in Poems, by Margarita Engle. See *Immigrant and Refugee History, Issues, and Rights* section. (**E, M, H**) bit.ly/3dhGw73

El Grito: A Lesson Plan, by Patricia Schwarz. See *Independence* section. (**TR**) bit.ly/1cNPPpp

En Comunidad: Lessons for Centering the Voices and Experiences of Bilingual Latinx Students, by Carla España and Luz Yadira Herrera. *En Comunidad* brings bilingual Latinx students' perspectives to the center of our classrooms and offers classroom-ready lessons that amplify the varied stories and identities of Latinx children. (**TR**) bit.ly/2Vyy22c

Funny Bones: Posada and His Day of the Dead Calaveras, by Duncan Tonatiuh. *Funny Bones* tells the story of how the amusing calaveras – skeletons performing various everyday or festive activities – came to be. They are the creation of Mexican artist José Guadalupe (Lupe) Posada (1852–1913). In a country that was not known for freedom of speech, he first drew political cartoons, much to the amusement of the local population but not the politicians. (**E**) bit.ly/2FKOXak

Harvest of Empire: A History of Latinos in America, by Juan Gonzalez. See *Immigrant and Refugee History, Issues, and Rights* section. (**H**) bit.ly/3dxD2Mi

Harvesting Hope: The Story of César Chávez, by Kathleen Krull. See *Labor and Economic Issues* section. (**E**) bit.ly/2qkxOfj; link to Teacher's Guide: bit.ly/1Qd1FZx

Indigenous Struggle and the Bolivian National Revolution: Land and Liberty! by James Kohl. See *Indigenous History, Issues, and Rights* section. (**H, TR**) bit.ly/3tn1XZT

Island Treasures: Growing Up in Cuba, by Alma Flor Ada. See *African and African Diaspora History, Issues, and Rights* section. (**E**) bit.ly/2JF664T

Martí's Song for Freedom/Martí y sus versos por la libertad, by Emma Otheguy. As a boy, José Martí found freedom in the river that rushed to the sea and peace in the *palmas reales* that swayed in the wind. Freedom, he believed, was the inherent right of all people. But his home island of Cuba was colonized by Spain, and some of the people were enslaved by rich landowners. Enraged, Martí took up his pen and fought against this oppression through his writings. By age 17, he was declared an enemy of Spain and forced to leave his beloved island. Written in verse, with excerpts from Martí's seminal *Versos sencillos*, this bilingual book is a beautiful tribute. (**E, M**) Teacher's guide from Lee & Low Books here: bit.ly/3dsPAFW

Migrant, by Maxine Trottier. See *Labor and Economic Issues* section. (**E**) bit.ly/32baKlB

Model Curriculum and Resources for Teachers. See *Labor and Economic Issues* section. (**E, M, H**) bit.ly/1mFT0W3

Mucho Mucho Amor: The Legend of Walter Mercado, directed by Cristina Costantini and Kareem Tabsch. This 2020 documentary film chronicles the life and career of Walter Mercado, one of the most influential and important astrologists in Latin America and the world. (**H**) bit.ly/3bL5NFM

Napí, by Antonio Ramirez. See *Indigenous History, Issues, and Rights* section. (**E**) amzn.to/39Ek6KV

Pablo Remembers, by George Ancona. This photodocumentary-style children's book follows Pablo and his family as they celebrate *Día de Los Muertos* by honoring his grandmother. (**E**) bit.ly/2LH9zBu

Resistencia: Poems of Protest and Revolution, edited by Mark Eisner and Tina Escaja, with an introduction by Julia Alvarez. An extraordinary collection, rooted in a strong tradition of protest poetry and voiced by icons of the movement and some of the most exciting writers today. The poets of *Resistencia* explore feminist, queer, Indigenous, and ecological themes alongside historically prominent protests against imperialism, dictatorships, and economic inequality. Within this momentous collection, poets representing every Latin American country grapple with identity, place, and belonging, resisting easy definitions to render a nuanced and complex portrait of language in rebellion. (**H**) bit.ly/3cTJKgw

Rethinking Cinco de Mayo, by Sudie Hofmann, Zinn Education Project. In this article, Hofmann critiques a stereotypical Mexican American event meant to celebrate Cinco de Mayo. Readers will find information about the history of Cinco de Mayo and how it is celebrated in the US, art depicting the events of the Battle of Puebla Day, and reactions from Chicana/o students. Links to related materials are provided. (**H, TR**) bit.ly/13VTKtX

Revolutionary Women of Texas and Mexico: Portraits of Soldaderas, Saints, and Subversives, edited by Ellen Riojas Clark, Kathy Sosa, and Jennifer Speed. This anthology embraces an expansive definition of the word revolutionary by looking at female role models and subversives from the last century and who stood up for their visions and ideals and continue to stand for them today. Eighteen portraits provide readers with a glimpse into each figure's life and place in history. (**H**) bit.ly/31DS51I

Sept. 14, 1911: El Primer Congreso Mexicanista Convenes in Laredo, by the Zinn Education Project. A short description of the first Mexicanist Congress meeting, along with related resources for teaching and learning. (**H**) www.zinnedproject.org/news/tdih/jovita-idar

Silver People: Voices from the Panama Canal, by Margarita Engle. See *African and African Diaspora History, Issues, and Rights* section. (**M**) bit.ly/1Bz0sVN; Teacher's Guide: bit.ly/2G0IqKf

Spanish-American War, teaching materials from the Stanford History Education Group. Although the sinking of the *USS Maine* provided an immediate trigger for the Spanish-American War, long-term US military and economic interests provide a more nuanced context for the US invasion of Cuba. In this lesson, students watch a documentary video, read a telegram describing Spanish treatment of Cubans, and examine an American campaign speech to explore the long-term reasons for the US invasion of Cuba in 1898. (**H**) stanford.io/2QfQBsn

Talking with Mother Earth/Hablando con Madre Tierra, by Jorge Argueta. See *Indigenous History, Issues, and Rights* section. (**E**) bit.ly/3d7dg2B

Teaching Central America, by Teaching for Change. More than four million Central Americans reside in the United States today, yet the lack of resources in most schools on Central American heritage make the rich history and literature of the region invisible. Teaching for Change launched a campaign to encourage and support teaching about Central America, with collected lessons, book lists, biographies of noted historical figures, and readings for free use by classroom teachers. (**E, M, H, TR**) teachingcentralamerica.org

The Christmas Gift/El Regalo de Navidad, by Francisco Jiménez. See *Immigrant and Refugee History, Issues, and Rights* section. (**E**) bit.ly/2Veahtj

They Call Me Guero: A Border Kid's Poems, by David Bowles. Twelve-year-old Guero is Mexican American, at home with Spanish or English and on both sides of the river. He's starting 7th grade with a woke English teacher who knows how to make poetry cool. (**E, M**) bit.ly/3rMhpNx

Tropical Secrets: Holocaust Refugees in Cuba, a novel in verse by Margarita Engle. Turned away from the shores of New York, a young Jewish boy seeks refuge in Cuba during WWII. Here in this tropical sanctuary, so far away from Germany, will he be safe from Nazi influence? (**M, H**) bit.ly/2R5lS1h

Viva La Causa, film kit by Learning for Justice. See *Labor and Economic Issues* section. (**E, M**) bit.ly/3hmif27

¡Viva la Causa! 500 Years of Chicano History, by the Southwest Organizing Project and Collision Course Video Productions. Based on the book *500 Years of Chicano History in Pictures*, edited by Elizabeth Martínez, this two-part video in English offers a compelling introduction to the history of Mexican American people. (**M, H**) amzn.to/XhUqfa

War Against All Puerto Ricans: Revolution and Terror in America's Colony, by Nelson A. Denis. The website for this book includes a historical overview of Puerto Rico's struggle for independence, and a wealth of related resources, including video clips and other multimedia. Includes a section on Albizu Campos. (**H, TR**) bit.ly/2lOJDVL

Literacy and Language

40 Books to Celebrate National Poetry Month, by Black Children's Books and Authors. Forty powerful poetry books by Black writers, which can be used during National Poetry Month and year-round. (**E**) bit.ly/2Ei0lXa

An Interview with Ralph Ellison, by Alfred Chester and Vilma Howard for the *Paris Review*. See *African American History, Issues, and Rights* section. (**H**) bit.ly/2P1liRw

Celebrating the Freedom to Read, by the Banned Books Week Coalition. Information and resources, including links to videos, related to increasing awareness of the annual celebration of the freedom to read, and the movement against book censorship. (**TR**) bit.ly/2Sm6s4x

Dear Banned Author, by the American Library Association's Office for Intellectual Freedom. During Banned Books Week, readers are encouraged to write to their favorite banned or challenged authors, sharing what their stories meant to them. (**E, M, H**) bit.ly/2SsnG0d

En Comunidad: Lessons for Centering the Voices and Experiences of Bilingual Latinx Students, by Carla España and Luz Yadira Herrera. See *Latinx/Latin American History, Issues, and Rights* section. (**TR**) bit.ly/2Vyy22c

Feed Your Mind: A Story of August Wilson, by Jen Bryant. See *African American History, Issues, and Rights* section. (**M, H**) bit.ly/3dWMlG8

Freedom Libraries: The Untold Story of Libraries for African Americans in the South, by Mike Selby. See *African American History, Issues, and Rights* section. (**H**) bit.ly/3se9QPV

Jump Back, Paul: The Life and Poems of Paul Laurence Dunbar, by Sally Derby. See *African American History, Issues, and Rights* section. (**E, M**) bit.ly/3mIhyAN

Little Libraries, Big Heroes, by Miranda Paul. The inspiring story of how the Little Free Library organization brings communities together through books, from founder Todd Bol's first installation to the creation of more than 75,000 mini-libraries around the world. Includes an author's note and bibliography. (**E**) bit.ly/3wUFeGQ

Love to Langston, by Tony Medina. See *African American History, Issues, and Rights* section. (**E, M**) Teacher's guide here: bit.ly/3ti1nMO

Rethinking Bilingual Education, by Rethinking Schools. See *Immigrant and Refugee History, Issues, and Rights* section. (**TR**) bit.ly/2njKRdr

Thanku: Poems of Gratitude, edited by Miranda Paul. An anthology exploring themes of thankfulness and gratitude through poetry written mostly by Black, Indigenous, and poets of Color. (**E, M**) bit.ly/2Fh30CM

The Dark Fantastic: Race and the Imagination from Harry Potter to the Hunger Games, by Ebony Elizabeth Thomas. See *African American History, Issues, and Rights* section. (**H, TR**) bit.ly/2BJY6gQ

Woke: A Young Poet's Call to Justice, by Mahogany Browne with Elizabeth Acevedo and Olivia Gatwood. Historically, poets have been on the forefront of social movements. *Woke* is a collection of poems by women that reflect the joy and passion in the fight for social justice, tackling topics from discrimination to empathy, and acceptance to speaking out. (**E, M, H**) bit.ly/3gnx3KI

Middle Eastern American and Middle East History, Issues, and Rights

A Little Piece of Ground, by Elizabeth Laird with Sonia Nimr. This novel is about a young boy named Karim, who is living through the Israeli occupation of Palestine. (**E**) bit.ly/2JC3zZf

A TED Talk by Manal-al Sharif. In this TED Talk from June 2013, Manal al-Sharif advocates for women's right to drive, male guardianship annulment, and family protection in Saudi Arabia. (**M, H**) ted.com/speakers/manal_al_sharif

American Islamophobia: Understanding the Roots and Rise of Fear, by Khaled Beydoun. See *Hate and Oppression* section. (**H, TR**) bit.ly/3fRy3Jx

An Interview with Nawal El Saadawi: "Do you Feel You Are Liberated? I Feel I Am Not." by Rachel Cooke for *The Guardian*. Video clips from a rich interview with Egyptian revolutionary Nawal El Saadawi with relevance to the issues of today. (**H**) bit.ly/3daNZ7J

Can Egyptian Women Start a Revolution Against Sexual Violence? By Nick Schifrin. In Tahrir Square, the center of the Egyptian revolution, women safely joined men to demonstrate for a new future. But that moment soon ended; hundreds, even thousands of female protesters were sexually assaulted. In some cases, activists believe the government used violence as a political weapon. Special correspondent Nick Schifrin examines how women have fought back through activism in this 10-minute video and interview with activists conducted for PBS NewsHour. (**H**) to.pbs.org/3wu7yzA

Celebrate Arab American Heritage Month, by Beatrice Alvarez for PBS. A collection of short films representing some of the millions of voices and diverse experiences of Arab Americans.

Celebrating Arab American Heritage Month, by Learning for Justice. A rich collection of resources, articles, lesson plans, and more to help educators celebrate Arab identity, counter negative stereotypes, teach about Arab history and cultures, and ensure an inclusive environment that supports Arab American students this month and throughout the year. (**TR**) bit.ly/3aO9wkX

Determined to Stay: Palestinian Youth Fight for Their Village, by Jody Sokolower. As Silwani youth and community members share their lives with us, their village becomes an easily accessible way to understand Palestinian history and current reality. Written with young people in mind, the richly illustrated text stresses connections between the lives of youth in the US and in Palestine: criminalization of youth, forced relocation, the impact of colonialism on Indigenous communities, efforts to bury history, and inspiring examples of resistance and resilience. (**H**) bit.ly/3410jSD

Egyptian Streets: The Podcast, by Noran Morsi. Featuring Egyptians around the world who fuel creative social change and their journeys that brought them there, from the intersection of Egyptian identity and creative social change, are stories from street to sound. (**M, H**) egyptianstreets.com/category/the-podcast

Except for Palestine: The Limits of Progressive Politics, by Marc Lamont Hill and Mitchell Plitnick. *Except for Palestine* deftly argues that progressives and liberals who oppose regressive policies on immigration, racial justice, gender equality, LGBTQ rights, and other issues must extend these core principles to the oppression of Palestinians. In doing so, the authors take seriously the political concerns and wellbeing of both Israelis and Palestinians, demonstrating the extent to which US policy has made peace harder to attain. They also unravel the conflation of advocacy for Palestinian rights with anti-Semitism and hatred of Israel. (**H, TR**) thenewpress.com/books/except-for-palestine

Other Words for Home, by Jasmine Warga. See *Immigrant and Refugee History, Issues, and Rights* section. (**M, H**) bit.ly/2DlV6Yu

Our Women on the Ground: Essays by Arab Women Reporting from the Arab World, edited by Zahra Hankir. A growing number of intrepid Arab and Middle Eastern *sahafiyat* – female journalists – are working tirelessly to shape nuanced narratives about their changing homelands, often risking their lives on the front lines of war. Nineteen of these women tell us, in their own words, about what it's like to report on conflicts. (**H**) bit.ly/3fZrkwV

Teaching with the News: The United States in Afghanistan: Analyzing Political Cartoons, by The Choices Program. This lesson enables students to analyze a series of political cartoons to understand different viewpoints on US involvement in Afghanistan. (**M, H**) bit.ly/9EeGIe

The Arab Spring: One Year On, by the CHOICES Program. In this unit plan, students learn about various Arab Spring protest movements in the Middle East and North Africa. There are additional general resources included, as well as country-specific resources and materials. (**H, TR**) bit.ly/3dTPPco

The Egyptian Revolution: An Interactive Timeline, by the CHOICES Program. Lesson plan and multimedia resources that engage young people in identifying core themes of Egyptian protest movements. (**H**) bit.ly/3fJqt3n

The Map of Salt and Stars: A Novel, by Zeyn Joukhadar. The story of two girls living 800 years apart – a modern-day Syrian refugee seeking safety and a medieval adventurer apprenticed to a legendary mapmaker – places today's headlines about Syria in the sweep of history, where the pain of exile and the triumph of courage echo again and again. (**H**) bit.ly/31M1WSZ

The Teach Palestine Project, by the Middle East Children's Alliance. The Teach Palestine Project website is a resource by and for K-12 teachers and teacher educators focused on bringing Palestine into our classrooms and schools. (**TR**) teachpalestine.org

Winter Soldier: Iraq and Afghanistan - Eyewitness Accounts of the Occupations, Illustrated Edition, by Iraq Veterans Against the War. In spring 2008, inspired by the Vietnam-era Winter Soldier hearings, Iraq Veterans Against the War gathered veterans to expose war crimes in Afghanistan and Iraq. These are the powerful words, images, and documents of this historic gathering, which show the reality of life in Afghanistan and Iraq. (**H**) bit.ly/3ucc1oC

Peace Education/ Counter-Recruiting

Essays on Nonviolence, by the Center on Conscience and War. Essays and statements by historical figures on nonviolence and conscientious objection. (**M, H**) centeronconscience.org/essays-on-nonviolence

Let the Faithful Come, by Zetta Elliott. See *African American History, Issues, and Rights* section. (**E, M**) bit.ly/2VZUGim

Mother's Day Proclamation – 1870, by Julia Ward Howe. Poem by Julia Ward Howe advocating for women around the world to organize to resolve conflicts peacefully. (**E, M, H**) bit.ly/eT5sy

Painting for Peace: A Coloring Book for All Ages, by Carol Swartout Klein and Robert O'Neil. A journalist and marketing professional by training, Carol Swartout Klein grew up in Ferguson, MO, and was so inspired by witnessing the spirit of hundreds of volunteers coming together to bring hope to a community in shock that she wanted to capture the story and the art for posterity. *Painting for Peace* is a coloring book that helps begin conversations with children and inspires adults. (**E**) bit.ly/3cIZHGw

Peace Tools for Teachers. This page on the peaceCENTER website offers a variety of peace teaching resources, including lessons, activities, dates, and quotes – all designed with teachers in mind. (**E, M, H, TR**) bit.ly/2HmWQSp

Project YANO – The Project on Youth and Non-Military Opportunities. Celebrate Veterans Day by helping students find alternatives to military service. Project YANO is a non-profit community organization that provides young people with an alternative point of view about military enlistment. (**H**) www.projectyano.org

Voices in Wartime, by *YES!* Magazine and Voices in Wartime Education Project. This site seeks to enable students to engage deeply with the subject of war by hearing and re-telling the personal stories of witnesses to war, encouraging students to imagine and create a less violent world. The site includes the film's trailer, curriculum materials, and poetry. (**H, TR**) bit.ly/1uCgCMY

Winter Soldier: Iraq and Afghanistan - Eyewitness Accounts of the Occupations, Illustrated Edition, by Iraq Veterans Against the War. See *Middle Eastern American and Middle East History, Issues, and Rights* section. (**H**) bit.ly/3ucc1oC

Police Violence and Prisons

13th Critical Viewing Guide, by Graduate Students at the Lynch School of Education of Boston College and Dr. Leigh Patel. Ava DuVernay's film, *13th*, provides a history of the establishment and maintenance of the prison industrial complex as an extension of chattel slavery in a racist, profit-driven society. This guide seeks to further elucidate several important themes not sufficiently covered in the documentary, but that undergird the structure of racist capitalism. The guide provides questions for reflection, readings, videos, infographics, and other materials, and aims to facilitate a more critical engagement with the film. (**H, TR**) bit.ly/2n1BZt8

Ahimsa, by Supriya Kelkar. See *Asian/ Asian Pacific Islander/Asian American History, Issues, and Rights* section. (**M, H**) Teacher's guide from Lee & Low Books here: leeandlow.com/books/ahimsa

An Outrage: A Documentary Film about Lynching in the American South, by the SPLC and the Smithsonian. See *African American History, Issues, and Rights* section. (**H**) bit.ly/3wSawy2

Attica Prison Uprising 101 - A Short Primer, by Mariame Kaba. This publication about the Attica Prison uprising of 1971 is not intended to be a curriculum guide, but a brief primer for educators and organizers. It includes a timeline of events (with primary sources); testimonies from Attica prisoners; poetry by Attica prisoners; sample activities for youth; and other suggested resources. (**H, TR**) bit.ly/3sZrlOT

Black Lives Matter at School Website, by a national coalition of organizers. See *African American History, Issues, and Rights* section. (**TR**) blacklivesmatteratschool.com

Death Penalty: What Is It? What Do We Think About It? by Marieke van Woerkom. This lesson was created in 2011 right after Troy Davis was executed. Still relevant today, the lesson involves studying Troy Davis's case and exploring different perspectives and facts about the death penalty. Resources include facts, readings, video links, and more. (**H, TR**) bit.ly/3cpIEb7

Every Mother's Son, by P.O.V. This film presents three primary examples of police brutality and what is being done about it. The lesson accompanying the video addresses actions that students can take. (**H**) to.pbs.org/1cNyCMD

Free Black Mamas: National Bail Out. This organization works to reunite families, create a national community of leaders who have experienced incarceration, and work with groups across the country to transform harmful systems to keep Black people safe and free. (**TR**) nationalbailout.org

Invisible No More: Police Violence Against Black Women and Women of Color, by Andrea Ritchie. A timely examination of how Black women, Indigenous women, and other Women of Color experience racial profiling, police brutality, and immigration enforcement. (**H**) bit.ly/3sUMYGr

Just Mercy (Adapted for Young Adults): A True Story of the Fight for Justice, by Bryan Stevenson. Stevenson's story is one of working to protect basic human rights for the most vulnerable people in American society – the poor, the wrongly convicted, and those whose lives have been marked by discrimination and marginalization. Through this adaptation, young people will find themselves called to action and compassion in the pursuit of justice. (**H**) bit.ly/3sO6kg7

Lessons in Liberation: An Abolitionist Toolkit for Educators, by the Education for Liberation Network and Critical Resistance Editorial Collective. The movement for abolition is expanding. Born from Black and Women of Color feminism, disability justice, and environmental movements, the call to end our reliance on imprisonment, policing, and surveillance and to imagine a safer future has a new terrain of struggle. This toolkit for educators, parents, and youth, shines a light on innovative abolitionist projects, particularly in the K–12 teaching and learning contexts. (**TR**) bit.ly/2ROijgp

Let Her Learn: A Toolkit to Stop School Push Out for Girls of Color, by the National Women's Law Center. This toolkit will help you determine if your school's discipline policy treats girls of Color fairly. Use this guide to learn your rights, ways in which you can change your school policy, and where to find help. (**TR**) bit.ly/2i1PIRG

Lynching in America, by The Equal Justice Initiative. See *African American History, Issues, and Rights* section. (**H, TR**) bit.ly/2JsovSt

Lynching in America: Confronting the Legacy of Racial Terror, by Equal Justice Initiative. See *African American History, Issues, and Rights* section. (**H, TR**) Report: bit.ly/3eDnvNu; Memorial: bit.ly/3eBGrvS

Mama's Day, by Strong Families. Each year artists are commissioned to create images that capture the full diversity of family arrangements. These images are offered as free e-cards; the site also offers the opportunity to send an e-card to an incarcerated or detained mama. (**E, M, H**) www.mamasday.org

Missing Daddy, by Mariame Kaba. In this picture book for readers ages 4-8, a little girl who misses her father because he's away in prison shares how his absence affects different parts of her life. She is most excited on the days when she gets to visit her beloved father. With gorgeous illustrations, this book depicts a little girl's love for her father from whom she is separated because of incarceration. (**E**) Resources and discussion questions here: missingdaddy.net

Resources from The Abolition and Disability Justice Coalition. See *Disability History, Issues, and Rights* section. (**H, TR**) abolitionanddisabilityjustice.com

"Riots," Racism, and the Police: Students Explore a Century of Police Conduct and Racial Violence, a teaching activity by Ursula Wolfe-Rocca for Zinn Education Project. In this lesson, students explore three documents produced in the wake of three major episodes of racial violence (1919, 1967, and 2014). The goal of the activity is to understand the long trajectory of police violence in Black communities. (**H**) bit.ly/3rLUHpl

Say Her Name, by Zetta Elliott. Inspired by the #SayHerName campaign, these poems pay tribute to Black women who are victims of police brutality, as well as Black Lives Matter activists. Elliott draws on the work of poets from the past two centuries to create a chorus of voices celebrating the creativity, resilience, and courage of Black women and girls. (**M, H**) bit.ly/3tcSQun

Soledad Brother: The Prison Letters of George Jackson. A collection of Jackson's letters from prison, *Soledad Brother* is a categorical condemnation of the racism of White America and a powerful appraisal of the prison system that eventually took his life but failed to break his spirit. (**H**) bit.ly/3qNNsfn

Steps to End Prisons and Policing: A Mixtape on Transformative Justice, by the Just Practice Collaborative. This mixtape is an offering of nourishment and care to the abolitionist community. Learn from some of the people who have been practicing and thinking about and creating organizations around Transformative Justice over the last two decades. (**H, TR**) bit.ly/3vsjVLb

Teaching for Black Lives, by Rethinking Schools. See *African American History, Issues, and Rights* section. (**TR**) teachingforblacklives.org

The Day Tajon Got Shot, by T'Asia, J'yona, Reiyanna, Jonae, Makiya, Rose, Najae, Serenity, Jeanet, and Temil (the Teen Writers of Beacon House). In March 2015, 10 teenage girls from Beacon House in Washington, DC started writing a novel during the rise of the Black Lives Matter movement. They began with one central question: What really happens in a community when a Black youth is the victim of violence by police? How are those lives affected? Each writer takes on the perspective of a central character – the victim, the police officer, the witness, the parent, the friend, the officer's kids – and examines how it feels to be a human being on all sides of this event. Their stories thoughtfully explore issues of race, violence, loyalty, and justice in a community torn apart but seeking connection. (**E, M**) bit.ly/2PArMXC

We Do This 'til We Free Us: Abolitionist Organizing and Transforming Justice, by Mariame Kaba. In this collection of essays and interviews, Kaba reflects on the deep work of abolition and transformative political struggle. The book asks questions about justice beyond the punishment system, transforming how we deal with harm and accountability, and finding hope in collective struggle for abolition. (**H, TR**) bit.ly/3lfelaV; discussion guide at bit.ly/3fDoUUK

We Still Here: Pandemic, Policing, Protest, and Possibility, by Marc Lamont Hill. In this urgent and incisive collection of new interviews bookended by two new essays, Marc Lamont Hill critically examines the "pre-existing conditions" that have led us to this moment of crisis and upheaval, guiding us through both the perils and possibilities, and helping us imagine an abolitionist future. (**H**) bit.ly/3sTMZua

When They Call You a Terrorist (Newly Adapted Young Adult Edition): A Story of Black Lives Matter and the Power to Change the World, by Patrisse Cullors and Asha Bandele. See *African American History, Issues, and Rights* section. (**M, H**) bit.ly/2Q6vOHr

Y'all Still Don't Hear Me Though, by Lecia Brooks. This text for grades 6-8 features a 2015 essay by Lecia J. Brooks as she recounts her perspective as a protester who participated in the Los Angeles Race Riots that followed the trial of those who had committed police brutality against Rodney King. Her account details the pervasiveness of police brutality and why demonstrators protest against it. (**M**) bit.ly/3thO8Mm

Queer History, Issues, and Rights

A Trans* and Gender Non-conforming Reading List for All Ages, by The Booklist Reader. The list highlights books by and about the trans*/GNC community for all ages. For non-trans readers with family members, friends, or colleagues who are trans*/GNC – actually, for all readers with open minds and hearts – these books can lead the way toward becoming well-informed allies. (**E, M, H, TR**) bit.ly/2oxQCnU

Am I Wrong to Love? by the UN Refugee Agency. A photo essay exhibit and collection featuring portraits and first-person stories of LGBTQI refugees and asylum seekers from around the world who are now living in Canada. (**M, H**) bit.ly/2PP2Mf6

An Audiovisual Collection on Mabel Hampton, by the Lesbian Herstory Archives. A collection of recordings of interviews and other source material by and from Mabel Hampton, highlighting her work as a champion for lesbian rights, and her career as a domestic worker and dancer. (**H**) bit.ly/3dpTmju

Asha's Mums, by Rosamund Elwin and Michelle Paulse. When Asha needs a signature for the permission slip for her school trip to the Science Center, she is questioned about which name on the form was her mom's. Asha undergoes the experience of teaching her fellow classmates and her teacher that she and her brother have two moms and they are both number one. (**E**) bit.ly/2KjEynm

Daddy, Papa, and Me, by Lesléa Newman. Rhythmic text and illustrations with universal appeal show a toddler spending the day with his daddies. (**E**) bit.ly/2qlJkHq

Day of Silence Website. This site includes information about the history of the Day of Silence, as well as FAQs, reproducible materials, an organizing manual for students, and more. (**M, H**) bit.ly/3SF54f

Gay, Lesbian, and Straight Education Network (GLSEN) Curriculum. This resource helps to ensure that LGBTQ students see themselves reflected in lessons and creates opportunities for all students to gain a more complex and authentic understanding of the world around them. (**E, M, H**) bit.ly/2RZG9nF

Gay, Lesbian, and Straight Education Network (GLSEN) Educator Resources. These resources help to ensure that LGBTQI+ students see themselves reflected in lessons and creates opportunities for all students to gain a more complex and authentic understanding of the world around them. (**E, M, H, TR**) bit.ly/2RZG9nF

Halal If You Hear Me, edited by Fatimah Asghar and Safia Elhillo. A BreakBeat Poets anthology of writings by Muslims who are women, queer, genderqueer, nonbinary, or trans. The collected poems dispel the notion that there is only one correct way to be a Muslim by holding space for multiple, intersecting identities while celebrating and protecting those identities. (**H**) bit.ly/2vdWYym

Hope Along the Wind: The Life of Harry Hay, directed by Eric Slade and produced by Jack Walsh. This documentary follows the life of one of the founders of the Mattachine Society, a highly successful gay rights organization. The website provides information regarding Hay's life and information on purchasing the film. (**H**) vimeo.com/48114440

Hope In a Box. A nonprofit that designed a primer in LGBTQ literature for young adults and now donates this set of 50 books to middle and high schools free of charge. They provide curriculum guides for selected texts and help purchase copies for the full classroom for teachers looking to include an LGBTQ book in a lesson plan. (**M, H, TR**) hopeinabox.org

InterACT, Advocates for Intersex Youth. A rich bibliography of resources, from academic papers and news articles to human rights rulings and policy statements related to intersex awareness and advocacy. (**M, H, TR**) bit.ly/1KUOkJN

International Day Against Homophobia, Biphobia, and Transphobia (IDAHOBIT) Website. Resources about LGBTQI injustices around the world and ways to contribute to campaigns fighting for LGBTQI justice. (**M, H, TR**) bit.ly/1i0e5IG

Intersex Stories, Not Surgeries, by Pidgeon. A YouTube channel by non-binary, intersex youth, Pidgeon is a humorous and humanizing way to learn more about intersex experiences from their perspectives. (**M, H**) bit.ly/2s2tcLq

Just Like You: A 60 Second Text, by Ki Gross, Woke Kindergarten. In 1-minute narrated images, Ki Gross translates "big concepts for little people." Designed for early childhood, this particular 60-second text features the important and beautiful lives of Black transgender people, and the ways in which these human beings are "just like you." (**E**) wokekindergarten.org/60secondtexts

King and the Dragonflies, by Kacen Callender. In a small but turbulent Louisiana town, one boy's grief takes him beyond the bayous of his backyard to learn that there is no right way to be yourself. (**M, H**) kacencallender.com/books

Mucho Mucho Amor: The Legend of Walter Mercado, directed by Cristina Costantini and Kareem Tabsch. See *Latinx/Latin American History, Issues, and Rights* section. (**H**) bit.ly/3bL5NFM

My Footprints, by Bao Phi. See *Asian/Asian Pacific Islander/Asian American History, Issues, and Rights* section. (**E**) bit.ly/3wJBsjm

On "Don't Ask, Don't Tell": Debating a Proposed Repeal, by Sarah Kavanagh and Holly Epstein Ojalvo for the Learning Network, *NYTimes*. From their description: Should gays and lesbians be allowed to serve openly in the military? What issues are at stake in this issue? In this lesson, students consider the law and the arguments for and against repealing it, then engage in a "structured academic controversy" about whether or not the "Don't Ask, Don't Tell" policy should be repealed. (**H**) nyti.ms/3rMXXQT

Queer America Podcast, by Learning for Justice. Without LGBTQ history, there is no American history. From Learning Justice and hosts Leila Rupp and John D'Emilio, *Queer America* takes listeners on a journey that spans from Harlem to the Frontier West, revealing stories of LGBTQ life we should have learned in school. (**E, M, H**) learningforjustice.org/podcasts/queer-america

Queer History of the United States for Young People, by Michael Bronski and Richie Chevat. This book explores how LGBTQ people have always been a part of our national identity, contributing to the country and culture for more than 400 years. Through engrossing narratives, letters, drawings, poems, and more, the book encourages young readers of all identities to feel pride in the accomplishments of the LGBTQ people who came before them and to use history as a guide to the future. (**M, H**) bit.ly/3aVl0S3; teacher's guide: bit.ly/3br8hXB

Schools in Transition: A Guide for Supporting Transgender Students in K-12 Schools, by the ACLU. This guide highlights best practices while offering strategies for building upon and aligning them with each school's culture. (**TR**) bit.ly/3dwMEak

Supporting LGBTQIA Youth: A Resource List, by the Harvard Graduate School of Education's "Making Caring Common" Project. How can educators support LGBTQIA-identifying middle and high school students and create more inclusive school communities? The list at this site offers a sample of resources and links to websites for teachers and students. (**TR**) bit.ly/3dtRkOh

Sylvia and Marsha Start a Revolution!: The Story of the Trans Women of Color Who Made LGBTQ+ History, by Joy Ellison. This book introduces children to the story of Sylvia Rivera and Marsha P. Johnson, two transgender Women of Color who helped kickstart the Stonewall Riots and dedicated their lives to fighting for LGBTQ+ equality. It introduces issues surrounding gender identity and diversity, accompanied by a reading guide and teaching materials to further the conversation. (**E**) bit.ly/38A7dkj

The God Box, by Alex Sanchez. Paul, a religious teen living in a small conservative town, finds his world turned upside down when he meets Manuel, a young man who says he's both Christian and gay – two things that Paul didn't think could coexist in one person. Doesn't the Bible forbid homosexuality? As Paul struggles with Manuel's interpretation of the Bible, thoughts that Paul has long tried to bury begin to surface, and he finds himself re-examining his whole life. (**H**) bit.ly/2SMcjAp

The Power of Love: Meet the LGBTQI Refugees Finding Love Beyond Borders, by the UN Refugee Agency. Photos and stories of LGBTQI people finding and making home in new countries after forced displacement because of discrimination. (**M, H**) bit.ly/3oxa5VZ

The Trans Educators Network (TEN) is a support and community-building focused organization for trans and other PK-12 educators who don't always fit neatly into systems of gender at school. The Network is open to trans educators or anyone whose gender exists outside prescribed lines of male and female, and who works with youth in PK-12 schools. TEN is firmly committed to trans justice, racial justice, and anti-oppression work in education. (**TR**) transeducators.com

They, She, He, Me: Free to Be! By Maya & Matthew. The authors have succeeded in creating a gorgeous and much-needed picture book about pronouns and gender fluidity. (**E**) bit.ly/3uSs4IB

Toolkit for "Being There for Nonbinary Youth," by Learning for Justice. This toolkit synthesizes the key tips and takeaways from a related article entitled, "Being There for Nonbinary Youth" and offers online resources for supporting transgender students. (**TR**) bit.ly/3sqIXbz

Travels In a Gay Nation: Portraits of LGBTQ Americans, by Philip Gambone. In addition to interviews with David Sedaris, George Takei, Barney Frank, and Tammy Baldwin, *Travels in a Gay Nation* brings us lesser-known voices – a retired Naval officer, a transgender scholar and "drag king," a Princeton philosopher, two opera sopranos who happen to be lovers, an Indie Rock musician, the founder of a gay frat house, and a pair of Vermont garden designers. In this age when contemporary gay America is still coming under attack, Gambone captures the humanity of each individual. (**H**) uwpress.wisc.edu/books/4771.htm

Troublemaker for Justice: The Story of Bayard Rustin, the Man Behind the March on Washington, by Jacqueline Houtman, Walter Naegle, and Michael G. Long. See *Civil Rights, Black Power, Student and 1960s Movements* section. (**E, M**) bit.ly/2Q0nSHA

Two Spirits, film directed by Lydia Nibley. See *Indigenous History, Issues, and Rights* section. (**M, H, TR**) bit.ly/1qA6uVK

Welcoming Schools. This is a guide for administrators, educators, parents, and guardians who want to strengthen their schools' approaches to family diversity, gender stereotyping, and bullying. It is specifically designed for use in K-5 learning environments and is inclusive of LGBTQI+ families and individuals in the broader context of diversity. (**E**) bit.ly/bN8CiT

When a Student Comes Out to You... Today or Any Day! by GLSEN. This blog post provides suggestions for how to respond when a student comes out to you. The post comes from GLSEN's Safe Space Kit available on their site. (**TR**) bit.ly/2Q1uwgl

Race and Ethnicity

The White Supremacy and Me Workbook, by Layla Saad. See *Hate and Oppression* section. (**TR**) bit.ly/2Agvf2C

White Anti-Racist Biographies: Early Grades, by Learning for Justice. For young White students, explorations of fair and unfair, just and unjust can go a long way in advancing anti-racist White identity. Purposeful use of literature and basic study of White anti-racists are among the ways educators can advance such aims. Learning for Justice presents four short biographies for early grades classrooms, with activity ideas. (**E**) bit.ly/3rSpLn0

White Rage: The Unspoken Truth of Our Racial Divide, by Carol Anderson. See *Hate and Oppression* section. (**H**) bit.ly/36ey6Xj

Religions

8 Ways to Include Vaisakhi in Classrooms, by Navjot Kaur and Saffron Press. Background information on the holiday, as well as eight meaningful activities for children, are included on this site. (**E, M**) bit.ly/2AqVjen

A Lion's Mane, by Navjot Kaur. This is a picture book that helps young readers journey to cultures around the world to explore the meaning of the *dastaar*, the Sikh turban. The second link is to a teacher's guide for the book. (**E, TR**) bit.ly/3cgyvvp; Teacher's Guide: bit.ly/V1oNIK

A Mountain of Blintzes, by Barbara Diamond Goldin and Anik McGrory. This children's book tells the story of a family saving up to make cheese blintzes, a traditional food eaten during Shavuot. (**E**) bit.ly/2RX0IB3

A Question of Faith: Books and Resources to Help Us Talk to Our Kids About Religion and Spirituality, by Olugbemisola Rhuday-Perkovich. How do we help our children process the messages they receive from media sources about religion and faith, its connections to conflict, history, and culture? Helpful tips, books, and other resources to support educators and families in talking to kids about multicultural faiths and spirituality. (**E, M**) bit.ly/3dRpITo

Apples and Pomegranates: A Rosh Hashanah Seder, by Rahel Musleah. This children's book acts as a guideline for celebrating the Jewish New Year. Traditional foods and the sequence in which they are eaten are described. Each chapter includes the history of the food, an activity, recipes, and more. (**E**) bit.ly/2ShDgLT

BBC Schools: Guide to Christianity. This site includes basic information about Christianity, including Lent and Easter, as well as links to classroom activities intended to help students understand the beliefs and practices of Christians. (**M, H, TR**) bbc.in/ROXVFb

Becoming Buddha: The Story of Siddhartha, by Whitney Stewart. This book follows Buddha from pre-birth prophecies through his pampered youth, his break with royal life, and his quest for enlightenment. (**E**) bit.ly/2IIlLOC

Cakes and Miracles: A Purim Tale, by Barbara Diamond Goldin. Purim is approaching and Hershel, the only blind boy in the village, wishes he could help his mother prepare *hamantashen* (a traditional pastry) for the holiday. With new courage, Hershel creates something more beautiful than anyone in the village can imagine. An Author's Note about Purim is also included. Reading guide included at this site. (**E**) bit.ly/2DCZ7XS

Celebrate Easter: With Colored Eggs, Flowers, and Prayer (Holidays Around the World), by Deborah Heiligman. This children's book uses *National Geographic* photographs to document the celebration of Easter around the world, including the White House Easter Egg Roll and traditional bonfires in Europe. (**E**) bit.ly/T4xiH4

Celebrations: Wesak, by Anita Ganeri. This children's book, part of the *Celebrations* series, explores the history behind Wesak (Vesak) and how it is celebrated today with special foods, clothing, songs, and rituals. (**E**) amzn.to/VAg7CL

Classroom Resources for Educating About Muslims, by teachingwhilemuslim.org. A compilation of resources, lesson plans, and curriculum guides to help fill the gap in educating about the experiences and history of Muslims all over the world, and to combat Islamophobia in our schools and communities. (**TR**) bit.ly/2JitGo4

Diwali: A Cultural Adventure, by Sana Sood. This book offers young readers a bright, beautiful introduction to Diwali and how and why it is celebrated. (**E**) bit.ly/2HY9NAU

Festival of Colors, by Kabir Sehgal and Surishtha Sehgal. Learn all about Holi, the Indian Festival of Colors, in this lush picture book from the bestselling mother/son duo. (**E**) bit.ly/2KO5lpt

Guru Nanak, by Rina Singh. The Sikh faith, the world's 5th largest religion, began with the teachings of Guru Nanak in the 15th century and evolved with the nine gurus who followed him. He grew up to be a great spiritual teacher, revolutionary for his time, declaring that there is no difference between Hindus and Muslims, that men and women are equal, and that caste is irrelevant. This biography, exquisitely illustrated in the Indian miniature-painting tradition, tells the story of his life. (**E**) amzn.to/1qMWw5Q

Halal If You Hear Me, edited by Fatimah Asghar and Safia Elhillo. See *Queer History, Issues, and Rights* section. (**H**) bit.ly/2vdWYym

Hanuman Jayanti. This is a religious website that tells the story of the life of Hanuman. Illustrations and links to other festivals and related topics are available on this site. (**M, H**) bit.ly/KntMvy

Hinduism, by The Pluralism Project, Harvard University. A comprehensive collection of essays and resources related to topics such as Introduction to Hinduism; The Hindu Experience; and Current Issues for Hindus in America. The site also includes resources for "America's Many Religions." (**H, TR**) bit.ly/2TQIG17

Holiday Inclusion Guide, by Tanenbaum. A planning sheet for educators to think ahead about how to include diverse holidays in the classroom. (**TR**) bit.ly/2s3t4uS

Holidays Around the World: Celebrate Hanukkah: With Lights, Latkes, and Dreidels, by Deborah Heiligman. This children's book features *National Geographic* photography to illustrate how Jewish people around the world celebrate Hanukkah. (**E**) bit.ly/2U0xkr3

How Teachers Can Support Students During Ramadan, by Rusul Alrubail. Ramadan is a month in the Islamic calendar when Muslims observe fasting from sunrise to sunset. It can be a difficult month for many to get through, especially students who have to go through a normal school day without eating or drinking. For schools, it's important to provide an environment for students where they feel safe to practice their religion, but maybe more important, one that ensures their well-being during the school day. (**TR**) to.pbs.org/3ujLfuC

Lailah's Lunchbox: A Ramadan Story, by Reem Faruqi. Lailah's hesitation about her faith and traditions is explained from a child's point of view. Though she is excited to begin fasting during Ramadan, she is unsure about how to explain this practice to her classmates or deal with the temptations of lunchtime. Eventually, with the help of her librarian and teacher, she gains confidence among her peers. (**E**) bit.ly/2kFmPLM; Interview with author: bit.ly/2kzsP6e

Lights for Gita, by Rachna Gilmore. This book introduces readers to Diwali, one of the most important holidays observed by Hindus all over the world, through the eyes of Gita, a young immigrant girl. (**E**) bit.ly/2rYz5Jm

Maintain Neutrality, by Teaching Tolerance. This link provides a collection of lessons designed to help teachers maintain the distinction between "teaching religion" and "teaching *about* religion." The site has a wide array of other lessons and resources on the topic. (**E, M, H**) bit.ly/2IIR7Wp

Muslim Booklist, by Teaching for Change. Teaching for Change carefully selects the best multicultural and social justice books for children, young adults, and educators. This list includes many titles about the Muslim holidays and experience. (**E, M, H**) bit.ly/2ShV61l

My Name is Bilal, by Asma Mobin-Uddin. In this book, Bilal feels the need to hide his Muslim religion for fear he will be teased by other students. (**E**) bit.ly/2JvurtS

Once Upon an Eid: Stories of Hope and Joy by 15 Muslim Voices, edited by S.K. Ali and Aisha Saeed. A collection of short stories that showcase 15 brilliant Muslim voices sharing tales about the most joyful holiday of the year: Eid! The anthology also includes a poem, a graphic novel chapter, and spot illustrations. (**E, M, H**) bit.ly/2TAkYrO

Ramadan Moon, by Na'ima Bint Robert. This lyrical and inspiring picture book captures the wonder and joy of Ramadan from the perspective of a child. Written and illustrated by Muslim people, this is a book for all children who celebrate Ramadan and those in the wider communities who want to understand why this is such a special experience for Muslim people. (**E**) bit.ly/39F2vCA

Religions in My Neighborhood, by Tanenbaum. A collection of recommended readings, multimedia, and lesson plans to explore religious tolerance. (**E**) bit.ly/2GiZAC0

Respecting Atheists and Nonreligious People, by Teaching Tolerance. Students often learn the importance of respecting people of different religions, but what about people who do not hold religious beliefs at all? This lesson introduces students to people who choose not to follow a religion. (**E, M, H**) bit.ly/nonrelig

Rethinking Holidays in Schools, a blog post by Alex Shevrin Venet. Reflection questions for educators that support schools in making intentional decisions about how to mark and celebrate holidays in classrooms. (**TR**) bit.ly/2PlSvaz

Salaam – A Muslim American Boy's Story, by Trish Brown. This is a biography about a Muslim American boy named Imran, who likes to do the same things that most children his age enjoy. Not everyone understands what it means to be Muslim, and through his story, Imran shows that Muslims strive to be good people, just as those of other faiths do. (**E**) bit.ly/2C8BsOk

Taking a Closer Look at Religions Around the World, by Teaching Tolerance. This lesson offers a starting point for exploring religions and faith traditions, creating an ongoing respectful dialogue about religious tolerance. (**M, H**) bit.ly/d0Wqlg

The Fantastic Adventures of Krishna, by Demi. *The Fantastic Adventures of Krishna* tells the enchanting tale of the child Krishna, who is sent by the God Vishnu to aid humanity. Hidden among the poor cowherds, Krishna uses his miraculous powers to fight an evil demon king who has overthrown the peaceful kingdom of Mathura. The story of Krishna, dating to the 8th century BCE, and forming an integral part of Hinduism, is beautifully brought to life by award-winning author and illustrator, Demi. (**E**) bit.ly/2VbP1ax

The Little Book of Hindu Deities: From the Goddess of Wealth to the Sacred Cow, by Sanjay Patel. See *Asian/Asian Pacific Islander/Asian American History, Issues, and Rights* section. (**E**) bit.ly/2D23VXI

The Proudest Blue: A Story of Hijab and Family, by Ibtihaj Muhammad. Faizah admires older sister Asiya's new, strikingly beautiful blue first-day hijab, finding inner strength and pride when facing bullies at school who make fun of it. (**E**) bit.ly/3d0n2RL

The Story of Passover, by David Adler. One of the most significant holidays in Jewish tradition, Passover commemorates Moses leading his people out of slavery in Egypt. *The Story of Passover* recounts the major events of the story in dramatic but accessible language, from Jacob settling in Egypt to the miraculous parting of the Red Sea. The text and images have been vetted for accuracy by a rabbinical authority, and the book includes an author's note about the modern Passover celebration, the seder, and how the different parts of the meal symbolize elements of the story. (**E, M**) bit.ly/3e8UtTS

The Very Crowded Sukkah, by Leslie Kimmelman and Bob McMahon. This children's book tells the story of a family celebrating Sukkot by building a *sukkah* (a temporary hut) outdoors. When the weather doesn't cooperate, the family makes a decision about the celebration that includes some surprising guests. (**E**) bit.ly/2rZHvQR

Under My Hijab, by Hena Khan. With cheerful rhyming text and charming illustrations, this picture book provides a friendly introduction to hijabs for all readers and celebrates the many Muslim women and girls who choose to wear them. Free teacher's guide at this site. (**E**) leeandlow.com/books/under-my-hijab

Under the Bodhi Tree, by Shi Jin Rou, Dharma Realm Buddhist Association. This book tells the story of the Buddha's life, from his birth as a pampered prince, through his cultivation and enlightenment, to his founding of the Buddhist *sangha* and his final *Nirvana*. (**E, M**) bit.ly/2MhVfQh

Sexual Violence

How My Third-Graders and I Address Consent, by Elizabeth Kleinrock. In the wake of #MeToo and the Kavanaugh hearings, Ms. Kleinrock shares her strategies for addressing consent with elementary students. (**E, TR**) bit.ly/2RQL8XV

NO! The Rape Documentary. This documentary explores the impact of sexual violence on Black women and girls. As incidents of violence and sexual assault increase in number, this film can be used to support people as they learn to navigate the challenging terrain of sexuality without violence. (**H**) bit.ly/2RXJUKi

The Reckoning: Teaching About the #MeToo Moment and Sexual Harassment with Resources from The New York Times, by the *NYTimes* Learning Network. In this unit, *NYTimes* staff pull together a wealth of *Times* reporting, opinions, and videos to suggest several ways to begin confronting the questions and issues the #MeToo movement raises. Christopher Pepper, a health educator in the San Francisco Unified School District, who helped design the district's high school sex education curriculum, co-wrote this piece with the Learning Network staff. (**H**) nyti.ms/2DD6eyi

The Arts

18 Multicultural Children's Books About Jazz, by Colours of Us. These fun books will inspire your kids (from babies to teenagers) to clap, sing, dance, and play their own Jazz! (**E**) bit.ly/2Vb1Keo

40 Books to Celebrate National Poetry Month, by Black Children's Books and Authors. See *Literacy and Language* section. (**E**) bit.ly/2Ei0lXa

Mahalia, a film produced by Robin Roberts. See *Civil Rights, Black Power, Student and 1960s Movements* section. (**M, H**) bit.ly/3rL2OTr

Mahalia Jackson: Walking with Kings and Queens, by Nina Nolan. Accompanied by John Holyfield's gorgeous illustrations, debut author Nina Nolan's narrative wonderfully captures the amazing story of how Mahalia Jackson became the Queen of Gospel in this fascinating picture book biography for young children. (**E**) bit.ly/3wyo2XA

Mama Africa!: How Miriam Makeba Spread Hope with Her Song, by Kathryn Erskine. See *African and African Diaspora History, Issues, and Rights*. (**E, M**) kathrynerskine.com

War and Imperialism

A Bowl Full of Peace: A True Story, by Caren Stelson. See *Asian/Asian Pacific Islander/Asian American History, Issues, and Rights* section. (**E, M**) carenstelson.com/books/

A Little Piece of Ground, by Elizabeth Laird with Sonia Nimr. See *Middle Eastern American and Middle East History, Issues, and Rights* section. (**E**) bit.ly/2JC3zZf

All He Knew, by Helen Frost. See *Disability History, Issue,s and Rights* section. (**M, H**) bit.ly/39HC4vZ

Arundhati Roy: A Digital Collection of Interviews and Conversations, assembled by Alternative Radio: Audio Energy for Democracy. See *Asian/Asian Pacific Islander/Asian American History, Issues, and Rights* section. (**H**) alternativeradio.org/speaker/arundhati-roy

Children's Books About the Holocaust, by the United States Holocaust Memorial Museum. See *Genocide* section. (**E, M**) bit.ly/2ImkJJH

Cinco de Mayo, Yesterday and Today, by Maria Cristina Urrutia and Rebeca Orozco. See *Latinx/Latin American History, Issues, and Rights* section. (**E, M**) bit.ly/2SFfXvSp

Constitution, War Crimes, and Guantanamo Justice, by Alan Shapiro, Morningside Center for Teaching Social Responsibility. Release of a Justice Department memo raises the issue of how the US treats "terrorist suspects." Two student readings are followed by discussion questions and other student activities. (**H**) bit.ly/3cidbpb

Fish for Jimmy: Inspired by One Family's Experience in a Japanese American Internment Camp, by Katie Yamasaki. See *Asian/Asian Pacific Islander/Asian American History, Issues, and Rights* section. (**E, M**) bit.ly/3mgFwTB

Fred Korematsu Speaks Up, by Laura Atkins and Stan Yogi. See *Asian/Asian Pacific Islander/Asian American History, Issues, and Rights* section. (**E, M**) bit.ly/30Ly0Wx

Gaijin: American Prisoner of War, by Matt Faulkner. See *Asian/Asian Pacific Islander/ Asian American History, Issues, and Rights section*. (**E, M, H**) bit.ly/3dMxPAA

Haiku and Hiroshima: Teaching About the Atomic Bomb, by Wayne Au. See *Asian/Asian Pacific Islander/Asian American History, Issues, and Rights* section. (**H**) bit.ly/2SdYmL4

In the Shadow of My Country: A Japanese American Artist Remembers, by Densho. See *Asian/Asian Pacific Islander/Asian American History, Issues, and Rights*. (**E, M, H**) Teacher's guide to the exhibit included here: densho.org/in-the-shadow-of-my-country

Multiple Perspectives of the War of 1812, by PBS Learning Media. This lesson plan, to be used in conjunction with the program *The War of 1812*, gives students background information about the diverse perspectives of those groups involved in the war: Americans, British, Canadian Colonists, and First Nations people. (**M, H**) bit.ly/3gZi7p9

Nuclear Weapons: What Should Our Policy Be? by The Choices Program. This unit engages students to consider a balanced range of views on the questions that surround the future of nuclear weapons. The material in this 2-day lesson is drawn from a larger curriculum called "The Challenge of Nuclear Weapons." (**H**) bit.ly/2Ex69w5

Rethinking Cinco de Mayo, by Sudie Hofmann, Zinn Education Project. See *Latinx/Latin American History, Issues, and Rights* section. (**H, TR**) bit.ly/13VTKtX

Righting a Wrong: Japanese Americans and World War II, by the National Museum of American History. See *Asian/Asian Pacific Islander/Asian American History, Issues, and Rights* section. (**E, M, H**) s.si.edu/3r9LW7v

Spanish-American War, teaching materials from the Stanford History Education Group. See *Latinx/Latin American History, Issues, and Rights* section. (**H**) stanford.io/2QfQBsn

Texas Revolution: A Lesson Plan, by the Stanford History Education Group. Why did Texans revolt against the Mexican government? In this lesson, students read the Texas Declaration of Independence, military commanders' letters, and an abolitionist pamphlet to explore causes of the Texas Revolution. (**H**) stanford.io/2RblRbV

The Diary of Anne Frank, Teacher's Guide, by PBS and Facing History and Ourselves. See *Genocide* section. (**H, TR**) bit.ly/3eWwoli

The "Hiding Place" Curriculum, by the Houston Holocaust Museum. The book, *The Hiding Place*, is the true story of the ten Boom family who were members of the Dutch Resistance during World War II. Their resistance group found shelter for dozens of Jews, including many children. Corrie ten Boom helped children find a safe house or passed them on to a representative from another area. The ten Booms also opened their home to many fugitives and Resistance workers. Holocaust Museum Houston has created and collected resources for educators who are teaching *The Hiding Place*. (**H**) hmh.org/education/hiding-place-curriculum

The People vs. Columbus, et al., by Bill Bigelow. See *Indigenous History, Issues, and Rights* section. (**E, M, H**) bit.ly/hRdbSf

The Teachers' Protest: How Norwegian Teachers Defeated Nazi Education, a film by Jon Seal. In 1942 Nazi-occupied Norway, teachers were forced to join the Nazi Teachers' League and teach Nazi ideas in their classrooms. 8,000 of them wrote protest letters. They were threatened with salary withdrawal and dismissal, but they refused. In a desperate attempt to break them, the Nazi government arrested 1,000 male teachers and sent them to prison camps, 300 miles above the Arctic Circle. This 75-min documentary weaves together archive footage, first-hand testimony, and the skillful animation of Herlov Åmland's poignant drawings to tell this gripping story to an international audience for the first time. (**H**) Film available for free here: theteachersprotest.com

They Called Us Enemy, by George Takai. See *Asian/Asian Pacific Islander/Asian American History, Issues, and Rights* section. (**M, H**) bit.ly/3eElaSf

Tropical Secrets: Holocaust Refugees in Cuba, a novel in verse by Margarita Engle. See *Latinx/Latin American History, Issues, and Rights* section. (**M, H**) bit.ly/2R5lS1h

War Against All Puerto Ricans: Revolution and Terror in America's Colony, by Nelson A. Denis. See *Latinx/ Latin American History, Issues, and Rights* section. (**H, TR**) bit.ly/2lOJDVL

We Shall Remain. See *Indigenous History, Issues, and Rights* section. (**H**) to.pbs.org/2SvdUu2

Weapons of Mass Destruction: A Resource Unit, by the Morningside Center for Teaching Social Responsibility. A substantive reader and activity guide on chemical, biological, and nuclear weapons. (**H**) bit.ly/3tsKDml

Write to Me: Letters from Japanese American Children to the Librarian They Left Behind, by Cynthia Grady. See *Asian/ Asian Pacific Islander/Asian American History, Issues, and Rights* section. (**E, M**) bit.ly/3d8XLY9

Women's History, Issues, and Rights

500 Years of Chicana Women's History, by Elizabeth Martinez. See *Latinx/Latin American History, Issues, and Rights* section. (**H**) bit.ly/3ba7sEh

A Black Women's History of the United States, by Daina Ramey Berry and Kali Nicole Gross. See *African American History, Issues, and Rights* section. (**H, TR**) bit.ly/3exil5r

A Litany for Survival: The Life and Work of Audre Lorde, a film by Ada Gay Griffin and Michelle Parkerson. See *African American History, Issues, and Rights* section. (**H, TR**) to.pbs.org/3ezIeBN

A TED Talk by Manal-al Sharif. See *Middle Eastern American and Middle East History, Issues, and Rights* section. (**M, H**) ted.com/speakers/manal_al_sharif

A Woman for President: The Story of Victoria Woodhull, by Kathleen Krull. A revolutionary woman in American history, Victoria Woodhull was many years ahead of her time, breaking boundaries. But her presidential campaign, and the backlash it sparked, left her in political ruin and bankruptcy. Acclaimed biographer Kathleen

Krull and beloved illustrator Jane Dyer combine their talents to bring her story to life for young readers. (**E, M**) Teacher's guide: bit.ly/3x1yJC1

Amelia to Zora: Twenty-Six Women Who Changed the World, by Cynthia Chin-Lee and Megan Halsey. Detailed collages and illustrations draw from various events of both hardship and triumph in the lives of 26 amazing women. (**E, M**) bit.ly/2EAyiCo

An Audiovisual Collection on Mabel Hampton, by the Lesbian Herstory Archives. See *Queer History, Issues, and Rights* section. (**H**) bit.ly/3dpTmju

Annotated Bibliography for Young Readers of Harriet Beecher Stowe Biographies, by the Harriet Beecher Stowe Center. See *Abolition and Slavery* section. (**E, M, H, TR**) bit.ly/3ecm32y

At the Mountain's Base, by Traci Sorell. See *Indigenous History, Issues, and Rights* section. (**E, M**) bit.ly/2Xc7hSp

Ava DuVernay on Her Journey to Become the First Black Woman to Direct an Oscar-Nominated Film, by *Time* Magazine. In this short interview, DuVernay talks about growing up in a matriarchy and breaking down barriers in the patriarchal film industry. (**M, H**) youtube.com/watch?v=J4Gh4WYvaDs

Before Rosa Parks: Ida B. Wells, by Learning for Justice. See *African American History, Issues, and Rights* section. (**M, H**) bit.ly/2J75IBk

Bessie Coleman Read-Alouds, from *Women and Girls are Changemakers*, created by Shay InLak'Ech. An exceptional collection of picture books on powerful women throughout history, each linked to a YouTube read-aloud of the book. The link on this page includes three read-alouds about Bessie Coleman. (**E**) bit.ly/2Qlav4N

Black Women in Science: A Black History Book for Kids, by Kimberly Brown Pellum. See *African American History, Issues, and Rights* section. (**E, M**) bit.ly/3rJKg55

Can Egyptian Women Start a Revolution Against Sexual Violence? By Nick Schifrin. See *Middle Eastern American and Middle East History, Issues, and Rights* section. (**H**) to.pbs.org/3wu7yzA

Chisolm '72: Unbought and Unbossed, a POV documentary. See *African American History, Issues, and Rights* section. (**M, H, TR**) bit.ly/2RW7q8z

Drummer Girl, by Hiba Masood. Young Najma loved Ramadan and had a secret dream. She longed to beat the drum that traditional male *musaharati* drummers use during the wakeup call for the pre-dawn meal. Supported by her loving family, Najma realizes her long-cherished dream and pushes the boundaries of what girls can accomplish. (**E**) bit.ly/2pDcQHq

First: Sandra Day O'Connor, by Evan Thomas. A vivid and personal portrait of the life of Sandra Day O'Connor, the first woman to serve on the United States Supreme Court. (**H**) bit.ly/3cLpOMR

Fannie Never Flinched: One Woman's Courage in the Struggle for American Labor Rights, by Mary Cronk Farrell. See *Labor and Economic Issues* section. (**E, M**) bit.ly/328Y6nn

Free Black Mamas: National Bail Out. See *Police Violence and Prisons* section. (**TR**) nationalbailout.org

Gender and Jobs – Women in the Workforce, by Learning for Justice. This lesson plan from Teaching Tolerance will guide students in exploring gender equity, reflecting on how gender-based injustice might affect them and exploring ways in which they can fight this injustice. (**M, H, TR**) bit.ly/1eNtNSW

How One Woman Fought One of the World's Biggest Oil Companies and Won, a story recorded for *Living on Earth* by Reid Frazier and Jared Goyette. See *Environmental Justice Issues* section. (**M, H**) bit.ly/3n1gRCS

Ida B. The Queen: The Extraordinary Life and Legacy of Ida B. Wells, by Michelle Duster. See *African American History, Issues, and Rights* section. (**M, H**) bit.ly/3wUMl1O

Ida B. Wells: Let the Truth Be Told, by Walter Dean Myers. See *African American History, Issues, and Rights* section. (**E, M**) bit.ly/3teCtNR

IntersectionAllies: We Make Room for All, by Latoya Council, Carolyn Choi, and Chelsea Johnson. Written by three Women of Color sociologists, *IntersectionAllies* introduces children to intersectional feminism. The nine interconnected characters describe themselves and their backgrounds, offering an opportunity to take pride in a personal story and connect to a collective struggle for justice. (**E**) bit.ly/2Q2iVOs

Introduction to Activism: A Closer Look at Dolores Huerta, a lesson by Eden McCauslin for The National Women's History Museum. Using videoclips and speeches, this lesson plan takes a closer look at one of the key activists in the Women's, Workers' and Immigrants' Rights movements in the 20th century. (**M, H**) bit.ly/2SlWgsN

Invisible No More: Police Violence Against Black Women and Women of Color, by Andrea Ritchie. See *Police Violence and Prisons* section. (**H**) bit.ly/3sUMYGr

Jewish Women: A Comprehensive Historical Encyclopedia, by the Jewish Women's Archive. Organized by categories such as activism, art, science, and sports, this online encyclopedia cataloguing the accomplishments of hundreds of Jewish women throughout history is a rich biographical resource. (**E, M, H**) jwa.org/encyclopedia

Key Facts About Women's Suffrage Around the World, by Katherine Schaeffer for Pew Research. See *Human Rights and Democracy* section. (**H**) pewrsr.ch/3u5K4zg

Let Her Learn: A Toolkit to Stop School Push Out for Girls of Color, by the National Women's Law Center. See *Police Violence and Prisons* section. (**TR**) bit.ly/2i1PIRG

Let It Shine: Stories of Black Women Freedom Fighters, by Andrea Davis Pinkney. See *African American History, Issues, and Rights* section. (**E, M**) bit.ly/3dYjmBQ

Life Story: Grace Thorpe, from Women & The American Story. See *Indigenous History, Issues, and Rights* section. (**M, H**) bit.ly/3dWMdXb

Lifting as We Climb: Black Women's Battle for the Ballot Box, by Evette Dionne. See *African American History, Issues, and Rights* section. (**M, H**) bit.ly/2PY7Yx9

Little Leaders: Bold Women in Black History, by Vashti Harrison. See *African American History, Issues, and Rights* section. (**E**) bit.ly/2p5UijE

Mama's Day, by Strong Families. See *Police Violence and Prisons* section. (**E, M, H**) www.mamasday.org

Mamie on the Mound: A Woman in Baseball's Negro Leagues, by Lean Henderson. See *African American History, Issues, and Rights* section. (**E, M**) bit.ly/3eCiva1

Mighty Justice: The Untold Story of Civil Rights Trailblazer Dovey Johnson Roundtree, by Katie McCabe, adapted for young readers by Jabari Asim. See *Civil*

Rights, Black Power, Student and 1960s Movements section. (**E, M**) bit.ly/32dGdDG

Mother's Day Proclamation – 1870, by Julia Ward Howe. See *Peace Education/ Counter-Recruiting* section. (**E, M, H**) bit.ly/eT5sy

NO! The Rape Documentary. See *Sexual Violence* section. (**H**) bit.ly/2RXJUKi

Open Wide the Freedom Gates: A Memoir, by Dorothy Height. See *Civil Rights, Black Power, Student and 1960s Movements* section. (**H**) https://n.pr/3diUnd0

Our Women on the Ground: Essays by Arab Women Reporting from the Arab World, edited by Zahra Hankir. See *Middle Eastern American and Middle East History, Issues, and Rights* section. (**H**) bit.ly/3fZrkwV

Revolutionary Women of Texas and Mexico: Portraits of Soldaderas, Saints, and Subversives, edited by Ellen Riojas Clark, Kathy Sosa, and Jennifer Speed. See *Latinx/Latin American History, Issues, and Rights* section. (**H**) bit.ly/31DS51l

Say Her Name, by Zetta Elliott. See *Police Violence and Prisons* section. (**M, H**) bit.ly/3tcSQun

She Sang Promise: The Story of Betty Mae Jumper, Seminole Tribe Leader, by Jan Godown Annino. See *Indigenous History, Issue,s and Rights* section. (**E, M**) bit.ly/2QVWKd6

She Was the First!: The Trailblazing Life of Shirley Chisholm, by Katheryn Russell-Brown. See *African American History, Issues, and Rights* section. (**E**) bit.ly/3laM7yj

Sylvia and Marsha Start a Revolution!: The Story of the Trans Women of Color Who Made LGBTQ+ History, by Joy Ellison. See *Queer History, Issues, and Rights* section. (**E**) bit.ly/38A7dkj

Teaching with the News: The United States in Afghanistan: Analyzing Political Cartoons, by The Choices Program. See *Middle Eastern American and Middle East History, Issues, and Rights* section. (**M, H**) bit.ly/9EeGIe

The Bobbin Girl, by Emily Arnold McCully. See *Labor and Economic Issues* section. (**E, M**) zinnedproject.org/materials/bobbin-girl

The Body Is Not an Apology, by Sonya Renee Taylor. See *Hate and Oppression* section. (**H**) bit.ly/2tDnzHU

The Reckoning: Teaching About the #MeToo Moment and Sexual Harassment with Resources from The New York Times, by the *NYTimes* Learning Network. See *Sexual Violence* section. (**H**) nyti.ms/2DD6eyi

The Women Who Caught the Babies: A Story of African American Midwives, by Eloise Greenfield. See *African American History, Issues, and Rights* section. (**E, M**) bit.ly/3wMGICZ

The Women Who Gave Us Christmas, by William Loren Katz. See *Abolition and Slavery* section. (**M, H, TR**) bit.ly/1QvQJe8

The Women's Army Corps: Female Soldiers in WWII, by National Women's History Museum. A multimedia slideshow that includes video clips, photographs, and other primary source documents about the Woman's Auxiliary Army Corps. (**M, H**) bit.ly/3srS4sK

They Dared! by PBS. A collection of 2-4-minute videos celebrating strong and determined Alabama women who dared to make a difference, including Amelia Boynton Robinson, Gwendolyn Patton, Hellen Keller, and more. (**E, M, H**) pbs.org/show/they-dared/

Title IX at 40, by Carrie Kilman for Teaching for Justice. An essay exploring the ways in which Title IX was never just about sports, and how it radically changed everything about education for girls and women. (**M, H**) bit.ly/3sWhi2p

Vanguard: How Black Women Broke Barriers, Won the Vote, and Insisted on Equality for All, by Martha Jones. See *Human Rights and Democracy* section. (**H**) bit.ly/39JVwse

Wake: The Hidden History of Women-Led Slave Revolts, by Rebecca Hall. See *Abolition and Slavery* section. (**M, H**) bit.ly/3s2TAB7

What Do You Do with a Voice Like That?: The Story of Extraordinary Congresswoman Barbara Jordan, by Chris Barton. See *African American History, Issues, and Rights* section. (**E, M**) bit.ly/3gd1qpt

When Saying "I Do" Meant Giving Up Your US Citizenship, by Meg Hacker for the National Archives. See *Human Rights and Democracy* section. (**H**) bit.ly/2PwFoDr

Women and Girls Are Changemakers, created by Shay InLak'Ech. An exceptional collection of picture books on powerful women throughout history, each linked to a YouTube read-aloud of the book. (**E**) bit.ly/390Wz6C

Women and Social Movements in the United States, 1600 to 2000. This *Teacher's Corner* website offers more than 100 documents and lesson plans for teaching the role of women in American history. (**M, H**) bit.ly/bmuSYJ

Women Who Soar: 30 Books About Boundary-Breaking Female Pilots, by A Mighty Girl. From the authors of this annotated list of recommended books: "In this blog post, we've featured our favorite books for all ages about trailblazing female pilots throughout history. Whether they were on the cutting edge of the development of flight, breaking records and testing the limits of what newer and better airplanes could do, or thrilling crowds with their daredevil maneuvers, these airwomen were bold and daring. And, for the mighty girls that read them, these books might just be the inspiration for their dreams of a life in the clouds!" (**E, M**) amightygirl.com/blog?p=20960

Women's Suffrage, by Justice for Education. See *Human Rights and Democracy* section. (**M, H**) bit.ly/2IOoO9c

Youth Activism

Determined to Stay: Palestinian Youth Fight for Their Village, by Jody Sokolower. See *Middle Eastern American and Middle East History, Issues, and Rights* section. (**H**) bit.ly/3410jSD

Finding Solutions to Hunger, by Kids Can Make a Difference. See *Labor and Economic Issues* section. (**M, H**) bit.ly/cYEDNd

Gun Violence in Schools, by Learning for Justice. Use these resources to help navigate conversations about gun violence, school safety, mental health, and how to take action after a school shooting. (**TR**) learningforjustice.org/magazine/gun-violence-in-schools

How to Change Everything: The Young Human's Guide to Protecting the Planet and Each Other, by Naomi Klein, adapted for young readers by Rebecca Stefoff. See *Environmental Justice Issues* section. (**H**) bit.ly/2S19nnJ

Kids on the March: 15 Stories of Speaking Out, Protesting, and Fighting for Justice, by Michael Long. From the March on Washington to March for Our Lives to Black Lives Matter, the powerful stories of kid-led protest in America. Kids have always been activists. This book shows that no one is too young to make a difference. (**E, M**) bit.ly/3lhzHVu

No Planet B: A Teen Vogue Guide to the Climate Crisis, edited by Lucy Diavolo. See *Environmental Justice Issues* section. (**M, H**) bit.ly/3mnvAHQ

No Voice Too Small: Fourteen Young Americans Making History, edited by Lindsay Metcalf, Keila Dawson, and Jeanette Bradley. Mari Copeny demanded clean water in Flint. Jazz Jennings insisted, as a transgirl, on playing soccer with the girls' team. From Viridiana Sanchez Santos's quinceañera demonstration against anti-immigrant policy to Zach Wahls's moving declaration that his two moms and he were a family like any other, *No Voice Too Small* celebrates the young people who know how to be the change they seek. (**E, M**) bit.ly/3uM5TU9

What Do You Do with an Idea? by Kobi Yamada. This story is about a child who one day discovers he has an idea. He wonders where the idea came from, but he is afraid to tell others about it because they might think it's silly. Instead of giving up, the child decides to nurture and feed the idea. Something magical happens – the idea bursts out into the world, bringing with it a miraculous change. (**E**) Find a read-aloud video and guidelines for a philosophical discussion from the Prindle Institute here: bit.ly/39YUmJg

View all these resources online with live links at:
www.edliberation.org/planbookresources

15 EVERYDAY WAYS TO AFFIRM TGNC (TRANS AND GENDER NONCONFORMING) STUDENTS

ONLINE VERSION WITH CLICKABLE LINKS: https://bit.ly/2KAeW3A

"Teachers are our nation's greatest resource and stand on the frontlines alongside our youth. They have the capacity to be the first source of affirmation and support for young people as they're discovering themselves, and I hope this resource encourages teachers and administrators to be advocates toward making our schools safe and welcoming spaces for all students, regardless of their gender identity, expression or sexual orientation."

- Janet Mock, *New York Times* bestselling author of *Redefining Realness*

1 Adopt an intersectional approach to supporting TGNC students. Sexuality and gender identities are related to the other identities that people hold, and the privileges associated with those identities. Individuals in our community hold not only LGBTQ identities, but are also People of Color, people with disabilities, immigrants, and people experiencing homelessness.[1] The supports needed by White TGNC people will likely be different from those for TGNC People of Color (PoC), and within PoC, a variety of experiences and cultural traditions can inform the supports they need. Kian, a member of GLSEN's National Student Council, advises us to "identify the intersections between class, race, and gender identity and listen to the voices often being marginalized and erased within your school community and the entire country." (GLSEN: "How to Support Transgender Students").[2]

2 Instead of calling roll, have students introduce themselves. Give students the chance to share their names and pronouns with you and their classmates, instead of relying on the information presented on school paperwork. It's an opportunity to affirm students, TGNC as well as many others, by centering their presentation of themselves to others in the way they'd like to be known. Try a name game to learn and practice name pronunciations. If asking students to write name tents, explicitly invite them to write the name and pronouns by which they would like to be known. **Resist assigning pronouns before asking.**

3 Introduce pronouns early and often through a game or a get-to-know-you worksheet. Model by naming your own pronouns and those of role models to whom you introduce students, taking care to include individuals representing a diversity of genders. Remind students that we wouldn't assume someone's name without asking first, so we don't assume their pronouns either.

4 Ask students how they'd like you to respond if someone misgenders them. If you've already gained the trust of a TGNC student and want to affirm their gender identity, **ask them** how they'd like you to do so. What name and pronouns would they like you to use in front of their classmates? What would they like you to do if a classmate or teacher misgenders them? What names and pronouns would they like you to use when speaking with their family members? Answers may change for an individual student over time, so keep lines of communication open.

5 Model accountability and affirmation. Did you mess up a student's pronouns? Apologize, correct yourself by repeating your statement using the student's correct pronoun, and *move on*. Dwelling on your mistake is self-serving and puts the trans person in an uncomfortable position. On the flipside, showing students that teachers can apologize and correct our mistakes, prioritize a moment affirming the student's gender, and then return to the topic of discussion will make it possible for students to repeat that behavior. To prevent future misgendering mistakes, practice on your own time so it doesn't happen again. This ally-focused resource[3] can help you make a personal shift. Help your students to practice this with the lesson: "Misgendering and Respect for Pronouns."[4]

6 Make your language more inclusive and reconsider gendered protocols. Instead of referring to your class as "boys and girls," try "artists, scientists, readers" – words that honor what students *can be* over what they have been *assigned*. Use GLSEN's "Pronoun Resource"[5] to learn more and for tips on gender-inclusive language. Do you line up students with a boys and girls line? Keep a boys and girls classroom closet? Consider new affirming, creative ways to divide your students into two groups.

7 Make your support of TGNC and all LGBTQ+ students visible. Let students know you are someone to whom they can turn for support by making your commitment visible. Hang up stickers and posters available from TSER[6], the GLSEN Safe Space Kit[7], or wear an "OUT for Safe Schools"[8] badge available in several urban school districts. Post pictures and quotes from noteworthy queer and trans leaders. Challenge gendered assumptions. When you hear, "Only girls wear nail polish," ask questions to dig deeper: "What makes you say that?" "Does anyone else feel differently?" Weave affirmations and entrances into your classroom conversations so it is obvious to students that you will welcome them if they choose to confide in you about their identity and about any support they may need.

8 Be prepared for a student to disclose their trans identity to you. Now that you've stood out as an ally, some TGNC students may choose to come out to you. Respect their privacy and recognize that they are entrusting *you* with this information, not everyone. You are not obligated to share this information; sharing the information without their consent could betray their trust and even put them in jeopardy if their families are unsupportive. Ask and support student decision-making about if, when, and in whom to confide about their identity. Self monitor your reactions to make sure you're not processing your own potential surprise or confusion with the student to keep their needs centered. For more information, check out "When a Student Comes Out to You."[9]

9 Teach about trans and gender non-conforming experiences and people. No matter what you teach, it's possible to make TGNC people visible in your curriculum. Share examples of gender variant role models[10] connected to your course topic who express gender in a range of ways beyond the binary. Representation enables reflection and expands what "normal" is! If your math[11] word problems describe stories of people, try referring to people in non-heterosexual couplings or describing a person using non-binary pronouns. Debunk the concept of a biological sex binary[12] in your biology class. Try studying the declassification of homosexuality as a mental illness[13] to start a discussion of science *vs* social constructs. If you need help, refer to the many curricular resources mentioned in this plan book to enhance your lesson planning, and reach out to other educators to do this work collaboratively![14, 15]

10 Become versed in your school and district policies addressing the needs of TGNC students, as well as their local, state, and federal rights. Despite current administration initiatives to undermine the rights of TGNC students, many legal protections remain in place, including the right to a safe and supportive learning environment. The ACLU and Lambda Legal are excellent resources for information and legal support. In some municipalities, supportive policies go beyond those of Title IX and 14th amendment rights, which remain in place.[16,17] GLSEN's "Model Policy" provides language you can use to advocate for affirming policies that center on trans students and provide best practices in regard to school records, confidentiality when speaking to parents and family members, gendered-spaces and response to bullying and harassment.[18] "Trans Inclusion in High School Athletics" focuses on supportive policies regarding bathrooms and locker rooms.[19]

11 Advocate for all-gender bathrooms that are consistently accessible to students, and uphold a policy allowing students to use the bathroom that matches their gender identity. Bathrooms have become a keystone issue in the struggle for trans inclusion. In the words of actress and LGBT advocate Laverne Cox, "When trans people can't access public bathrooms we can't go to school effectively, go to work effectively, access health-care facilities. It's about us existing in public space." All-gender restrooms are a beacon to TGNC students[20] that their school has a vested interest in supporting them by making school facilities accessible, as is signage affirming that all individuals can use the bathroom that matches their gender identity. In addition to your students who may identify outside the gender binary,[21] all-gender restrooms can be supportive of disabled students as well as cisgender and heterosexual students who are bullied for their gender expression. As a supportive educator, don't wait for a student who needs it to ask. Proactively work with administrators and building officials to remove the obstacles surrounding affirming bathroom access at your school.

12 Combat bullying with LGBTQ-Specific Support. Your support can be life-saving. While young people are brilliant and resilient, LGBTQ and gender nonconforming students face high rates of bullying and discrimination at school, and this victimization can lead to higher rates of depression and even suicide. Make sure that your school counselors have been trained in LGBTQ-specific supports, and that all of your students have access to suicide prevention resources, such as the Trevor Project.

13 Start/Support a Gender and Sexuality Alliance (GSA) at your school. Create a GSA[22] in your school community where LGBTQ students and allies can gather to center student voices, leadership and needs. Federal law protects the right of all schools to establish a GSA as part of an extra-curricular program. Moreover, schools with GSAs have reduced suicide risk for *all* students, including heterosexual boys.[23] To develop your GSA,[24] establish norms for students to assure mutual respect and affirmation. Try to build administrative and collegial alliances so that the student participants feel supported by many entities. Discuss what students need in terms of interaction with parents while also building home connections when possible and safe. Connect students with outside organizations developing LGBTQ youth affinity,[25] youth leadership development,[26] and establishing networks and events for GSAs and queer youth.

14 Facilitate training for colleagues (pedagogues and all staff) and families. Connect with national organizations and local LGBTQ organizations and centers in your city to see if they offer training on gender inclusivity for schools and PTAs. Consider attending training with the goal of teaching them to your colleagues. There's always more to learn, as affirming terminology and current legal rights are ever evolving. Consider forming a collegial group (e.g., an inquiry group or equity committee) that stays in touch with current best practices.

15 Advocate for restorative justice, rather than punishment. Building community gives TGNC students a safety net when life gets challenging. Restorative practices help all students in ways that don't single out TGNC students. Zero tolerance policies aren't effective[27] and often result in pushing unresolved conflicts into other schools, in addition to falling disproportionately on students of color. Moreover, bullying can be a complex dynamic that includes situations in which a victimized LGBTQ student may, in turn, respond with harm that is pathologized or criminalized.[28] Mediation and facilitation practices support overall school climate and give all students a tool for their own self-advocacy.

THIS FEATURE WAS ORIGINALLY PRINTED IN OUR 2018-19 EDITION.

Contributions and editing by

NYC Educators Jae Berlin, Sage Forbes-Gray, Kit Golan, Kelinda Schuster; as well as Eli Erlick, *Trans Student Educational Resources*; Becca Mui, *GLSEN*; Sophie Labelle, *Assigned Male Comics* (www.assignedmale.tumblr.com); and Janet Mock, *NYT Bestselling Author.* Coordinating Editor: Jae Berlin.

Citations and Resources

1. *Coming Out*, by GLSEN – bit.ly/2yfjKZg
2. *Supporting Trans and GNC Students* by GLSEN – bit.ly/2um7aXY
3. *Trans Allyship Workshop: Building Skills to Support Trans People in Our Lives* by Think Again – bit.ly/1MQ0FPY
4. *Misgendering and Respect for Pronouns* by GLSEN – bit.ly/2pFJskp
5. *Pronouns: A Resource for Educators* by GLSEN – bit.ly/2G7SwJ7
6. *Trans Student Educational Resource (TSER)* – transstudent.org
7. *GLSEN Safe Space Kit: Be an ALLY to LGBTQ Youth!* – www.glsen.org/safespace
8. *OUT FOR SAFE SCHOOLS® Get the Badge* – bit.ly/2DTtbgd
9. *When A Student Comes Out to You...Today or Any Day!* by GLSEN – bit.ly/2GahasN
10. *Meet 10 Black Transgender Figures from History Who are Role Models for Resilience* by Ashlee Marie Preston, Mic Network – bit.ly/2plrca9
11. *How Do We Make Math Class More Inclusive of Trans and Non-Binary Identities?* by Kyle S. Whipple, GLSEN – bit.ly/2GwD350
12. *Trans women are not "biologically male"* (video), by Riley J. Dennis – bit.ly/2mSoSwk
13. *Charles Silverstein and the Declassification of Homosexuality as a Mental Illness*, by Anti-Defamation League, GLSEN, and StoryCorps – bit.ly/2pMkLIR
14. *6 Ways I Make My Science Class LGBTQ-Inclusive as a Trans Teacher*, by Lewis Maday-Travis, GLSEN – bit.ly/2pP2ofT
15. *Beyond the Gender Binary*, by GLSEN – www.glsen.org/article/beyond-gender-binary
16. *How Schools Can Support Transgender Students*, by Lambda Legal – bit.ly/2pN2qFX
17. *Transgender and Gender Nonconforming Student Guidelines*, by NYC Department of Education – on.nyc.gov/2Cv0Mxb
18. *Model District Policy on Transgender and Gender Nonconforming Students*, by GLSEN and National Center for Transgender Equality – bit.ly/2pPiFIO
19. *Trans Inclusion in High School Athletics*, by GLSEN – bit.ly/2GyTv4H
20. *How to Support Transgender Students* (video), by GLSEN – youtu.be/kq19QdOfH1Y
21. *I'm Non-Binary, and "Trans-Accessible" Restrooms Should Include Me, Too*, by Keress Weidner, GLSEN – bit.ly/2IbLik2
22. *10 Steps for Starting a GSA*, by GSA Network – bit.ly/2b1uSeS
23. *Simply Having a Gay Straight Alliance Reduces Suicide Risk for All Students*, by Rose Eveleth, Smithsonian.com – bit.ly/2HODPb3
24. *Jump Start Your GSA*, by GLSEN – www.glsen.org/jumpstart
25. *The Center: The Lesbian, Gay, Bisexual, & Transgender Community Center* – gaycenter.org/family-youth#youth
26. *National Student Council*, by GLSEN – www.glsen.org/article/national-student-council
27. *Why Zero Tolerance Is Not the Solution to School Bullying*, by Carolyn Laub, *Huffington Post*
28. *Dropout, Push-Out, and the School-to-Prison Pipeline*, by GLSEN – bit.ly/2pRxhAI

Additional Resources

GLSEN: GLSEN is a leading national education organization focused on ensuring safe and affirming schools for LGBTQ students. www.glsen.org

Lambda Legal: Lambda Legal is a national organization committed to achieving full recognition of the civil rights of lesbians, gay men, bisexuals, transgender people and everyone living with HIV, through impact litigation, education and public policy work. www.lambdalegal.org

New York City Oral Trans History Project: NYC Oral Trans History Project is a community archive devoted to the collection, preservation and sharing of trans histories, organized in collaboration with the New York Public Library. www.nyctransoralhistory.org

The Center: The Center in New York City is a community center focused on the needs of the LGBT community, offering services as well as a wealth of resources. gaycenter.org/resources#gender-identity

The Trevor Project: The Trevor Project is a leading national organization providing crisis intervention and suicide prevention services to lesbian, gay, bisexual, transgender and questioning (LGBTQ) young people ages 13-24. www.thetrevorproject.org

Unheard Voices: GLSEN, the Anti-Defamation League (ADL) and StoryCorps have collaborated to create *Unheard Voices*, an oral history and curriculum project helping educators integrate lesbian, gay, bisexual and transgender (LGBT) history, people and issues into their instructional programs. www.glsen.org/unheardvoices.html

Comic created by Sophie Labelle of Assigned Male Comics
www.assignedmale.tumblr.com

Freedom Fighter Award

This recognition goes to

____

Who stood up for freedom and justice by

____

____

"It is our duty to fight for our freedom. It is our duty to win. We must love each other and support each other. We have nothing to lose but our chains."
- Assata Shakur

Knowledge Is Power Award

This recognition goes to

____

for using knowledge to make a difference.

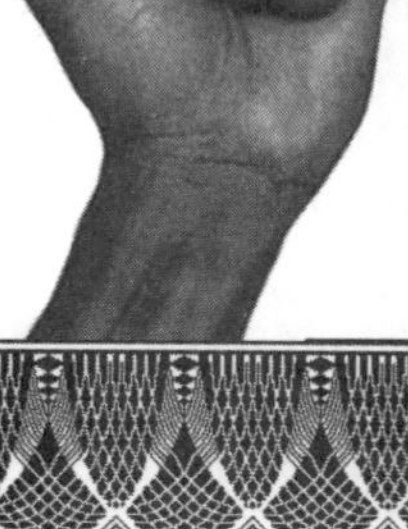

"The end of all education should surely be service to others."
- César Chávez

Person in the Mirror Award

This recognition goes to

____

for having the courage to self-reflect and transform.

"Revolution begins with the self, in the self."

- Toni Cade Bambara

Say It Loud, Say It Proud Award

This recognition goes to

____

for speaking up and taking risks in the name of justice.

"Our lives begin to end the day we become silent about things that matter."

- Martin Luther King, Jr.

List of organizations

Education for Liberation Network recommends the following organizations and resources.

Teacher organizations:

Association of Raza Educators (Los Angeles) - an association that believes in community change through critical consciousness and a democratic education. www.razaeducators.org

Educators Network for Social Justice (Milwaukee) - a network of practicing educators promoting pro-justice curricula and policies so that all students in the Milwaukee area are better served. www.ensj.org

Educators for Social Justice (St. Louis) - the only organization in St. Louis connecting educators across districts to focus on social justice curriculum and change. www.educatorsforsocialjustice.org

Metro Atlantans for Public Schools (Atlanta) - a network of progressive public school employees, parents, students and allies who believe that public education should be democratic, well-funded and community-supported. https://sites.google.com/site/metroatlantansforpublicschools

People's Education Movement (Los Angeles) - educators seeking to create sustainable liberatory spaces inside and beyond the classroom to promote growth, healing and transformation. www.peoplesed.org

Teacher Action Group (Boston) - a group of Boston-area educators and allies who work together to organize around our principles of social justice and education for liberation. www.tagboston.org

Teacher Action Group (Philadelphia) - an organization that seeks to strengthen teacher voices in schools and policy decisions. tagphilly.org

Teachers for Social Justice (Chicago) - an organization that works to fight for social justice in Chicago, and gets the voices of educators into the public discussion of school policies. www.teachersforjustice.org

Organizations that publish curricula and teaching resources:

Teachers 4 Social Justice (San Francisco) - a grassroots, non-profit teacher support and development organization. www.t4sj.org

EdChange - an organization promoting equity and justice in schools and society. Their website includes many resources for integrating social justice in schools. www.edchange.org

Facing the Future - offers sustainability and global issues curricula, professional development, service-learning and free K-12 lessons. www.facingthefuture.org

Gay, Lesbian and Straight Education Network (GLSEN) - a network that focuses on ensuring safe schools for all students, regardless of sexual orientation or gender identity. www.glsen.org

IndyKids - a free newspaper and teaching tool that aims to inform children about current news and world events from a progressive perspective. www.indykids.net

Institute for Humane Education - a non-profit educational organization dedicated to creating a humane world through humane education. www.humaneeducation.org

Learning for Justice - an organization that promotes and supports anti-bias activism and provides online resources and ideas for teaching tolerance. learningforjustice.org

National Center for Fair and Open Testing - works to reform/end standardized testing and promote other methods of evaluation. www.fairtest.org

Project Look Sharp - a media literacy initiative of Ithaca College that develops and provides lesson plans, media materials, training and support for the effective integration of media literacy with critical thinking into classroom curricula at all education levels. www.ithaca.edu/looksharp

Project South - a leadership development organization based in the US South that publishes teaching materials on organizing and global issues. www.projectsouth.org

Rethinking Schools - a national publisher of education materials that is committed to equity and to the vision that public education is central to the creation of a humane, caring, multiracial democracy. www.rethinkingschools.org

Safe Schools Coalition - an organization that is working to make schools safe places for all children, regardless of gender identity or sexual orientation. Their website contains a large collection of resource materials for educators. www.safeschoolscoalition.org

School of Unity and Liberation - a youth organizing training center that publishes teaching materials on youth organizing and global issues. www.schoolofunityandliberation.org

Teachable Moment - a project of Morningside Center for Teaching Social Responsibility that fosters social responsibility by sharing free K-12 classroom lessons, activities and ideas with educators. www.morningsidecenter.org/teachable-moment

Teaching for Change - a provider of curriculum guides and other resources to help teachers engage students in innovative classroom activities that deal with issues of equity and social justice. www.teachingforchange.org

What Kids Can Do - an online publication that features young people's lives, learning, and work, and their partnerships with adults both in and out of school. www.wkcd.org

Zinn Education Project - promotes and supports the use of Howard Zinn's best-selling book, *A People's History of the United States*, and other materials in middle and high school classrooms. zinnedproject.org